DEAR SAUCY PAT

DEAR SAUCY PAT

The Life of Patrick Brontë

Coreen Turner

The Book Guild Ltd
Sussex, England

First published in Great Britain in 2003 by
The Book Guild Ltd
25 High Street
Lewes, East Sussex
BN7 2LU

Typesetting in Baskerville by
SetSystems Ltd, Saffron Walden, Essex

Printed in Great Britain by
Bookcraft (Bath) Ltd

A catalogue record for this book is
available from the British Library

ISBN 1 85776 689 X

To the memory of

GEORGE THOMAS FUERY
1868–1952
inspiration and example

and
ADRIAN VALE
1928–2000
who had such good ideas

FOREWORD

All the main events of this book are based on facts known about the Brontës. It differs from biography in the interpretation. Barry Unsworth said in *Losing Nelson*, 'All the imagination needs is the stimulus of facts.' For well over a hundred years the facts about Patrick Brontë were interpreted negatively, particularly in their treatment of his marriage to Maria Branwell. There is no shred of evidence that the marriage was anything but happy; even the greatest manifestation of their happiness, their six children, has been used against him. This is to disregard the fundamental nature of Victorian marriage: babies were born because couples had sex and it is possible that women, while regretting frequent pregnancies, were nevertheless enthusiastic about what caused them. Contraception has dulled our empathy.

Some of the dialogue is taken straight from primary sources: the conversation between Tabby and the old man when Patrick is ill is recorded by Charlotte; the testimonies of the servants about Patrick's kindness and goodness as a husband are also recorded; but there is, for instance, no evidence that Patrick met Lord Byron, but they were contemporary at Cambridge in 1805, were both writing poetry and passionately fond of dogs for the rest of their lives. Patrick came to England in July 1802, well before the start of the Cambridge term in October. There has to be an explanation for this, and I think mine is plausible. His change of name from Brunty to Brontë can be seen in the registers of St John's College, Cambridge. His French phrase book still exists as does Emily's carefully fingered piano music. Any reader who has not visited the Brontë Parsonage Museum in Haworth should go immediately; it is surely our most evocative literary shrine.

All writers on the Brontës owe huge debts to a century of interest and scholarship. I acknowledge these debts humbly and gratefully.

For Patrick, the greatest service came from Juliet Barker, who started to set his record straight. He would have been courteously grateful to her, but he would regard it as unnecessary. He was, after all, solely concerned with his children.

ACKNOWLEDGEMENTS

Many people have helped me during the writing of this book; particular thanks are due to: Jo Leveridge and Geoffrey Palmer for their time in reading the manuscript and their unstinting encouragement; Sebastian Moffett for sound professional advice; Lucy Moffett for accompanying me on my very first visit to Haworth; Rachel Terry and Ann Dinsdale for help in the Brontë Parsonage Museum and Library; Brenda and Alan Fox, the present owners of Hill Top, for nurture during my treks to Haworth, and for lending me Freda, Bess and Moss for a very Brontë dog experience on the moors; Louisa and Alan Stoney for nurture at the Irish end where ideas come more easily in the pure air of Rosturk and Peter Turner, who, having an obsession himself, is tolerant of mine.

PROLOGUE

Three children in the National Portait Gallery, painted by a fourth: a unique achievement for the Reverend Patrick Brontë.

Born on St Patrick's Day 1777 to a barely literate Irish peasant family, he leapt a social chasm through his passion for learning. Blacksmithing, weaving and teaching were his preparation for St John's College, Cambridge, where his gracious spirit charmed educated men and won their support and approval. His moral courage inspired fear and respect.

He was 'Papa' to Charlotte, Emily and Anne, and to Branwell, his only son, a brilliant, flawed spirit with ambition devastated by drink and drugs. He was 'dear saucy Pat' to his beloved wife, before her untimely death left him with six children under the age of eight. To those children he was father, teacher, priest, companion, guide and a lighter of fires. The world he created for them fuelled their genius.

They hated to be away from his home. In all their prolific writing there is no word of criticism of him. And yet, because he was unconcerned with the world and cared little for opinion, he left unchanged the reputation so mischievously created for him. No longer through a glass darkly, we now see him face to face.

Part One

The Wandering Years

1

Papa will perhaps think it a wild and ambitious scheme; but
... when he left Ireland to go to Cambridge University, he
was as ambitious as I am now.

Charlotte Brontë, letter to her aunt Miss Branwell,
29th September 1841.

The blood from his mouth spattered his fists as he struggled while
they bundled him into the cart. He fell against the damp wall with
a thud; in the stifling gloom he could now make out the features
of the three men who had brought him to the thatched cabin at
the foot of the mountains. The stink of bodies, smoking-wet turf
and the unventilated atmosphere which was made necessary by the
Irish winter overcame him, and he retched.

'I'm sorry, Pat,' said Michael Sullivan, 'but you would not have
come if we'd asked you nicely.'

'You're right, Michael,' Patrick Brunty replied. 'Never in a
thousand years. Cattle maiming and gun smuggling are not my
interests. I understand your cause, but I detest your methods.'

'Your brother Billy's not so unsympathetic.' The burly man's
face was angry, although his voice was steady. 'Billy is a United
Irishman, loyal and true, but unfortunately illiterate like the rest of
your family. But you – you write and speak the language of the
enemy as easily as an Englishman, and you keep the Gaelic only
for entertainment...'

'What do you want?' Patrick interrupted. He rose, towering over
all the men. 'I will not remain here to listen to your views on the
Act of Union or the varying politics of my family.' His pale blue
eyes, discernible in the gloom, were cold, and the single candle
shone on his red hair. His attempt to reach the door was blocked
by the solid bodies of the four men.

'You'll write for us, Pat,' the smallest one said. 'If you won't join us, you can help us. We'll make sure that your superior Protestant education with the Reverend Thomas Tighe will help our rebellion.' He laughed at his own wit, seeing the Drumballyroney minister as an insurrectionist.

'I could read and write well enough before Thomas Tighe taught me Latin and Greek.' Pat stood over Michael, threatening and fearless, staring down into his black eyes. 'Tell me what you want before I knock you down!'

Sullivan raised a clenched fist and then dropped it.

'You'll write a letter for us to the garrison, in English, setting out our demands. It's a great weakness in our cause, not knowing the language of our enemy. We have pen, ink and paper.'

'It certainly created a stir when Mick bought them,' said Liam McGuire. 'Mrs Neeley thought he was going soft in the head and was all for refusing to sell them to him.'

'Shut your mouth,' growled Sullivan. 'Write what we want, Pat, for although I've known you all my life, I'll maim you like the cattle if you don't.'

'I'll do it,' said Patrick. *There is a world elsewhere*, he thought. 'But I won't write threats and you'll be polite. What you are engaging in is politics, and the language of politics is reason.'

'Not in our experience,' said Sullivan grimly. 'But as you wish, as long as the meaning is clear.'

They moved a wooden box towards him, on which were ranged the writing tools. He wrote, not at their dictation, but with his own interpretation, slowly, deliberately, his eyes close to the page in the weak candlelight, the quill scratching regularly in the silence as only the occasional foot shifted. At last he sat back, scattering the sand across the paper. Suddenly he laughed. 'You wouldn't know if I had offered a surrender! I could have written it in Greek and you wouldn't know. If ever there was an argument for opportunity for education!' And he wiped the mirth from his eyes.

McGuire snatched the paper up and pushed him roughly towards the door. 'You were always too clever for your own good, Brunty,' he said, 'even in the hedge schools.' He thrust a lantern into his hand and threw him out into the sheeting rain.

෴

He covered the six miles back to Ballynaskeagh in less than an hour, his long legs and sure feet instinctively skimming the bog and stones, finding the straightest route by following the familiar horizon which was lit by the moon. The beating rain streamed down his face, plastering his red hair until it was black against his skull, and he felt relief spread through him as the cold and wet cooled his anger. The lantern swayed with the movements of his body and gave tipsy, fleeting pictures of the sheep that huddled into the turf and stones. Joining the road, he kept his pace and arrived at the Brunty house.

He entered the kitchen and doused his head and hands, rubbed his hair roughly and took a dry shirt from the horse in front of the fire.

'I'm going to Tighe's,' he said to his mother.

'Be careful, Pat,' she replied. 'Billy and his friends are out tonight, and the Whiteboys are about. There's trouble.'

'I know.' He smiled. 'I've had it.'

She saw the cut on his lip but said nothing, only looked at him and crossed herself. He kissed the top of her head and went back out into the pelting rain.

☙

Instead of going up the backstairs to the schoolroom where he taught the rector's sons, Patrick went through the deserted kitchen and entered the stone-flagged hall. He stopped before the mahogany door on the left, his hand brushing his soaked hair as he pulled his wet coat into shape. He knocked gently and barely paused for Thomas Tighe's invitation to enter.

'Patrick!' he said, turning from his desk and removing his spectacles. 'I didn't expect you so late. Sit, please.' He rose and brought the candles over to where his dripping tutor hovered. The dog in front of the fire dragged itself out of sleep and wagged its way towards him, resting his head on his knee with a confidence that expected kindness.

'I'm sorry,' Patrick said. 'I know it's late. I've just come from a meeting of the United Irishmen.'

'You've joined them?' Tighe's white eyebrows shot up, only his inbred courtesy and affection for his protégé preventing further comment.

5

'No – it wasn't that sort of meeting. An enforced one. They wanted me to use my skills in writing English to send their demands to the garrison. I did it. I'm ashamed.' A sudden squall sent rain spattering down the chimney, hissing on the turf. There was no other sound in the room. Patrick drew his fingers slowly along the dog's head, watching the hairs flatten then recover.

'I know we'd planned that I should teach the boys until I left for Cambridge at the end of September.' He had to break the silence, for the first time finding it hard to talk to this trusted friend and priest.

A nod.

He swallowed hard. 'I think I must go sooner. I'm being drawn more and more into the troubles here. If I stay for the next few months I fear I could lose everything I have worked for – you and I have worked together for. It was bad enough after Ballynahinch when I had to close the school and you saved me by letting me tutor the boys.'

'That was entirely our gain, Pat,' said the rector. 'They had a learned and enthusiastic teacher, and I have taught Greek and Latin to the ablest man I have met since I came here over thirty years ago. And when you go to St John's, eventually God will have a good worker in his fields. I still remember the day when Andrew Harshaw told me he had found you in the woods reciting Milton to the trees.'

Patrick blushed. 'I wanted to hear the sounds, not merely read them on the page. I could hardly do it in the kitchen at home. That is part of the problem. I cannot hate England with Billy and the rest of them when everything I love is in her language.'

The rector nodded again.

'I've never met a man with such a passion for literature as you, Pat; and you absorbed Latin and Greek effortlessly. Sometimes I feel you understand their poetry better than I do myself. God has given you great gifts. Will your father mind you leaving before the harvest?'

'We are five boys, so he will have help. He is fair and just. He's proud of my achievements; he never pushed me to work longer hours with him if I wanted to study. Like me, he could scarcely believe that St John's would take me on your recommendation. He's always understood my passions. His own is storytelling, Gaelic or English; he keeps the family and his friends spellbound for hours. His great regret is that he can neither read nor write, and that my brothers and sisters are limited to their signatures.'

Thomas Tighe sighed. Leaning his elbow on the beam above the hearth, he kicked the dying embers of the fire with his boot, creating a brief flaring.

'It is a great sadness, this lack of education for the Irish people.' Patrick smiled to himself, remembering his own utterances earlier, in different, less pleasant circumstances. 'The division between Protestant and Catholic in this land, and the two nations of Ireland and England, has led to great injustice, although I wouldn't want you to repeat that I said that,' he added hastily. 'It should not be that only a man of your calibre can get an education despite his low birth.' Patrick smiled again at the rector's easy statement. If he had been another man, he might have punched him. 'But once you had the basics there was no stopping you. Working in the forge and weaving left little daylight for your study, but you soon had a school of your own . . .'

Brunty leaned forward in his chair, elbows on his knees, his hand movements reflecting the excitement he recalled. 'Sometimes in the depth of the winter it was hard, rising with no hope of natural light before I left for work, reading by a single candle. But for the rest of the day the poetry was with me. You know,' – and he looked with real pleasure at the intent rector – 'the rhythm of the loom used to help me to remember the poetry; I would repeat it in lines or phrases as the shuttle flew back and forth. Sometimes I was barely aware of the weaving, which had its own consequences!'

'And you are anxious to retain your opportunity,' Tighe probed gently, 'so you want to leave now?'

'I don't want to leave; but if I stay even for a few months God alone knows how things will shape here. My poor mother – a Catholic as you know – is desperate at the division in the family. I'm not as tolerant as my education should make me; I should be able to argue rationally with Billy, but I've a hot temper and the rows flare. Only last week she took a pan of water to us, like two fighting dogs. But what I experienced tonight is worse than family rows.'

'So?'

'So, if you'll allow it, I'll go to England soon – in July. I know I can't reside at St John's until I register in October, when the terms of my sizarship start. But I can work at something, in the fields and on the roads; I've done it all before. I'm not running away, but I can't stay and be a pawn in a game I see no point in. Violence will ruin all our lives.'

'You are right to go, my boy. I will see everything is in order for your arrival in Cambridge in October.'

The tension in Pat's body broke and he fell back into the depths of the chair. 'I'll be in to say goodbye to the boys,' he said gratefully. 'I shall miss all of you. Without you I wouldn't be going to Cambridge. Whoever heard of a man of my origins doing that?'

'It's a rum system, Pat, that prevents a man of your talents from using them. This time it has been prevented.' The dog shifted from its secure sleep on Patrick's feet as he rose to go. Letting himself out at the back door, he bent down to give the velvet ears a final caress and disappeared into the unrelieved darkness, alert to every sound and movement.

2

But I was . . . a stranger in a strange land.
Patrick Brontë to the Reverend John Buckworth,
27th November 1821.

The packet rode the swell of the harbour well. With his modest box stowed, Patrick had been gazing interestedly at the cattle huddled on the deck; suddenly he turned and looked towards the disappearing Irish coastline. The tears in his eyes surprised him, and he was filled with a mild panic. He had scarcely ever been out of County Down, and then only twice to Belfast to sell the linen he had woven and to buy books from his wages. He turned his back on the retreating coast and breathed deeply. He began to feel mildly queasy and welcomed the sickness as a distraction from his surprising emotions. Several groups of passengers precipitately sought their cabins, handkerchiefs to mouths. Those without cabins, like Patrick, vomited over the rails, unable to reach the tin pans provided.

'Here,' said a voice at his elbow, 'try this.'

He looked up from his misery to see a ruddy-faced man offering him a small bottle.

'It's the strong stuff,' he said amiably, 'it will settle you eventually.' As Patrick looked doubtful the man went on, 'Go on, take it – I do this crossing every year, and it never fails.'

Patrick swigged. 'You're kind,' he said, for the man looked as if surplus was strange to him. 'Have you enough for yourself?' He breathed deeply again. He did indeed feel better.

'I've enough of this,' replied the man, laughing. 'But not enough of anything else. I go to work every year in England. The landlord puts up the rent, and we can't pay it from the crops we grow, so here I am. What about you?'

9

'I'm going to Cambridge, to the university.' It sounded odd, as if he were telling a story. 'I'll be gone four years. I don't expect I'll be back before then.'

'To Cambridge?' His new friend drew back a little, fearing he had been familiar with a gentleman, despite the rough but clean homespun clothing.

'Yes,' said Pat, sensing the unease. 'But like yourself, I think, I have worked on the land, in the smithy and in the weaving shed. I've been incredibly lucky.'

'And clever, to be sure,' said the man. 'Luck will only take you part of the way. Are you not anxious at mixing with the gentry at the university? The English gentry at that? From what we see in Ireland there is little love of the Irish in them.'

Pat sighed. 'I just don't know. I have to take my chance, whatever it is. I have endured difficulties to get there, and if necessary I'll endure more to get a degree.'

'What will you be in the end?'

'A poet,' Pat said without hesitation, his eyes lighting up. 'Or a clergyman,' he added with a little less enthusiasm.

'You'll be a gentleman if you're a clergyman,' replied the man. 'I'm not so sure about poets.'

Patrick dug in his pocket and brought out the bread wrapped in a cloth that his mother had pressed on him. His stomach had recovered. 'Here,' he said, 'share this with me. I'm Pat Brunty.'

'Sean Laughlin. That's good of you. A dram is easy come by, but we did not have bread to spare; there are eight children. They're a gift of the Lord, but a terrible responsibility. You will no doubt find that out!'

'Perhaps, ' said Patrick, frowning. 'There's a lot to do before that.'

☙❧

The coachman had not wanted to take his box at Liverpool, making it plain that his coach was for travellers who were generally precluded from having luggage by their poverty. 'I can see that,' said Pat angrily, looking at the bony horses and the ill-fitting harness which chafed their breasts and faces. His love of animals had often set him at odds with his family, who regarded them as slaves to be worked, seldom as companions and friends. 'But I would be obliged if you would let me travel with you; I cannot afford the mail. I will pay you extra for the box.'

The coachman accepted his money grudgingly and left him to stow it away as well as he could. He resented the manners of the man – bog Irish, but with the air of a gentleman. And he wanted to travel on the top of the coach, to keep the costs of his journey down still further. Growling softly to himself, the coachman turned his back on Patrick and heaved himself onto the ancient coach's creaking box and whipped up the horses.

Five hours later they had completed the first stage. Patrick paid his fare and dismounted. His legs were numb and his body aching from the jolting and swaying, which required him to hold himself stiff all the time as he gripped the slim rail provided to help the passengers balance when the coach hit the biggest bumps and holes and the tightest corners. The sun had been hot, but he had removed his hat for fear of losing it to the rushing air: his fair skin was burning and his pale blue eyes watering from peering into the sun and absorbing the alien sights and sounds which were England. He stamped his booted feet to bring the feeling back into them and watched his fellow travellers gather in the inn yard. Those from within the coach had immediately gone inside to order food and drink; Pat and the other 'outsiders' strolled about in the yard. He noticed that some brought out bread from their bundles. It was too early for him to eat; he could save it for later. He would not start paying for food until hunger really drove him.

He walked over to the stable yard and watched the ostlers working with the horses. The standard of care was reasonable; horses which were not fit enough to travel fast in a team were nothing but trouble to a jobmaster. He leaned on the door of a loose box and breathed in the grassy smell of warm sweaty horse which enveloped him like a comforting blanket, reminding him of home. Reaching in to touch a sinewy black neck, he patted it with a satisfying dull slap and breathed gently into the animal's nostrils. Its ears came forward, and Patrick breathed again. He would miss the horses, the farm, the life he had made in the school and with the Tighes. He was suddenly overwhelmed by the unknown life in front of him: he didn't know a soul; no one knew him. He was a stranger in a strange land. His empty stomach lurched, and his face burned. What if he did not succeed? What if Thomas Tighe, resident in the backwoods of County Down for thirty years, had misjudged his abilities? What if the English despised him, as they seemed to despise the rest of his kinsmen?

Suddenly the horse shook its head, the collar jangling and breaking into his nightmare. He reached for its mane and gave it an affectionate tug. He breathed in the smell he loved and looked the horse straight in the eye. *Thank you,* he said softly, *for stopping my fear. There is no 'What if?' It is up to me.*

Rain and mud sometimes forced him to buy a night's lodging. He had hoped to pass the nights in hedges or barns near the inns where the coach changed horses, but this night his clothes would have suffered lying in a field and there was no barn. His own fastidiousness demanded it, too. He had to arrive in Cambridge looking as near to a gentleman as he could get with his country clothes. He had kept clean by washing under inn-yard pumps and in streams, and his fair skin produced little beard, which prevented an unkempt look. His fellow sleepers were less fastidious: he lay close to the edge of the mattress, trying to avoid the sweaty body of the man next to him who rolled and groaned as he slept; he shut his eyes and ears to the noisy couplings of the inn miss and his fellow travellers. She had offered, but Pat reasonably judged that if he could barely afford food and lodging he certainly could not afford her pleasures. His box was beside him on the floor; suddenly he was awake, startled, staring into the darkness, roused by the giggles and groans from the corner; he caught a gleam of moon-light which silvered a hand approaching the belongings that lay on top of his box. He grabbed the hand, twisted it hard and, rising up, thwacked its owner across the head. He pushed the man into a corner of the room and punched him again, until he dribbled down the wall and onto the floor.

'Don't,' he said, holding the head back by its hair, 'ever do that again, to me or to any other man who has worked for his money and needs it!' The other sleepers protested at the noise, and Pat returned to the mattress, clutching his goods to his chest.

The rain had stopped in the morning, and he was back to the jolting and the burning heat. He had grown used to the English countryside, friendly huddles of cottages and houses around a church, grouped as if they were in conversation with each other. In Ireland villages were strung out along roads; cabins isolated in the midst of fields. *Isolated like me,* he thought. *Will I ever become convivial with the English? Or will I always be alone as I am now?* By the time the coach reached London he was a few pounds lighter from his frugal diet and aware that his lightly covered frame had been scant protection against the rigours of the outside ride. When he made his final descent into the yard of the Cock and Hen in Fleet Street, he could barely lift his box onto his shoulder without steadying himself on some railings. It surprised him, for he had always worked with his father even when he was a schoolmaster, and he thought he could lift anything. Four days and four nights without food, rest or exercise had left him as weak as a puppy.

The river drew him, and he walked through the crowds towards London Bridge and gazed on the city he knew from his reading. He leaned on the rail, his box at his feet. *Sweet Thames*, he murmured, marvelling at the dome and spires. St Paul's gleamed white in the sunlight; the water was churned and chopped by the river traffic, noisy with human cries and trading boats. He breathed in the rank smell of the water, his eyes sharp and his heart beating fast with excitement. His box was heavy, and the Chapter Coffee House near St Paul's, recommended by Thomas Tighe as a comfortable lodging for a gentleman of literary interests, would have cost him more than he dared spend without a fuller knowledge of the expenses ahead of him at Cambridge. It would have to be a lodging house, the sort of accommodation he had experienced on the journey, and he dared not leave his box while he roamed the city. He would have to keep it with him.

He cut a strange figure: tall, slim, graceful, shining red hair, immaculate coarse black coat and hat. He swayed slightly as he manoeuvred the box on his shoulder, stopping to identify landmarks, his face both grave and delighted as he passed from one to another, resting the box from time to time but ever wary of its separation from him. By afternoon he had to buy both water and bread from street sellers; his foreign speech brought joking responses which he barely understood, and he felt exhausted with the strangeness of it all. He had barely spoken to anyone since he came off the boat. His fellow travellers on the stage had been too poor and too uncomfortable to bother with him, and Londoners seemed humorously hostile and always in a hurry. He reached St Paul's, where he knew the bookshops were. Having examined all the titles on the hinged shutter outside one on the corner of Paternoster Row, he cautiously entered, breathing with satisfaction

13

the smell of new paper and leather bindings. He tentatively asked the bespectacled man reading behind the scuffed wooden counter if he minded if he put his box down while he looked at the huge assortment of books.

'No, sir,' said he, 'for no one buys a book by its cover, and you need two hands to open it with. You're travelling?' he asked in a friendly fashion, which encouraged Patrick. It was the first sensible reaction he'd had all day.

'Yes,' he replied and, risking what had become the inevitable reaction to his nationality, he continued: 'I've come from Ireland. I'm going to the university at Cambridge. St John's College.'

'Ah,' said the man. 'You are Irish. A very literary nation.'

Pat was disarmed; relief flooded his features.

'You think so?'

'I know so. Dean Swift, Oliver Goldsmith, for two. And all the friends I ever made in the pubs of Dublin on my book-buying visits!'

'I want to write,' Pat said hesitantly, 'but first I have to get a degree and a profession. I would like to write like Scott, poetry and narrative combined.'

'When you publish, let me know. I'm George Moffett. Look as long as you like, and let your box rest from your shoulder.'

'I won't be buying.' He was apologetic. 'I'm Patrick Brunty. I have to wait until I know what my expenses will be. But I will be back, and thank you for your kindness.'

Well over two hours later, Moffett shut up the shop, smiling to himself as he watched the tall figure steady his burden and move off in search of his mean lodgings.

∽

He arose as soon as it was light, examining himself carefully for fleas and then making use of the pot and bowl of grey water on the landing outside the room he had shared with eight others. He left the house quietly – lodgers were relieved of their two-pences on arrival so there was nothing left to pay – and he was glad of the cool air which hit him as a contrast to the thick, warm, noxious atmosphere he had slept in. He had bound his box to his wrist with a book strap he had packed and brought with him, but had still only felt secure enough to sleep fitfully. He walked

14

back to Fleet Street and found the coach bound east for Cambridge.

The coachman was used to young men with boxes, but not to Irishmen. 'Stow your box there, Paddy,' he said, indicating a space in the pile of luggage. The short night had sharpened Patrick's temper.

'My name is Patrick Brunty,' he snapped.

'That's what I said, Paddy,' replied the coachman laconically, as he swung himself up onto his worn seat and alerted the horses; soon the coach crunched, creaked and jingled on its way to the eastbound road.

Patrick marvelled. Apart from George Moffett in his bookshop, whose natural courtesy and literary interests precluded prejudice, he had met with nothing but ridicule and misplaced witticisms whenever he opened his mouth. *Please God*, he thought, *let Cambridge be different, because if it is not I will knock down the first man who mocks me.* He clenched his fists in his pockets as he braced himself against the swaying coach; his set face had the cast of his brother Billy.

But greater than his problem with the indigenous population was his need to survive until the beginning of October, when he would move into St John's. Finding work did not worry him; there would be plenty in the fields for the rest of the month of July and in August, possibly well into September, and his acquaintance on the boat proved to him that Irish labour was expected and acceptable; but what of his box? He could not carry all his possessions with him as he tramped the countryside looking for work. Did he dare ask at the college if they would keep it there for him? But whom would he ask? How would he ask? He could hardly say he needed to leave it while he roamed the countryside looking for labouring work.

By the time the coach rumbled into the Market Square in Cambridge, he had made up his mind. (*Not for nothing*, thought Patrick grimly, as he eased his aching body to the ground, *that the second most frequent admissions to Bedlam are coachmen whose brains have been shaken into madness.*) Ever since he was a small child he had watched his father assume a character as he told his stories and sang his songs, convincing his listeners of every character he played. When Pat first read *Hamlet*, he had thought of Hugh Brunty as the First Player, who:

. . . in a fiction, in a dream of passion
Could force his soul so to his own conceit . . .
And all for nothing.

In the absence of solid information, he would assume a part. No
longer the supplicant Irish peasant, but a gentleman and a member
of the college. Asking the coachman in clear tones where St John's
lay, he retired into a doorway and removed from his box a few
essential personal items, including a pencil and notebook, and
stowed them about him; he brushed his hair, retrieved a clean
neckcloth and wound it round his neck, straightened his coat and
set off.

The pale stone was bathed in afternoon sunlight, and the lines
of the buildings took his breath away. The colleges he passed
to reach his own were finer than he had been able to imagine.
The town was quiet, deserted by undergraduates and populated
mainly by dons and dawdling servants, who showed little interest
in the black-clad figure with its burden perched easily on his
shoulder. *Four years here*, he thought. *What greater blessing could I
have?*

Tighe had told him that the first person he should meet was the
porter, so he approached the door at the left of the arch resolutely.
He tapped lightly on it, and the man inside looked up.

'Good day,' he said in his best town Irish. 'I shall be an
undergraduate here in October, and as I was passing through
Cambridge on another journey, I took the opportunity to bring
with me this small box to lighten the load when I finally come up.
Would you be able to store it for me?'

'Your name, sir?'

That's better, thought Pat. *Sir.*

'Patrick Brunty,' he replied, looking the man straight in the eye.

'Yes, sir, I can help you with that,' the porter eventually replied,
after a silence in which Pat's heart beat fast while the man searched
slowly among great curls of paper spread across the counter he was
leaning on. 'We have a boxes room, and this can go in there to
await your other luggage. I see you are a sizar, sir. You'll be glad
they've abolished the tasks the sizars had to do for the other
gentlemen, I'm sure.' There was a hint of condescension. He
paused. 'Are you Irish, sir?'

16

Patrick groaned inwardly. 'I am,' he said, 'but I will be staying in England until I register. I have business in London.'

'Indeed,' said the porter, without interest. 'I hope you will be happy here. Good day, sir.'

Patrick deposited his wordly goods and turned back onto Trinity Street.

3

Mr Brontë . . . his manner and mode of speech always had the tone of high-bred courtesy.

Ellen Nussey, Reminiscences of Charlotte Brontë, 1871.

Relieved at the success of his performance, Patrick sat beneath a willow which trailed its branches into the river and contemplated his next few weeks. He had left Ireland with ten pounds for his four years in England; but, having left earlier than he had intended, he must survive the intervening months without spending that money. He had stitched it into the inner pocket of his coat and would have to work out a solution for its security while he laboured. His inclination was to go towards Ely and then on to the Norfolk coast. He longed to see the place where Admiral Nelson was born. Sometimes he was disturbed by his addiction to heroes: Nelson, Wellington, even Jesus. Wellington had been born in Ireland, an Irishman who had been sent to England to polish his speech and his manners. Patrick sighed, hands clasped round his knees as he scanned the water for rising fish: these things did seem to matter, but how he could acquire this polish he was none too sure. Nelson, he had read, was a parson's son from a remote village by the sea. He would start to walk that way and pick up work as he went. There was little point in remaining in Cambridge; it would be expensive, and he could hardly risk labouring there and being recognised when he eventually went into residence.

Dusting the grass from his coat and breeches, he enquired the way for Ely. It was fine, clear, sunny. The flat golden fields, as different from his home's rocky and mountainous landscape as possible, stretched towards the great ship of the cathedral which rode the fens. That night he slept in a barn, warm, peaceful, cleansed in the river, at ease with himself for the first time since the start of his journey. There were groups of men in a field, working under the blistering sun. He approached.

'Does your master need more men?' he asked, shading his eyes.

'He may not think he do, but we do!' answered a man leaning on his scythe. 'This needs to be in before the rain, and there's too few of us to cover a field at the moment.'

'Who's asking for work?' A shout from nearby.

'I am, sir,' Patrick shouted back. 'I can work today, or for longer, as you need.'

The burly farmer came over, inspecting him closely as if he were an animal in a market.

'You're big enough,' he said, 'and you look strong. Your speech is strange. Where are you from?'

'Ireland, sir, I . . .'

'We get a lot of Irish,' the farmer cut in. 'Desperate to send money back for the rent, which the big, bad English expect them to pay, and they, it seems, expect to have for free. What do you ask for the day?'

Patrick's anger had started to rise as he picked up the tone of the man's opinion. But he had to have work, and what if they were all like this? He would have to tolerate it.

'Whatever you pay,' he replied quietly.

'Your countrymen will usually take a shilling or two less on the week. You can have a week's work for two shillings less.'

Patrick could hear the men behind him, intent on this conversation, start to grumble. They knew it would be the thin end of the wedge. Theirs would soon be reduced too.

'I won't work for less,' he replied with dignity. 'I'll work for the same rate as everyone else.'

'Suit yourself, Paddy,' was the reply, and the farmer turned on his heel and strolled towards his cart. A small dark man came forward from the group.

'He always tries it with the Irish, boy. Start to walk away, and he'll come after you.'

Patrick grinned at the men and picked up his bundle and his coat from where they lay at his feet. He walked as nonchalantly as he could in the direction of the road. He heard a horse and cart rumble behind him, and the farmer drew level.

'You can work today,' he shouted. 'At the men's rate. I'll see if you're any good.' He cracked the whip on the old mare's rump and was gone.

Thank you, said Pat to himself, *for no one will ever cheat me again.* He had realised with disgust that the apprehension bred in him by this new, strange country had inclined him to take the farmer's insulting offer.

'And thank you,' he said, as he returned to the men. 'I'm not yet used to customs here and I could have fallen for that one.'

'Stick with us, boy,' said the dark man, 'and you won't get wrong.'

By the end of the day Pat's hands were streaked with blood and his back ached, but he was at ease with these men and the common physical labour dispensed with the need for conversation. They liked him for his height, strength and tenacity. Whenever one needed a rest, Pat would cover his place and keep his own in the cutting line, swaying rhythmically as he scythed both sides, never pausing so that the operation proceeded unhindered. His height, and the muscles he had from working in Ireland and covering huge distances without a horse, made him a giant among these pigmy fen dwellers. By evening, as the sun sank into the stubbly field, they were asking him where he would stay for the night.

'There's a barn near the cottages where Nero lives,' said a little old man, sweat running through the dust on his seamed face, indicating the dark man.

'Nero?' said Pat in astonishment. 'The Roman emperor?'

'Don't know about that,' said Nero. 'That's what they've always called me. But you can sleep in the barn, there's a pump in the yard, and we'll take you to the inn my brother has, and you'll get food there.'

Now if this is what the English are really like, I shall be happy here, Pat thought. He spent the evening in the inn, which, they told him, had been built as a lodging for the men who dug out the Bedford Levels. Below the waterline, the brick floor of the inn shone with the damp which penetrated from the river. After a few drams Pat felt he was among friends enough to treat them to a song.

'My father,' he said, very deliberately, carefully focusing on his hands, which were clasped in front of him on the table, 'is a singer and a storyteller. You will not hear better songs than his.' He stood up. Swaying a little, his light tenor voice rose clearly as he sang of the land he had left and the girls he had loved. Silence fell in the little inn, broken only by the gurgling of the water outside and the melody within.

'Stop it, Pat,' said Nero. 'You'll have us all a-weepin'. Sit down and have some more whiskey.'

'A dram,' said Patrick nostalgically, 'a dram is what it is. The best friend a man ever had.' So saying, he attempted to rise to propose a toast to them all, but instead disappeared beneath the table and was carried to his barn and gently deposited in the warm straw by his new friends.

⚭

When he reached the coast he had three more guineas in his pocket to add to his ten pounds. He had not only kept himself, but added to his store. The stony road crawled and snaked away from the sandy beaches as if it feared the wind; the trees grew low and lean, with an excessive slant away from the sea. The little houses crouched low, too. At Burnham Thorpe he saw the parsonage where Nelson was born, where his father had been the parson until he died. The old house was being pulled down and, gazing on the ruins which were being created, Patrick reflected that they might one day regret the loss of such a birthplace.

He took the road to Overy Staithe where he knew the brave sailor had first seen the sea. He watched the boats and the tide, which left them stranded and then trickled back around them until it suddenly obliterated the creeks and marshes. He helped an old fisherman and his son unload their catch as rain fell unexpectedly; eventually the two younger men sent the old man off to get dry while they continued to work with the nets and boxing the fish. They were both thoroughly soaked, and the young man offered Pat a bed in the cottage that faced towards the sea.

'Just by the fire, mind,' he said, 'we only got the one bed, and you won't want to bed with my old gaffer.'

Pat laughed. 'The fire is fine,' he said.

Later that night, when they had eaten a fish stew with coarse bread, Pat took out his bottle and shared a dram or two with Matthew, who produced a jug of beer. Unable to restrain himself, in the happiness of warmth and simple hospitality, he started to sing 'The Red-haired Man's Wife' in Gaelic.

'Where you from, boy?' asked Matthew in surprise. 'Tha's a foreign language. What's your name?'

'Patrick Brunty,' he replied.

'Brontë?' queried Matthew. 'You'm like the good admiral up at the parsonage. He got called the Duke of Brontë. They say he writes himself Nelson and Brontë now.'

'That's right,' Pat said slowly. 'I am Patrick Brontë.'

4

Mr Brontë . . . whose bills I have borrowed, has been at the college three years. He came over from Ireland with 10£ in his pocket, and has no friends or any income or emolument whatever, except what he receives for his Sizarship; yet he does support himself, and that, too, very genteelly.

Henry Kirke White, letter to his mother, 26th October 1805.

'Branty? Or is it Brunty?' queried the registrar testily. 'It looks like Branty here. Parents then? Branty or Brunty? County? Ireland will do. Never mind – we'll call you Paddy. Who's next?'

Patrick's fair face flamed, and he was sweating inside his fresh shirt despite the chill of the autumn day. His arrival at St John's to register had been humiliating. He simply couldn't make the sounds they expected to hear. He would have to do something about the speech. He would have to remember to play the part. He would do better then. He would be Brontë. That would remind him of his hero and distract them from the Irish sounds they did not understand and the Irish jokes they loved to make. He was walking through the meadows, soothed by the familiarity of the gentle cattle grazing; he cut a stick and thwacked the reeds growing by the river. He would try again. Stick in hand, he walked firmly back to the porter's lodge.

'Good morning, Mr Brunty,' said Tompkins; he had not forgotten the red hair and sharp blue eyes.

'Good morning,' Patrick replied deliberately, in his best town Irish. 'Actually it's Brontë.'

'I'm sorry, sir,' came the reply, 'it must be a mistake. I'll alter it here, and then it will be right for residence day,' and without asking further he dipped his quill and scrawled on his long curl of paper. 'Your other luggage hasn't arrived yet.'

'Has it not?' Patrick was vague. 'Perhaps you will tell me where my rooms are and have it sent there.'

'Third Court, Staircase D, top floor. The sizars are usually there. Small rooms, but the gentlemen seem to manage.'

'My thanks to you,' said Pat, doffing his hat. *Nothing to be lost by politeness.*

Since his return from Norfolk four days ago he had paid for a room in the town with Mrs Kelly. Hearing her talking in the street he had been overwhelmed by a wave of homesickness which surprised and shocked him. He followed her into Green Street, where she unlocked a door and paused to heave her basket of washing back onto her hip. He offered to help her up the steps with the burden and then daringly asked her if she knew of rooms to rent for a short time. She was garrulously glad to talk to a compatriot and soon had him inside and seated at her kitchen table with a brew of tea.

'You'll stay here with me!' she said. 'Nowhere else. Sure the English do not understand hospitality the way we do. I take gentlemen for time to time, and I've a room free.' She was almost as excited about him going to St John's as he was.

'A great achievement! I don't know of another Irishman in the university. Francis and I came here because of the river work for him, and I thought that a university would need washerwomen. But I've not met another Irishman. You'll be a sensation, with that lovely red hair and those blue eyes . . .'

'I hope not,' said Pat fervently. Suddenly the door opened and in came the most beautiful girl he had ever seen. Golden curls framed her fine-boned face, and the rest of her hair was tied towards the top of her head. Her dark brown eyes gazed expressionlessly at him; her skin was pale but glowing.

'It's Mr Brontë, Mary. This is my daughter, Mr Brontë. Mary, he's to be a student at St John's, and we must prepare his clothes for Thursday. And look after him until then.'

Mary looked at Pat. 'You're older than most students,' she said, with just a trace of Irish. 'Most of them look sixteen or seventeen and behave like it.'

'Go and start scouring Mr Brontë's coat, Mary,' said her mother swiftly, as if anticipating more views which she did not think proper. She sighed after the girl had gone. 'Young girls today have no sense of their betters. She gets impatient with the rich young men we see round here.'

'Then she'll have no trouble with me,' laughed Pat, 'for I am old to her, and poor, and I shall be industrious, as this is the best chance I've had in my life.'

⟲⟳

The residence day dawned cool and bright; autumn leaves had begun to fall, and the town was noisy and bustling in contrast to the tranquillity Pat had seen in July. Carriages jammed Trinity Street and Patrick sidled his way between them, noticing the coats of arms painted on the doors of some and even a coronet entering the gates of Trinity next door. He felt unnerved. There were servants everywhere: coachmen, grooms, footmen, valets with hat-boxes, college servants, men everywhere juggling with boxes and trunks. Out of the carriages stepped young men with fine coats and brightly coloured waistcoats flashing beneath their well-cut cloaks. Many of them reminded Pat of pictures he had seen of the Prince Regent: curled hair, silver-topped canes and careful postures. He hung back, waiting for a moment when he could break through the crowd and enter the gate. His own plain black coat and breeches, white shirt and stock, were almost like a servant's in their simplicity.

I must play the part, he thought. He gripped the stick he had cut by the river and standing tall, hat in hand, he pushed through the crowd to the porter's lodge.

'Brontë,' he said, clearly. A different man peered at the papers.

'Branty?' he said, holding the paper to the better light at the window.

'No,' said Pat, strictly, 'that's an error. B-R-O-N-T-E. Please don't let it happen again.'

'Sorry, sir. Here's your key. I think your luggage is there. It's a small room. You may be able to change later. It's a sizar's room,' he added quietly.

Patrick walked through First Court and Second Court, revelling within himself at the beauty and dignity of the place. In Third Court he found Staircase D and climbed the wooden stairs to the third floor. Entering the room, he breathed out in pleasure. Small, yes, but about as big as the house he was born in at Emdale. And

25

he had never had a room to himself before. He had written and read at the kitchen table with the hubbub of eleven others about him, and slept with his father and four brothers. The nearest he had got to privacy was the Tighe's schoolroom when the boys were absent for a while. But here – he looked out of the window into the courtyards and over the rooftops still touched by the autumn sun – what more could a man want?

Almost bursting with happiness, he unlocked his box and started to make his new life.

◌◌

The boom of many male voices, laughter and talk, encouraged Patrick next day to leave his rooms at the dining hour, and walk towards Hall. As a sizar he had free rooms and meals, and he had heard from Mrs Kelly that these were ample. Coming to the passage between the Hall and the kitchens, he stood stock-still; the conviviality of the young men, who all seemed to know someone, and in some cases many, made his stomach lurch as he reviewed the problem before him. *Of course*, he thought, *they have all come from schools which have sent many of them together to this and other colleges. I have barely been to school. And I know no one.*

Since he arrived the day before he had been happy arranging his few possessions, fetching his cleaned clothes from the Kellys (*touched and smoothed by the hands of the delectable Mary*, he had thought with pleasure) and rereading books he had brought with him. There had been no one in the room opposite him on the staircase, and although he had heard sounds below, the sight of a young man accompanied by a family servant whom he ordered about with scant respect had driven Patrick back to his room. He was always uncomfortable in the presence of men who treated their inferiors badly, his ambiguous position making him fragile. Rising early, he had drunk his breakfast milk and looked forward to his first dining in Hall.

But how would he breach this wall of socially superior, confident young men, to whom dining with servants in attendance was habitual?

He hung around on the fringes of the crowd passing into Hall. No one looked at him; no one spoke to him. Would he go with the throng and take a place, attempt a conversation and wait for the first assault on his Irish accent? Even if he did his town Irish slowly,

26

they might still mock him. His empty stomach rumbled with hunger and anxiety. For the first time in his life, his courage failed him.

He walked slowly back through the deserted courts and, miserable with loneliness and failure, turned left and made for the kitchen bridge. Leaning on the parapet, he watched the weed-strewn water flowing past.

I am a fool, he said to himself. *It is ridiculous that I am standing here, hungry and alone because I fear ridicule. I call myself Brontë, and I have not the courage to face a few rich young men, when Nelson himself will face the Spaniards on a burning ship with no thought for his life. I will screw my courage to the sticking place.* He watched the boatmen for a while and walked back to his room.

When the supper bell rang, he walked determinedly across the courts. The throng was less for this meal, and he took a place at the end of a table where there was no one on his right, his heart pounding but his exterior calm. He ate little, spoke only a few necessary words to his neighbour and marvelled at the beauty of the candle-lit hall, glowing with paintings and suffused with the soft light of silver. He was glad he had seated himself at the end of the table: the light was dim and, with no one on his right, it was possible to observe carefully the manners of those around him. He ate nothing until observation gave him the confidence to do so. It was a world away from the spoons and bowls of his mother's kitchen, even from the plate of cold meat in the Tighe schoolroom. Relieved at having regained his self-respect, he walked in the dark around the college, smelling the sharpness of autumn and the wood smoke from the fires in numerous rooms, loving the glowing windows and murmuring voices within.

5

My Prize Book, for always having kept in the first Class, at St John's College – Cambridge – P Brontë A B. To be retained -semper-.

> Inscription in the front of the *Iliad*, given to Patrick Brontë as a prize when he was a student.

The day Henry Purefoy Browne left a pair of herrings on the staircase was the day Patrick became a legend in the college. He had found the eighteen-year-old aristocrat irritating in many ways; yes, he did mock Patrick's accent and talked loudly of his father's estates in Ireland and the feckless tenants; yes, he slept most of the day and broke the nights brawling with his drunken friends in his finely furnished rooms at the bottom of the staircase; and his late arrival back from the inns and stews of the town woke everyone, although Patrick was often up and at his books by then. But Patrick's happiness in his studies, and the poetry he was writing in the little leisure time he allowed himself, made him tolerant despite his lack of sleep. The herrings, however, were not to be tolerated.

Gathering them from each landing as he took the staircase in flying leaps towards Browne's rooms, he found the unsuspecting young man in the Court.

'Paddy,' he drawled, 'I thought you'd find them tasty. I meant to get you a potato as well. Next time, maybe.'

'There will be no next time,' growled Pat, seizing him by the collar with one hand and propelling him swiftly towards the bridge round the corner. He was much taller and stronger than the foppish young man, and he lifted him effortlessly onto the parapet. Steadying his victim with one hand as he writhed and protested, he stuffed the herrings one by one down the front of his fashionable silk waistcoat and then tipped him into the fast-moving river.

'Don't ever try anything like that again,' he called as Browne splashed his way towards the bank. 'I'll do worse next time. Be assured of that,' and, hands in pockets, he strolled back to Third Court.

Nunn, his fellow sizar and opposite neighbour on the staircase, had watched the whole business and was laughing tearfully.

'I expect I shall hear from Wood about this,' said Patrick ruefully. 'But I can't bear his manners; he's noble and educated. He should be polite, tolerant and fair.'

'You're an idealist, Pat,' said Nunn. 'For half the people here it's like casting pearls before swine. I think it is we who set them an example.'

'Come on,' said Patrick. 'I have the dregs of a bottle I brought from Ireland, and the day is getting colder. Did you know the Irish only drink to keep the damp from their bones and the fairies away? And I'll sing you a song.'

Nunn started to laugh again, as they took the stairs two and three at a time in a race to the top.

ᕲᕬ

Patrick did indeed hear from Wood about the incident on the bridge. His tutor had been a sizar himself, and through sheer academic brilliance was now a Fellow of the college and destined for even greater things in the university. He had been not only an excellent tutor but also a good friend to Patrick in his early days. When Patrick next visited him with his Vergil, he braced himself for a reprimand.

'I understand your feelings, Brontë, but I'm disappointed at your behaviour towards Browne,' he said. 'The number of times we have together deplored the development of violence in your country!'

Pat rallied a little to defend himself. 'Hardly violence,' he ventured, 'I only dropped him in the river.'

'But the herrings . . .'

'He obtained the herrings. I only returned them to him.'

'I only mention it', said Wood, 'because you're doing so well. Your diligence and discipline produce excellent results. You've been in the First Class twice now. So such behaviour, for an intending clergyman . . . And Tompkins has spoken to me about

29

the dogs again...' The good, mild man looked slightly embarrassed.

'I've never brought one in since the first time. I really didn't know the rule about them then. I thought he would be quiet and I could feed him up a bit. I always leave them at the gate now.' Pat was contrite. 'But Browne is a silly boy. I only wanted to teach him a lesson. He has been quieter since.'

'He needs to be,' replied Wood. 'His work, or lack of it, will have him sent down. But you – are you managing your bills Patrick? I know you have nothing but your savings and the exhibitions you have won in college.'

'I'm fine,' said Patrick. He didn't tell him about the vacation work, which had continued from time to time with his friends near Ely. 'You know I now have twenty pounds a year from Mr Wilberforce and Mr Thornton?'

'Yes. I'm glad of that. They were very impressed with you.'

'Your advice has been valuable, and I do very well,' said Patrick gratefully.

He returned to his rooms and followed one particular piece of Wood's advice. With candles at 2s 10d a pound, even allowing for the ends he bought off the college servants, lighting his studies was a great expense in the winter. He and Nunn took it in turns to sit on the stairs, feet wrapped in straw for warmth, to read by the flicker of the rushlight on the landing, as Wood had done when he was a sizar. Patrick actually enjoyed it: the landing window had a sheer drop to the river below, and he loved to watch the light fade and the reflection of the water dapple the walls. He heard the coughing from the neighbouring rooms, and joined in with his own Cambridge hack. Every man seemed to have a cough, bred by the dampness of the misty, foggy fen town. The infection he had had in Ireland protected him from the worst cough of all.

His relationship with the puerile Browne took a surprising turn. One day he heard unfamiliar, slow footsteps coming up the stairs, which hesitated at his open door. Patrick looked up from his writing, pushed his red hair out of his eyes and saw Henry Purefoy Browne looking decidedly sheepish.

'Brontë,' he said, 'I'm in an awful fix. My tutor has written to my father that I will be sent down if I don't do some work. I can't do it, Brontë. Never could, not even at Harrow.'

'And?' said Pat.

30

'And I wonder – and don't take offence, please,' he added nervously, taking a step backwards as Patrick rose and walked towards the window, 'I wondered if you'd do it for me if I paid you. Other fellows do – I don't mean to be insulting.'

Patrick laughed. 'Education! Will it ever be right? Those that don't have it desire it thirstily, and those who have it can't abide it. No – it's all right, I'm not going to hit you. But I've a better idea.'

'You have?'

'There's no point in me doing the work. Catton will soon know it's not you when he talks to you and you don't know one writer from another. But Latin can be learned. It's a matter of memory and application in the early stages. At least you could do that, even if the finer points of Pliny escape you.'

Henry looked blank.

'I will teach you – don't look so desperate – I will teach you and help you do the work yourself. You'll have learned a little at Harrow. We'll build on that. Twice a week at two o'clock, before dinner. Think how virtuous you'll feel, and what an appetite you'll have!'

And so it was: twice a week at two o'clock, Henry meekly climbed the stairs to Patrick's rooms (for he would not go down) and worked for two hours until his tired little brain sagged with the effort Pat drew from him. He even enjoyed it, for Pat was a skilled and enthusiastic teacher whose love of his subject was infectious. And every week Henry paid Pat half a guinea, and Pat paid his college bills. His contempt for the rich and foolish became tempered to an amused affection.

31

6

Mr Helstone . . . had missed his vocation: he should have been a soldier, and circumstances had made him a priest.

Charlotte Brontë, *Shirley*, Chapter 3.

'Brontë,' said Lord Palmerston, turning to Patrick who was seated on his right in Hall, 'you are the best, you know.'

Pat stared into the depths of his empty tankard, eyebrows raised in surprise.

'I mean,' continued Palmerston, 'you are the only volunteer in the corps who can load four to the minute. That's a professional standard. Bircham says some very good things about you.'

Patrick's career as a volunteer in the gentlemen of the university's volunteer corps had given him immense satisfaction. His strong body welcomed the physical challenge, and it was a world away from his other accomplishments, his Greek, Latin, mathematics and divinity. Although no regiment would have looked at him because of his social status, he had an undiminished passion for the military and his heroes, Wellington and Nelson. His height, enthusiasm and commitment soon made him the star of the Volunteers. He loved the scarlet tunic, he worked hard at the shooting practice, and no drilling was ever too tedious for him.

'As our best man,' – Palmerston interrupted his day dream – 'I would like you to assist when we present Captain Bircham with two hundred guineas.'

Two hundred guineas! thought Pat. *These people understand precious little about real money.*

'We shall muster at Parker's Piece, perform the usual manoeuvres and then form a hollow square. You will come forward, salute and present the purse.'

Pat tried not to show his pleasure. He had found it amusing that the scarcely bearded Palmerston should at eighteen be the officer in charge of the St John's Volunteers. But his social status, and the threat of an invasion by Napoleon, made it appropriate that the importance of the corps should be emphasised by his noble birth.

The crowd which gathered to see the presentation to Captain Bircham included Mary Kelly. Later, when she and Pat walked by the river in the cool evening, well away from the prying eyes of St John's, she teasingly reminded him of his social progress since the day they first met in her mother's house.

'Handsome you always were, Pat, and clever, but such a gentleman now, and even more since you've become a soldier.' When she was with him, her eyes lost the blank look she kept for the admiring young men who were naturally drawn by her beauty. Pat had never seen so much beauty with so little vanity.

'You're mocking me,' he said quietly, 'and you well know I've had enough of that. Shall we talk instead of the poetry you like?'

She had strong views on the wasted opportunities she saw all around her in Cambridge. She had learned to read and write in a dame school but had read eagerly on her own, and, although his Latin and Greek were beyond her, she loved Patrick to tell her about the poetry he read and the writing he did.

'Your poetry is not very like you, Pat,' she said, frowning. 'You're religious, and you'll be a clergyman, but I thought your poetry would be more ... well ... passionate, about nature and about love.'

He sighed. 'It should be. But the part of the church to which I now belong, and whose members help me to stay here, believes that the purpose of literature is not entertainment, but improvement. So I shackle my feelings and write what it is appropriate.'

'It shows,' said Mary. 'Knowing you, I would expect great love poems and sweeping descriptions of our great country!'

'Inside I am full of those, especially love,' he murmured as they reached a thickly fronded willow which almost enclosed them. He pulled her arm up to his chest and then encircled her completely; his red hair mingled with her shining golden curls as he kissed her with all the passion missing from his poetry. He kissed her again and again, until the spell was broken by the entrance of three noisy young men into their leafy privacy. They moved apart.

'You shouldn't, Pat,' she said. 'You will soon be a gentleman clergyman and you can't be friends with a washerwoman's daughter. I shall marry the boring Thomas Robinson, cook at Trinity, to please my mother and to escape from her. I shall forget about poetry and spend the rest of my life in this town watching wasted opportunities and envying the young cubs who fritter them.'

Patrick felt a lump in his throat for he knew that she was right. His loving friendship with Mary had sweetened his time at Cambridge, for he loved the company of women and sorely missed them in the frequently monastic college life. How the other men did without their company he did not know – at least he did know, for many of them boasted of their evenings in the bordellos of the town – but the others seemed unconcerned by the unrelieved maleness of their lives. Pat liked women. He had five sisters at home and he loved his mother's company. He found them good listeners, good friends and often with a great longing for the things of the mind which they were, by their exclusion from education, denied. He had vowed that if ever he had a daughter and a son, they would be treated equally when it came to learning. He understood Mary's longing: she was barred from it by her sex; he had nearly been barred by his poverty.

'Come,' he said, pushing away his distracting and unanswerable thoughts, 'let's walk back to Green Street.'

⚭

Patrick looked up from feeding the dogs that were gathered round the impervious butcher in the Market Square. The man watching him had tears in his eyes. *Not for the dogs*, Pat thought.

'Nelson is dead,' said the stranger.

He walked back to St John's with Rafferty at his heels. It was the same all along the way. Stranger spoke to stranger, 'Nelson is dead', like a litany. At the gate the porter helped Rafferty on his way with his boot, and for once Pat was too absorbed to notice. There were tears in his eyes and a sickness in his stomach. He had loved that man. What of the Brontë name now? It would surely die with Pat.

⚭

The beautiful Lord Byron, limping through the town with his black hair bobbing, fascinated Patrick. Not his nobility, for he knew now

34

that rank and wealth were merely the shell of a man. But his verses, which were published privately, had the effortless grace which Patrick would have nearly given his soul for. Watching him from the wall at the front of King's where he sat with Rafferty and his friends, Pat reflected that there was a paradox in Byron's lameness and his fluent verses, and his own swift, unimpeded gait and his halting lines. Suddenly, the young Lord was upon him.

'You're Brontë of St John's,' he said pleasantly. Stumbling a little as he got down on his haunches to caress the dogs, he seemed at ease with both the man and the animals.

'You've got quite a reputation,' he said smiling up at Pat, dark eyes friendly but complex. 'I hoped I'd see you. All that romantic stuff about coming from the mists of Ireland with only a shilling in your pocket, pushing the rich and noble out of the First Class and keeping the strays dogs of Cambridge fed and watered. Now *that* I understand.'

'It was hardly a shilling.' Pat was amused. 'But the general theme is true. I've read some of your verses,' he ventured.

'And I expect you think, Mr Intended Clergyman, that I am very, very bad. But I am good to dogs, you know, always. I tried to keep one here, but they won't allow it. Next year I intend to bring a bear and keep that in my rooms – they don't actually forbid it. I'll tell them he's come for a Fellowship. But dogs – all man's virtues without his vices, don't you think?'

'I do indeed!'

Byron had his arms round the skinny shoulders of one of Rafferty's friends, scratching the black chest fur absently.

'You read Wordsworth, I suppose, one of your college's alumni,' he said. 'Good free stuff but rather worthy don't you think?' He didn't wait for Pat's reply. 'Rather severe, but I shall make up for that!'

He laughed and stood up, bending slightly with one hand still in contact with the ecstatic dog. He smiled at Pat and gave a deep, mock-heroic bow, the black curls cascading and springing back as he straightened up. 'I'm glad we've spoken. When contemplating my debts the other night I thought about the legendary Brontë with his shilling,' – he laughed – 'and I thought you must be a frightful bore. But I think you are far from that and a great friend to these poor creatures. When you go down I shall still be here

35

and I shall continue the good work.' He paused, a shadow crossing his handsome face. 'Although people will think it is just an affectation.'

'Never mind that,' retorted Pat. 'Just do what you think is right and take no heed of what men say. If I had done that I would have caught the next boat back to Ireland.'

Byron's dark eyes widened. 'You *are* a good man,' he said; 'Good day and thank you.'

And settling his wide-brimmed hat, he was gone.

∞

Nunn came into his room and stopped amazed at the lean figure huddled near the window.

'You haven't been to bed,' he said in surprise. 'I fetched the breakfast milk and thought we would brew a little coffee as a treat.' He took Pat's hands between his own and chafed them. 'Look,' he said, 'they're bloodless and like marble. Will you sacrifice your health for your ambition?'

Patrick rose from the chair and sat on the edge of his bed.

'I suppose,' he said, stretching his huge frame till it cracked the cold out of him, 'it is ambition. I just wanted to see if I could do as well as those who have had formal, expensive education before coming here. Then I wanted to do better. And I never thought I was clever. I never felt clever. I expected clever people to have some sort of shining light bursting through their brains. Perhaps it is a sin,' he said with a regretful grin, 'pride and all that.'

'You've done better than any sizar since Wood; in the First class every term and here we are approaching the last one and it looks as if you will do the same again. I can't do it,' he added ruefully, 'and I have at least been to a grammar school.'

'Maybe the freedom I've had to learn at my own pace and in the ways that I wanted has helped rather than hindered me. It's always intrigued me that Shakespeare, without a university education, was a better poet and playwright than Marlowe or Ben Jonson, who both came here. Maybe too much structure hinders rather than helps.'

'Maybe, maybe,' said Nunn passing him the milk he had warmed on his own fire, as Patrick had none. 'I shall miss you Pat; you to Essex and me to Shropshire. About as far as we can be apart.'

'Jowett's curacy at Wethersfield seemed like a great gift at the time,' said Patrick, 'but it could be like going back to Ireland. No music! I really hadn't heard any music until I came here. All I'd heard was the scraping of the fiddlers in the Drumballyroney church, and my father's singing.' He got up and went to the west window, which looked out onto the river and across the meadows that stretched beyond. 'Sometimes I feel guilty that my reasons for ordination are all the wrong ones. I've had help here from devout members of the Church of England; she's seduced me with her marvellous liturgy and the unbelievable sounds in the chapel here and in King's. Will my faith survive in the real world?'

'You're not the only one, Pat,' said Nunn gently. 'Don't forget the youngest sons always go into the church as there is nothing else for them, and many of us do it for social and educational opportunities. You love the words and the music, and I think you love God, too.'

'I think I do. But sometimes I hate the way His world is for poor people.' He looked at Nunn, his blue eyes troubled, but finding no answer in his companion's face he picked up his black coat, and they took the stairs in a series of leaps which soon banished the sombre mood.

When the lists were published, Pat had indeed remained in the First Class every term. He tried not to seem too pleased. And Henry Purefoy Browne had a modest degree, too.

7

This is to certify, that public Notice was given by me, in the Parish Church of All-Saints in the town of Cambridge on Sunday the twenty-ninth day of June last, that Mr Patrick Brontë Intended to offer himself a Candidate for Holy Orders and no impediment was alledged.

Samuel Chilcote, curate of the parish of All Saints,
Cambridge, 4th July 1806.

The thunder cracked in the summer sky, and the rain began to fall in slow fat drops as the congregation filed out of Drumballyroney church. The Mourne Mountains, blue bulk visible through the misty rain, rumbled their response.

Hugh Brunty shivered slightly, but he smiled despite his moist eyes. Billy Brunty's eyes were not moist.

'You did not have to come,' Hugh hissed, watching his younger son nervously.

'I wanted to see the new Englishman,' laughed Billy, not even quietly. 'I wanted to see with my own eyes my gentleman brother.' Patrick, clad in his robes and bidding the congregation farewell, looked apprehensive.

'Stop it,' said Hugh, 'for the love of God, stop it. Your mother' – he indicated with his head and his eyebrows – 'is having the time of her life. Don't spoil it.'

'She never could see the way that Pat was going: she loves the Catholic Church, yet there she is, listening to the Anglicised Protestant Pat,' muttered Billy.

'Your tongue will be the death of you,' his father whispered. 'If you don't get it from the English, you will from your own family. This is your brother!'

Patrick had finished his courtesies and joined the two men, his eyes troubled but determined as he sensed the matter between them.

'Billy, be friends for the short time I'm here, whatever you think of me and my life. I'm willing to be pleasant for our mother's sake. Won't you?' He extended his hand. Hugh looked on, his eyes wary.

'So be it,' said Billy, slapping his shoulder and taking his hand. 'But don't think I'll ever welcome English rule in this country, or that I won't do everything in my power to get them out.' He laughed and, smiling, said pleasantly, 'I regard you as a traitor, Pat, but you are still my brother!'

Patrick winced. 'Strong words,' he said, 'and unfair to use on a man who has merely seized his opportunities.' He dropped the hand, looking towards the Tighes and the group of neighbours and friends which surrounded his mother. *This is a mistake*, he thought. *I am dividing my family. It's better they forget me.*

Later, he found it hard to concentrate on the conversation at the Tighes'. The old man, thrilled by his success, was urgent in his questioning about the college he had left himself thirty-five years ago. He spoke of God and theology with such enthusiasm that Pat was embarrassed; he was supposed to be red-hot himself, having just been ordained, and he was outdone in enthusiasm by this old man. The poetry he was writing would have been his preferred topic.

At last he rose to go, gently easing the little dog off his lap and patting it affectionately for its yelping welcome and fine doggy memory. They walked across the hall, Tighe's arm around his shoulders, although now he seemed smaller and was making an effort to reach up to Pat.

'To see you has been such joy,' he said. 'You've done so well! One day you will be a bishop, I'm sure. The church is in a difficult period, and a clever man like you will help her back to righteousness.'

'It's all because of you,' he said, patting the old man's arm affectionately. 'I'll never forget you or cease to be grateful.'

'But you'll be back, Patrick. You make it sound as if we will not meet again. You'll be back!'

෴

Outside in the darkness, he pulled his coat close around him to shut out the buffeting wind which wailed and sang around him.

The banshee, he thought. He smiled. *I really am back in Ireland.* The icy wind in Cambridge, straight from Russia they said, had not the spirit of this wind. Neither had the flat fens the excitement of the mountains and the rugged Irish landscape. His long strides soon took him to his parents' home, his feet remembering every step of the way in the darkness. He did not feel threatened. He believed Billy would honour their truce while he was visiting. When he reached the house, a single candle burned in the kitchen. On the table lay the documents he needed to complete his ordination papers: no record of his birth existed, and this was his father's statement, witnessed by his friend John Fury. *I doubt Lord Byron had such a problem,* he thought wryly, holding the paper up to the candlelight. The memory of the generous and talented young man suddenly flared. What a world away from here. He sat at the table, looking at the room in the shadows, remembering the past.

Suddenly the outer door opened, with a rush of wind and quick slam. Billy leaned against it and stood smiling at his brother. In his hand was a bottle. 'I thought you'd be back from your dinner with the gentry,' he said. 'So I've a dram or two here for us to take before we sleep. I may never see you again, Pat.'

'Why do you say that?' Pat was startled. He reached for the bottle.

'Because you've decided not to return, haven't you? It adds up. You're a gentleman now, an English clergyman; the world over there is open to you with your good Cambridge degree. If you come back here you will gather a reputation as a native sympathiser.' He took the bottle back from Pat and swigged. 'And I have to say that I won't make life easy for you: if I get into trouble I might even use your grand new name.' He laughed and passed the whiskey. 'It's over for you here; you can't have it both ways.'

Patrick rose and stood over the fire, the flickering embers lighting his thoughtful face, so like Billy's in features yet unlike in the eyes. There was nothing to say: reason only brewed anger with Billy. He did not want this, this alienation from his family to whom he could easily have remained loyal and loving. But Billy was a man to whom compromise was unknown, his passion for a free Ireland transcending family loyalties.

'Let's finish the bottle,' he said gently. 'Let's sing. That's the best of the Bruntys, our storytelling and singing. That we both have from our father.'

40

Billy nodded, and as the bottle emptied their voices mellowed, and Hugh, lying upstairs awake in the darkness, was glad that they were in harmony for this last night. When Patrick stood on the packet's deck next day and watched Ireland disappear into the mist, the tears streamed freely down his cheeks.

ᏊᏉ

His ordination in Fulham Palace had been the first chance he had to return to London. Not one to forget kindness, he returned to Moffett's bookshop in Paternoster Row. He entered hesitantly, despite his changed circumstances, unsure if he would be recognised, or indeed if Moffett himself would be there. But the last four years might not have passed, for there he was, spectacles on the end of his nose, book in hand, mind so completely engaged that he appeared startled when the door opened.

'I remember you,' he said, staring at Pat. Gradually his eyes focused. 'I'm sorry, sometimes I forget that the shop is open to the public. But I do remember you – you had come from Ireland and were going to Cambridge. You wanted to write,' he added.

Pat beamed at his recognition. 'That's exactly right. And now I'm ordained and my college has given me four pounds for my graduation, and I'm going to spend it on books.'

'I take it you want my theology or Classics sections?'

'I don't,' said Pat firmly. 'I want *The Lay of the Last Minstrel*. It's just published. Scott is the greatest writer of the last century and this. Such feeling, such fire, such . . .'

'Is that how you write?' asked Moffett, smiling.

'No. My only hope of publication is to please the evangelical wing in my church. They only approve of writing which aims at moral improvement,' he intoned mockingly. 'I have been told' – and he thought longingly of Mary Kelly – 'that I write stiffly because of this.'

'You'll have to choose,' said the bookseller, swinging his legs over the counter and taking the ladder to the shelves full of novels. 'Church or writing. You'll never write well if you don't express your feelings.'

Choices, thought Pat. *Ireland or England. Church or writing. But I have to eat.*

'You're right.' He looked up at the gold-tooled titles on the leather and linen bindings above his head. 'I just want the name

Brontë on one of those one day.' They both chuckled, and Patrick soon had this chosen volume in his hand, securely tied in brown paper.

Replacing his hat, he said goodbye and made his way back to the Chapter Coffee House. He had allowed himself two nights there; he was, after all, solvent, and had sixty pounds a year at Wethersfield for the future. He settled himself in the window seat of the public room and, opening his new book, prepared to spend an afternoon reading and watching the publishers and writers who, he knew, gathered there.

8

I see you still as you once were – affectionate, kind, and forgiving, agreeable in person, and still more agreeable in mind. I cannot forget our walks from Wethersfield to the Broad, and some of our interviews there.

Patrick Brontë to Mary Burder, 1st January 1824.

'Mr Brontë!'

Patrick's pen fell from his hand like a stone, spattering his poem, which should have been his sermon, with ink. Leaping from his chair, he knocked the inkwell and prevented permanent damage to his precious copy of Wordsworth only by a dexterous grab as he made for the backstairs of Miss Davy's house. His effort to smooth his coat and run his hand through his tousled red hair failed to contribute to his dignity for, in his eagerness, he nearly fell down the stairs. Miss Davy, pleasant, friendly and motherly, turned from her loaded kitchen table and dusted the flour from her arms.

'Ah – Mr Brontë. I thought you would want to know that Mary was here. She wondered if Mrs Windle needed a visit today for some reading?'

Patrick could scarcely look at the aunt for needing to look at her niece. 'Yes, yes,' he said, 'she needs someone to read her circulating library book as well as to have the collect read to her. Perhaps Mary will accompany me and remain after I've left?'

Miss Davy saw nothing wrong with her niece walking through the village with a clergyman twelve years older than she was. She nodded assent, and Mary picked up her empty basket and went out into the spring sunshine with Patrick.

Pat had found the life of a curate in an Essex village about as dull as anything he had yet experienced. He missed his Cambridge friends, he missed the beauty of the buildings, he missed the opportunity to talk and drink and sing his Irish songs. He thought, after the first few months in Wethersfield, that his brain would atrophy, and his efforts to keep it alive resulted in long hours spent at his writing. His congregation was small, for, however assiduously he visited its inhabitants, the village's strong Nonconformist tradition stolidly withstood the blandishments of the Established Church.

He lived well with Miss Davy, who was kind, as lonely as he was, and would talk to him in the evenings while he ate the simple food he had requested. When he returned to his warm, well-lit room, he tried to appreciate his good fortune but in truth he had been happier when cold and dark in his rooms in St John's. And then, as Miss Davy brushed his coat and then handed him his hat as he prepared for his afternoon visiting, Mary had arrived with the gift of a duck.

She was pretty rather than beautiful, but her tawny hair curled tantalisingly beneath her bonnet, and her wide smile and frank eyes were enough to disarm Patrick. Introducing her to Pat, Miss Davy took the duck into the kitchen and was absent long enough for Mary to find the curate's tall figure, red curls and lively pale blue eyes deeply attractive. It became easy for Pat to create meetings and walks, and he closed his mind to the difference in their religion in his desire for her company and his strong physical desire. She was also a clever girl like Mary Kelly (*Why are they always called Mary?* he pondered), educated like her at a dame school, but curious and intelligent to a degree which gave Pat ample opportunity to play the tutor. When he took her back to her mother's farmhouse home, the Broad, he went alone with her through the woods which led there.

As the year wore on Patrick battled with his inflamed desire and hot dreams and, because he was an honourable man, he soon became engaged to Mary Burder. He had decided it was better to marry than to burn and, while celibacy had been tolerable in the stimulating environment of Cambridge, he was somewhat fearful of giving in to the very great temptation of ravishing her when they were alone on their green summery walks. So he proposed to her after consulting a delighted Miss Davy, who said she would mention it to her brother-in-law.

Up the backstairs again.

44

'The man's Irish, Mildred. Whatever were you thinking of? Just because he covers it with his Cambridge airs and Anglican graces he's still potato and herring through and through. And he has sixty pounds a year to offer our Mary? The man's a fortune-hunter!'

A murmur from the distressed Miss Davy. A clatter of boots as Patrick descended the stairs, eyes blazing.

'I heard that Mr Burder! You insult me. I love your niece and only want what is honourable. I am a gentleman, a clergyman, a graduate of the finest university in Europe. And what is more, I'm proud to be Irish.'

'I don't care that you heard what I said, Mr Brontë. Every word I would have said to your face. Where is your family, Mr Brontë? Just understand that I don't want my family marrying parsons with no connections and no land. When Mary marries it will be to a man of substance, who will have land to join ours. That is not you, Mr Brontë! And we shall want to know his family!'

Mr Burder's face, fleshy and sun-burned, shone with anger, and his fist thumped the kitchen table, making the pans rattle. Pat's face burned, and his hands were clenched at his sides, in a desperate attempt to stop himself using them. Silent tears ran down Miss Davy's face. At the sight of her distress, Pat's anger abated, and he threw up his arms in exasperation.

'What will you have me do, Mr Burder?' He tried to sound reasonable, attempting to find the right tone for a future in-law, albeit a barely educated one.

'Do? I'll have you do nothing, Mr Brontë, absolutely nothing. Mary will come to stay with me at Great Yeldham, and there will be no more meetings. My sister,' – he threw her a fierce glance from beneath his shaggy brows – 'is to blame for this nonsense, almost as much as you. To think that I cannot send my niece to visit her aunt without her being thrust into danger and temptation. Good day to both of you!' And ramming his hat hard upon his head, he was gone with a slam of the door and a crack of his whip.

Pat and Miss Davy sat at the table in silence. Eventually she heaved a windy sigh and he patted her shoulder.

'We'll look at this again,' he said, but she appeared so anxious at his words that he added, 'In a way Mr Burder will not know about. Don't worry. You didn't deserve that,' he said gently. 'But then neither did I. Your brother is a passionate man.'

'Oh Mr Brontë,' she sniffed, starting to cry again. 'I was so pleased for you and for Mary. I thought you made a lovely couple and that she would be such a good parson's wife. He should be glad that Mary has met a real gentleman.' (Despite his anger Pat couldn't suppress his smile.) 'And I hate all this nonsense about different religions. When I was a girl I'm sure Protestants were all one and the same.'

'Don't cry any more,' said Pat soothingly. 'I'll find a way.' He sat her in the chair by the fire and poured milk into her little pan. 'You drink this and forget all about this evening. I will always be thankful that you introduced me to Mary, and I will find a way.' She still looked fearful. Patting her hand again, and closing the door softly behind him, he mounted the stairs to his room, where he spent the rest of the evening finishing his bottle of whiskey and hating the bucolic and powerful Mr Burder.

Patrick felt fragile in the morning and for several mornings to come, as he wrestled with the problem of Mr Burder and his attitudes. It was as if he was back on the journey from Liverpool when he endured the Paddy jokes, or in the early days at Cambridge when his poverty, rather than his ability, was noticed. To be treated like this by a semi-literate yeoman seemed to wipe out the effort and achievement of the past five years. He could not accept it. Every time he thought about the man and the virtual imprisonment of Mary, his thoughts were so dark that he was shocked by his primitive anger and lack of faith.

∽

'No, I can't manage any more,' said Nunn, smiling as he slid the bottle across the table. 'It makes you happy, whereas it makes me sad, and that won't do.'

They were in the room at the back of Nunn's lodgings in Shrewsbury; Patrick had walked from Wellington to spend the day with him, enjoying the wooded countryside and the fast-flowing rivers. Through Nunn's contacts he had moved to the busy industrial town of Wellington and put Wethersfield behind him. He took the bottle and poured the last of the whiskey into his own glass.

'And Pat,' said Nunn, 'I have to tell you that I am getting married in the spring.' He was looking warily at Patrick.

Pat burst out laughing. 'And you think I shall be sour about it! Just because I lost Mary. Surely you know me better than that. I

46

loved her, and lost her because my pride couldn't take the assaults Mr Burder made on my new respectability. I would probably have behaved differently now. Then, my only solution was to leave and deluge her with letters she may never have been allowed to see. It was a foolish way to act for a man of my age. I should have stuck it out and made the man respect me.'

'Why didn't you, if you loved her so much?'

The shadows were lengthening in the little room. Pat stood up and walked towards the window, hands in pockets, his straight back to Nunn. 'Pride, the same pride you so effectively exposed in Cambridge, John. I couldn't bear to be condescended to when I thought I'd achieved so much. I put it above my personal happiness. I told you before that I was concerned about my reasons for ordination. I certainly acted without humility.'

'And you had a hard lesson!'

'I lost a lovely girl. I hurt her as much as I hurt myself, despite my letters and promises. I justified it to myself on the grounds that we would have been "unequally yoked" because of her Nonconformity.' He turned back into the room, his eyes sad. 'I suffered more than I ever thought possible. It will be a long time before I let myself fall in love again.'

Nunn laughed. 'You don't *let yourself*, Pat. It just happens. Men like you usually fall harder than the rest of us. All that Irish passion – I wouldn't like to be around when it happens!' And he picked up both their hats so that he could start Pat's homeward journey with him.

The population of Wellington was amused these days by the figures of the two curates as they walked the town together. Patrick, tall, stately, dignified, his immaculate black clothes emphasising his height and slimness, and the cheerful, plump, rosy-faced William Morgan, almost bouncing along at his side. Pat loved Wellington: the busy town, the new, classical All Saints' church, the sense that there was a real job to do among the poor of the town; if he had ever doubted that he had a true vocation, here he could convince himself that practical Christianity could help their suffering.

The evenings, when he was not writing, were spent with the Welsh and garrulous Morgan and John Fennell, the headmaster of the school. Pat found he was remarkably at ease with Fennell, a large, kind man to whom he was able to talk about education, revealing his own background with a frankness that surprised him.

'You are hot on this one, Pat. You'll be joining the revolutionaries for Liberty, Equality and Fraternity!'

'That I will not. If you had come from where I have you would never think of revolution. If I achieve anything for the poor, it will be through reason and politics.'

Fennell had come from Penzance where he had met and married a Cornishwoman, Jane Branwell.

'A Celt like yourself, Patrick!' said John. 'With Nunn engaged, and me married, and William . . .'

'William nothing,' interrupted Morgan shortly. 'I am definitely a bachelor.'

'I'm merely observing that Cornishwomen would make good wives for the Irish and Welsh,' murmured Fennell, smiling. 'But Pat is more interested in his writing and singing.'

'And drinking,' muttered Pat looking sternly at his empty glass. 'Fill it up, John.'

'I think you've had enough if you're to walk through the streets of the town to your lodgings without disgracing your cloth,' replied Fennell firmly. 'Give us a song, Pat, instead. Anything you like.'

Deciding not to fight Fennell for the extra dram, Pat heaved himself out of his chair, and with his thoughts back in Wethersfield, he cursed his pride in his light tenor:

> *I intend to stay single for the rest of my life:*
> *The shells in the ocean will be my death bed*
> *And the fish in the water swim over my head.*

When Morgan turned off to his lodgings, and his own feet alone echoed in the still street, the night sky was still bright enough for Pat to see the outline of The Wrekin. In his slightly drunken state, any hill would remind him of the hills of his homeland and he was seized by an aching longing for home, for human love, for someone to be with. Staring at the great mound and brushing the tears from his eyes with his sleeve, he was sorry to find that he was not a man who wanted to be alone forever. Blaming the whiskey, he went sadly to bed and suffered fleeting dreams of both the Marys and a girl he had loved in Ireland.

9

As to the sufferers, whose sole inheritance was labour, and who had lost that inheritance, – who could not get work, and consequently could not get wages, and consequently could not get bread – they were left to suffer on . . . Misery generates hate.

Charlotte Brontë, *Shirley*, Chapter 2.

The boot was now truly on the other foot. The Yorkshire people spoke from behind their clenched jaws, and Patrick was at a loss to understand much of what they said. The open Essex vowels and the Welsh lilt of Shropshire he had conquered easily, but these tight sounds and strange words baffled him. Remembering the abuse he suffered in his early days in England, he was patient and courteous; less so his new parishioners.

He had been flattered to be asked to go to Yorkshire, the centre of the evangelical movement within the Church of England. It suited him, the emphasis on salvation through conversion, regardless of rank and possessions, to which he could add a concern for the poverty and disease which spread through the industrial north, where men grew rich on the backs of others.

He was a faithful visitor of the sick and dying. He was often moved to tears by the plight of little children and their young, sick parents: families surviving on threepence a day, with bread at over a shilling, and no money for an apothecary or laudanum to still the crying of the hungry and sick. The generosity of his own pocket was known but not abused. He reasoned that, without a family of his own, his family was his parish.

There had been moments when the rancorous nature of the local population had collided with Pat's pride.

'Keep a dog and bark yourself? Off with you, Mr Brontë!'

Thus Mr Halliley, the gentleman father-in-law of Pat's vicar, John Buckworth. Pat and young Joseph Tolson, who loved to ride the moors with him between the chapels of ease for the pure pleasure of having Pat teach him as they journeyed, had taken a service at Hartshead and ridden back through a storm in which the blazing lightning divided the dark sky, terrifying the horses who stumbled over the moor with their ears back flat, the rain flowing from their sodden coats. The men's clothes clung to their chilled bodies like second skins, and Pat knew that Joseph would have eaten little before they left Dewsbury in the morning. Wellington would have said the boy and the horses should be looked after first. He called at the Hallileys, where the Buckworths were dining, and, knocking on the door with his shillelagh as the rain ran down his arms and legs and into his boots, he asked Mr Halliley if John Buckworth could, after all, take the evening service at Dewsbury.

'Keep a dog and bark yourself?' And the door was slammed in his face.

Pat clenched his fists and, returning to the church, took the service, his hair black with rain and his saturated clothes steaming in the brazier's heat. He had sent Tolson home with the horses. At the end of his sermon he faced the congregation, his blue eyes black in the dim candlelight.

'I have been grievously insulted,' he told them. 'I will never again preach in this church.'

And he did not, although it was difficult, for he had to take services, and he loved Buckworth, who was frequently ill and as frequently absent. He lived with the Buckworths and, when they were away, comforted the little pining dog, Robin Tweed, with caresses and extra food and a letter in verse to his mistress to persuade her to return.

> *Each night I lie*
> *With sleepless eye,*
> *And poke my nose,*
> *And smell your clothes*
> *And howl aloud for sorrow.*

And he also dealt with the Dewsbury bell ringers. On reflection, Patrick was not proud of that. Incensed by their assumption that because the vicar was away they could decide on an extra practice without reference to his surrogate the curate, he had ended up swinging from the end of the bell rope, which he had seized to stop the ringing. It was only when his feet were skimming the astonished men's heads that he realised his temper had made him ridiculous. But he could not accept flouting of his authority or condescension to his person.

And who am I, to feel as outraged as I do? Is it my vanity or my fragility? he thought as he tramped the moors in the late afternoon, watching the pale sun sink into the heather. He greeted the sheep as he went so that they baaed in response, and kept Robin Tweed close to him. *Perhaps I am too much alone so that I have no one to cut me down a little.* But that would soon change, with the arrival of. William Morgan in Bradford, and John Fennell at the Woodhouse Grove Academy as headmaster. They would have laughed at him, but with affection, and that would have soothed his fractious spirit.

⚬⚬

When Buckworth gave Pat his own curacy at Hartshead within the year, he took up lodgings at Lousy Thorn farm with the Bedfords. The unprepossessing name belied the comfortable house and well-run farm which surrounded it. Patrick was soothed by the revolution of the farming year, and Mr Bedford was amazed at his knowledge of crops, methods and animal husbandry.

'Whativer next, Mr Brontë!' he said one night as they sat companionably in front of the fire, enjoying a dram and watching the flames being sucked tall and straight up the chimney by the wind which roared across the moor. 'We'll have you behind the plough with the horses!' And he puffed hard on his pipe and chuckled into the beard which framed his chiselled, weather-beaten face.

'I wouldn't mind at all, if ever there was the need. But seriously,' and he lowered his voice with a glance towards the kitchen where Mrs Bedford was supervising the little maid as she rattled away at clearing their dinner, 'I fear my parishioners are getting into deep water.'

Bedford shifted in his chair, which creaked beneath him. He was a big man, shaped by years of labour before he could employ others; he blew the smoke out of his mouth in a fragrant cloud and sighed.

'You mean the Luddites?' He, too, lowered his voice. The rumours of attacks and shootings were not what he wanted his wife to hear; she was often alone in the house when he was out lambing on the moor. 'You preached a good sermon on Sunday, Mr Brontë. That should put them in their place.'

'I didn't mean to put any one in his place,' protested Pat. 'I urged moderation. I even spoke from notes, to avoid inflaming their passions. They all grumbled and grunted and fidgeted, as it wasn't what they wanted to hear.'

'They have no respect!'

'No, Mr Bedford, they have no bread. They can have little respect for a system which takes their jobs and lets their families starve. Machines mean that to them. But my purpose was to avoid violence. If you had been in Ireland and seen what I have, you wouldn't want these people to split their families and risk their lives through violence. They need a solution through politics, not violence.'

'You have a good heart. But nothing can justify the destruction of another man's property.'

'Not to those who have it,' replied Pat, rising as Mrs Bedford entered. He turned his back to the fire, raising his coat tails and enjoying the warmth seeping through his breeches. Mrs Bedford was as good-humoured as her husband, but tiny, fine-boned and surprisingly elegant. Her good taste and aspirations had put her a little apart from her neighbours. She appreciated Pat as a lodger: her tasteful house was undisturbed by his quiet habits and his courtesy delighted her.

'If you have nothing,' continued Pat, 'that argument is not so strong.' He lifted a little black terrier from the floor and reseated himself with it on his lap, to the creature's ecstatic satisfaction. 'I want my parishioners to have jobs, decent houses and food for their children. I don't want violent protest to destroy their family life and communities.'

Mrs Bedford shivered slightly and went to the window, fastening the shutters with a clang as she dropped the metal bar into place. She pitied her poor neighbours, but would not want her property and possessions damaged in their cause.

'I'll put the dogs out,' she said, gathering up Pat's friend as the two mastiffs followed. her. 'That way we'll hear if there's owt about outside.'

⟲

'I love you, your reverence,' shouted the unsteady Jackson, clinging onto the pulpit as he strained to reach it from the back of his horse. The congregation whooped and yelled their encouragement as he planted a smacking kiss on the outraged Buckworth's face. Pat quickly moved towards the horse and, seizing the slack reins, led it away so that the man fell off and hit the floor with a resounding thud, and the preacher's virtue was intact again.

'I'm hurt, Mr Brontë, I'm hurt,' complained Jackson loudly. Struggling to keep himself from laughing out loud, and straight-faced with the effort, Patrick led the frightened mare out of the west door, where he tethered her to the railings, patting and soothing her before he returned to the church. *Play a part*, he thought desperately, viewing the mayhem with dismay. The drunk man was still crawling around on the floor, and the worshippers howled with mirth, pelting him with Bibles and any other book they could lay their hands on.

Pat grabbed the warden by his gown and said in a furious whisper, 'Get him out! Get him out! I can't do anything while he provides a show!' The warden looked belligerently at Pat, disinclined to do anything; but looking up into the furious blue eyes, he collected his assistant and they dragged Jackson by his coat tails out of the door.

Pat slammed it behind them, intending to make a great noise, ancient wood reverberating on cold metal. The congregation turned to look and momentarily stopped shouting, and Pat seized the silence to say loudly, 'Stand still, and we will sing our final hymn!' He stormed towards the altar, cuffing the heads of two of the noisiest lads as he went. It worked.

Patrick had quickly come to understand the garrulous and noisy nature of Yorkshire congregations and had perfected a style of preaching to deal with them. He spoke without notes and looked directly and deeply into the eyes of individuals. They were mesmerised, as they never knew on whom he would fix his gaze next. Other preachers had more trouble, and Buckworth, saint that he was, had no skills to deal with the challenges frequently provided by the lively congregations. He assumed it was Pat's Irish affability which made him the master of the unruly congregations they both faced from time to time. Pat often reflected that had he wished to be reminded of Ireland, he could have chosen no better place than Yorkshire: wild beauty in the landscape, and lawlessness among the people.

❧

The church door had been wide open on the warm August morning to dilute the strong smell of the congregation. Jackson, riding back drunk from visiting a friend languishing in Rothwell Gaol, had ambled in on his horse and been overcome with a strong desire to kiss the vicar. When he was locked up afterwards, the shock caused by this turn in the fortunes of her otherwise law-abiding husband made his young wife give birth prematurely, dying in the attempt. Jackson, appalled at the consequences of his actions, had a convulsive fit and died, too. Rancorous gossip in the town resulted in an exhumation for a poison suicide.

The stuff of a good novel, thought Pat, *if it were not so tragic.* 'Stand back!' he growled, pushing his way through the onlookers to the grave. 'Can't you let him rest in peace?'

The crowd, grey-faced in the twilight, shifted and muttered, their tattered clothing blowing with the sacking around the edge of the grave. There was little light relief in their care-worn, hungry lives and they resented the parson's implied criticism of their activity. Two men tried, for a second, to block his way, but fell back, recalling his reputation. The drunk he had felled in the path of the Sunday school Whit walk, and his rescue of a boy from the foaming River Calder, stood him in good stead. A young man, standing apart from the others beneath a dripping tree, had the grace to lower his eyes to avoid Pat's outraged stare.

William Nowell would be glad that Pat had the writer's habit of observation. It gave him the alibi he needed to get out of Wake-field's House of Correction when he was wrongly imprisoned for desertion. He was glad too of Patrick's passionate opposition to injustice in any form: he fought for the boy for months, using every connection he had, and rounding off his victory with a letter to the *Leeds Mercury*.

'I like it, Mr Brontë, I like it,' said Bedford that night, chuckling to himself as he held the newspaper nearer to the candle. 'To have a letter published in the newspaper is a great honour. 'Tis a great honour indeed.' He gripped his pipe's stem with his teeth, screw-ing up his eyes in the smoke, and his lips moved as he read and reread. 'And I like that bit at th' end – about the giant . . .'

'That's Shakespeare, Thomas, not Mr Brontë,' interrupted Mrs Bedford knowledgeably from her seat by the fire, continuing to stitch rapidly as she recited faultlessly:

> 'Oh, 'tis excellent,
> To have a Giant's strength: but 'tis tyrannous
> To use it like a Giant.

'And I love your *Cottage Poems*, too,' she continued. 'I've never had a book of poems before, and to have one by you, with my name inside in your hand!' And she shook her head with the wonder of it.

Pat couldn't hide his pleasure. 'I've been trying to publish for years. I hope it's the start of a writing career for me. Although, of course, it will be second to my ministry . . .' He didn't sound entirely convinced.

☙

If he were scrupulously honest with himself, Pat was not sure if he had started to carry a loaded pistol because of the Luddites or because he enjoyed the feel of the cold steel in his pocket and the exhilarating memories it brought of the volunteer corps in Cambridge. He certainly enjoyed his target practice on the Bedford's old apple-tree behind the house.

'What made you into a parson, Mr Brontë?' Bedford shouted from the upstairs window which he was leaning out of. 'Tha'd make a reet good soldier! The frame breakers'll never get thee. I'd quite like to see 'em try!'

Pat shot his last apple with precision and walked back to the house. He shouldn't really enjoy it this much. Carrying the pistol, in a special pocket he had sewn into his coat tails, was as much an act of violence as those committed by the desperate followers of Ned Lud. He often thought of the dark, glowing eyes of Byron these days: the young lord had made a passionate opposition to the Framebreakers' Bill in the House of Lords, reported in *The Times*. 'I have been in some of the most oppressed provinces in Turkey,' he had thundered, 'but never under the most despotic of infidel governments did I behold such squalid wretchedness as I have seen since my return in the very heart of a Christian country.' Byron's home near Nottingham was close to the weavers' misery.

But there was a genuine danger in the villages surrounding these Yorkshire mills, particularly the ones owned by William Cartwright. Mounting the polished staircase to his bedroom, Pat laid his watch and pistol on the table by his bed, as he would do for the rest of his life.

∽

He knew that the machines bound for Cartwright's mill at Cleckheaton had been smashed as they were carried over the moor, so when he came out of Hartshead church one moonless night he was immediately alert to the muffled tramping of feet in the distance. He stepped behind a tree, holding the dog's muzzle tightly in his hand. He crouched low, arm round the little terrier. Man and dog were transfixed.

Hundreds of people – for Pat was sure some of them were women well-muffled in tattered clothing – were tramping in silence, disciplined, determined, desperate. It was like a batallion, resolutely going to war, armed with anything they could lay their hands on, old muskets, pistols, clubs, even sticks with a single nail on the end. He shuddered against the dog's warm body. *I am in sympathy with these men, but I can't be with their actions. Will there ever be a time when politics will work and bring education, food and shelter?* He was not sure if his poor parishioners wanted them in that order, but his experience told him they certainly wanted them.

The attack on Cartwright's mill took place a few hours later. He was ready for them: dark and handsome, his polished manners betraying his French upbringing – a further alienation from his mill workers who hated him already for his devotion to the new factory methods. Yes, he was ready, almost longing for it, they said: five soldiers inside with a few faithful employees and two sentries on guard. He had been lodging there himself so that his wife and family were safe in their home.

Patrick had returned with the dog and told the Bedfords what he had seen. Thomas shook his head.

'It's like a civil war,' he said sadly. 'Many of these men are our friends and relatives. I can't abide it.' And seizing his candle he went up the stairs to bed. Mrs Bedford followed him.

'No woman can bear to see her children starve,' she murmured. 'I don't know what to think. There's good women with not a crust of bread to give their bairns and childer. That can't be right.'

'It's not right,' said Pat firmly. 'But we must make it right.' He took his own candle and went towards the back door of the house. 'I'm going out for a while. I'll take the key so that the house is locked.'

Bedford looked down from the top of the stairs, his shadow huge against the panelling. 'Be careful,' he said. 'For God's sake be careful.'

As Pat shut the door softly behind him, he thought of his mother's warning the night he decided to leave Ireland.

෨

The attackers threw themselves on the mill in a frenzy, smashing windows, hacking down doors, all through a hail of bullets which raked through them from the inside. From his position on the hill in the darkness, Pat could see the first burst of gunfire from within, the shots breaking the darkness of the night and the crackling of the bullets splitting the silence. Nothing seemed to penetrate the men inside, but the men outside were soon shot to pieces, and after only twenty minutes they fled, dragging the wounded with them, abandoning two who were too badly injured to carry. Pat could hear their screams and moans: he sat numbed in body and mind, surveying a scene more terrible than any he had seen in Ireland. He walked back to Lousy Thorn with a heavy heart, a confused mind and a bitter regret that he was living again in a community torn by violence.

Next day, Cartwright was publicly hailed as a hero for the defence of his property. However, there were many whose loyalties were as divided as those of the young soldier who was condemned to three hundred lashes for not firing on the attackers for fear of killing his brother. The pale pink dawn had risen on fields smeared with the blood of the wounded; their mutilated bodies lay in cottages and barns, secretly tended by friends and families.

'Out again Mr Brontë?' queried Tom Bedford as Pat took his stick from the stand by the door. 'Ee lad,' – he looked apologetic that his concern had revealed his affection for his young lodger – 'tha must take care. 'Tis difficult times for us all, not knowing what's best to do. Can tha not stay in tonight and tek a drop with me? Tha knows my whiskey's good!'

Pat smiled at his landlord's attempt at seduction, usually completely successful.

'I must go,' he said, picking up his second-best hat and adjusting it to a firmer hold to withstand the wind which was wuthering outside. 'I don't sleep well if I don't walk before I go to bed.' His words produced a sigh but no further protest. He closed the door carefully behind the black mastiff's solid body and headed off towards the church.

He was aware before he got there that he was not alone. No speech, only movements in the graveyard: outlines of men bearing bulky burdens on their shoulders, and the scrape of spades on earth. *Dear God*, he thought, *the poor wretches are giving their dead a decent burial in my churchyard!* He pulled in close to the wall; the dog, despite her size, was gentle and biddable, glad to stay close to him on such a troubled night. The men dug on, spades chinking occasionally as they hit stones, the earth pattering in a heap as it was flung away from the grave. Finally they stood back; they lifted the bodies gently into the grave, and for the first time a muttering broke the silence as they said brief prayers before the filling-in. When that was done, a different sound arose – choking, strangled sobs from men gripped by grief. Pat's throat ached. His hand moved instinctively, and he crossed himself.

He walked back to Lousy Thorn and shouted into the wind in frustration. The men were committing an illegal act – they were wanted men; but despite his conviction against violent protest, he would not betray this brave and desperate band. He slammed the door unnecessarily hard and stared hard at his pistol when he placed it beside his bed.

Early the next morning, he smoothed the grave and scattered grass across the disturbed earth before the sexton came on duty.

10

Papa put into my hands a little packet of letters and papers –
telling me that they were Mama's and that I might read them
. . . They were written to Papa before they were married –
there is a rectitude, a refinement, a constancy, a modesty, a
sense – a gentleness about them indescribable. I wished She
had lived and that I had known her.

Charlotte Brontë, letter to William Smith Williams,
3rd July 1849.

Patrick could only liken the experience to the conversion of St
Paul. One minute he was carelessly bowling along on a fine spring
day in the company of William Morgan, the next a blinding light
had changed him and his life forever. The light shone from Maria
Branwell.

'Pat,' said Morgan for the fifth time, trying to gain his attention,
'will you stop fooling? I'm trying to tell you a serious thing.'

'Not you, my little one,' replied Pat as he seized Morgan's hat
and threw it up in the air, 'you were never serious in your life. The
Welsh never are. Only the Irish are serious and know how to suffer
and live with the fairies.' And so saying, he replaced the hat on the
little Welshman's head back to front.

They had met at the gates of the Woodhouse Grove Academy:
Patrick had walked the twelve miles from Hartshead, and Morgan
had contrived to get himself there somehow from Bradford. The
day was beautiful, and the grounds of the school for Methodist
boys, where John Fennell now taught, were full of flowers and trees
in their early-summer leaves. Morgan made a final attempt.

'I am to be married,' he said, in a rush, neatly sidestepping an
assault that Patrick was clearly going to make upon his small

person. 'Stop it, Pat – you are making me look a fool, and the LADY IS WITHIN!'

'THE LADY IS WITHIN!' bellowed Patrick. He suddenly sat down on the grass in front of Morgan. 'Explain yourself!'

'For goodness sake, Pat,' his desperate friend whispered, 'I am engaged to the niece of Fennell's wife, and she is at the window now!'

Pat's eyes swivelled from where he was still sitting to the window of the fine grey stone mansion in the distance. Indeed, he could see the outlines of not one but two female figures in the window on the right of the door. He stood up, brushed his clothes, replaced Morgan's hat the right way round, and said:

'Your old friend Patrick will not let you down, William. I will be so well behaved you will not know I'm there. Curmudgeonly old Patrick wishes you well and will die himself alone, writing bad poetry, eating burnt porridge and longing for his novels to be published. I shall just enjoy the sight of you and Miss . . .?'

'Jane Branwell. You remember John met his wife in Penzance . . . . . . It's her niece.'

Pat could remember some remarks Fennell had made about the suitability of Celtic Cornishwomen as the wives of the Welsh and Irish. Clearly he had had Morgan in mind for his niece then.

'I shall just enjoy the sight of you and Miss Jane drooling over each other, and I will sit as a sober chaperone. Fear not.'

They had reached the door, and the maid was there to take their coats and hats. She showed them into the drawing room on the right-hand side of the front door. The light began immediately. Sun and flowers lit the spacious room.

'Who is the other lady?' whispered Patrick.

'Come in, Pat,' said Jane Fennell, 'and meet my cousin Maria. She has come from Penzance to stay with us a while.'

Pat bowed deeply, gazed into her eyes, and the light exploded within him.

'Mr Brontë,' she murmured, 'what a pleasure to meet you.'

◦◦◦

'He's been out nearly every night this week,' sighed Mrs Bedford, as she put the plate of cold meat and potatoes, under their white napkin, on the gleaming mahogany table in the parlour. She placed a lighted candle next to them and stood back, as if she were seeking a way to improve upon what she had done. ''Appen that Mr Fennell's wearing him out with all that work he has to do with the boys at that school. As if there weren't enough to do here, without him tramping the moor night and day to see to their Latin or whativer it is.' She sniffed, smoothed her apron and moved as if to put the dogs out for the night.

Her husband, seated in his usual chair beside the roaring fire, examining the newspaper myopically in the weak candlelight, gave his throaty laugh.

'You're always the last to hear,' he chuckled. 'If you gossiped more you'd know more. They do say there's a young lady staying with the Fennells, and that the twelve mile there and back seems nothing to our lightly stepping parson.'

Mrs Bedford stopped dead in her tracks as she went to expel the reluctant dogs out into the cold night air.

'Mr Brontë!' she exclaimed. 'Mr Brontë with a lady! He hasn't time for that sort of thing. He's devoted to his church, and his poetry writing. You know as well as I do that he is!'

'Mr Brontë's a proper man, Agnes. That's why you like him so much.' He peered closely at his wife, smiling to see a faint blush spread over her pretty features. 'He's made of flesh and blood, and he'll need a wife like the rest of us.' He rose and pulled her to him. 'It's grand if he's found someone. He's too much alone, and he can't spend the rest of his life drinking whiskey with me in the evenings and writing poetry. He needs a loving woman.'

'Well,' breathed his wife, 'I hope she's worthy of him. I should hate to see him with a woman who isn't.'

Bedford chuckled again and led her up the stairs. 'That's for him to decide, not you. You're lucky enough to have a perfect husband. Mek the most of him!'

༄

'Your stick, Mr Brontë? I'll go and look. 'Will you wait in the drawing room?'

The Fennells' maid was surprised to see the young red-haired clergyman back again the next day. She liked his blue eyes and good figure, his height and open manners. *He's got some energy*, she thought, *to walk twenty-four miles for a stick.* She opened the drawing room door for him and said, 'Miss Branwell, Mr Brontë's going to wait a moment while I look for the stick he left behind yesterday.'

61

It had worked. Patrick now knew enough of the routines of ladies to know that at this time of day she might be doing a little sewing in the drawing room. And she was there without her cousin. She looked up from her work as Pat entered, tiny hands fluttering among the yards of hemming she willingly did to help her overburdened aunt. Her eyes, warm and glowing in her small features, welcomed him, and her wide mouth, with its slightly crooked teeth, smiled at him serenely.

'Come and sit down, Mr Brontë. What a long walk you've had to get your stick. I believe it's twelve miles to Hartshead and the same back. William says your colleagues call you Old Staff because of the miles you walk over the moors with your stick. You must certainly have it back.'

Silence. The birds sang heartily outside. Inside, Patrick, preacher, teacher, writer, singer, worker with words, was completely lost for them.

'Do you like Yorkshire, Mr Brontë?' continued Miss Branwell calmly, minutely inspecting her stitches; her head was down now, soft brown hair curling gracefully over her head and neck. His heart was thudding. 'I find it very different from Cornwall.'

'Yes, I find it different from Cornwall too . . . I mean . . . I have never been to Cornwall . . . I mean I find it different from Ireland. That is where I come from,' he stammered, unable to play a part as he now always did when unsure of himself.

'I know it is where you come from,' said Maria with a laugh, her eyes alight, the good-tempered mouth curving. 'No one can mistake your speech. Do you find mine strange?'

Like an angel's, he thought. 'I find it refreshing,' he replied. 'Yorkshire speech is hard. Yours is soft, like the Irish.' He stopped, amazed. Why was he talking about Ireland? He never did except when he'd been drinking too much and singing. But he wanted to tell her his whole life story . . .

'Here's your stick, Mr Brontë,' said Ellen, entering the room with his battered old shillelagh. 'If you start now, 'appen you'll be home before the rain.'

༄

For the next two weeks Patrick performed the relatively easy duty that John Fennell had requested of him with an assiduity bordering on obsession. Almost every other day he walked the twenty-four miles to set the examinations, and mark them, Greek one day, Latin the next; he discussed with Fennell exhaustive measures to improve the curriculum, counselled the appointment of a new Latin master to replace the incompetent Burgess, advised on the appointment, filled in with teaching to improve the results until the master arrived. He caught cold in the rain and the wind. He had a barking cough that would not go away. John Fennell was concerned that he was asking too much of him. He said so to his wife.

'It's Maria, John,' she laughed, sitting back in her chair for a moment to rest from the endless accounting and checking which was her lot as part of their joint hundred pounds salary. 'It's as plain as the nose on your face. He's fallen in love with Maria. When we're having tea he scarcely takes his eyes off her. He gets later and later starting on his return journey to Hartshead. He loves Maria!'

'Well,' replied the bemused husband. 'In that case we must speak to him. We can't let him suffer. And what about Maria? What else have I missed?'

'Maria looks more radiant then she ever has in her life. Presumably she cannot believe her luck – she came to visit her ancient aunt and uncle, to be a useful spinster after the death of her parents, and she meets Patrick! She adores him. Her eyes shine when he enters the room. She is so careful not to push herself that I sometimes wonder if he realises how she feels.'

'I'll speak to him, before he catches pneumonia and becomes the husband she never had.'

He took his hat from the table and went out of the house and over to the barn which had been made into a schoolroom. Patrick was there with eleven boys; they had packed away their books and were animatedly discussing the possibilities of walking by the River Aire with him and seeing the birds he described. He shooed them off when Fennell entered, and they fell out of the room in a good-natured heap. Fennell sat on the desk, one knee clasped in his hands, the other foot on the floor.

'It's quite late, Pat,' he said. 'I worry that you spend too much of your valuable time on us, and that the walking will wear you out. We had no idea the task we asked you to undertake would prove so onerous.' He kept his head turned to hide the smile he could not suppress. Pat walked towards the new bookshelves and bent to examine the big atlases stored upright on the bottom shelf.

He is on to me, he thought. *What do I do now?*

Fennell suddenly burst out laughing. 'I can't pretend any more,' he chuckled. 'Jane tells me that I'm as blind as a bat and that you love Maria. You know – if you wish to get to know her, we are her guardians and can allow it. Both her parents are dead.'

Pat's blush ebbed a little. 'I have never met a woman like her,' he said simply. 'It is as if I have known her all my life. I can talk to her about anything. I think about her all the time.'

'Well, then, do as you wish. You have our blessing, and if Jane isn't wrong – and she seldom is about human affairs – you won't receive a rebuff from our niece.' And jumping from the desk, he squeezed Pat's shoulders and was gone, out into the garden and back to the main house. Patrick sat down in the nearest chair, for he felt quite weak.

It's happened at last, he thought joyfully. *This is going to go right, and I'm going to be happy!*

༺༻

The summer months passed in a whirl of delight: there could hardly be a better courting place than Woodhouse Grove. The grounds spread down to the River Aire, and there were woods and copses all around. There was Kirkstall Abbey nearby for more formal excursions and picnics. He could not have been happier, surrounded by the beauties of nature, which he had loved all his life, in the company of Maria, whom he was going to love for the rest of his life. The sun shone, the birds sang; they were able to walk at sufficient distance from her cousin Jane and William Morgan for their conversations to be intimate and fun.

'Brunty,' she said, amused when he told her about changing his name. 'Brunty indeed. You're not a woman, Pat; you have no need to change your name. But Brontë is good. I like it. Bron,' she pronounced experimentally, 'it's not far from Bran-well.'

'Would you change yours then just a bit?' he ventured. 'It would not be a big change, from Branwell to Brontë. Same initials.'

She looked up at him, smiling her wide smile, the large eyes glowing. 'That is a definite offer of a name change, then,' she replied slowly. 'I think I might.'

Suddenly he was thrown into confusion. 'I was going to tell you other things,' he said warmly, 'I . . .'

'What, more name changes?' she laughed. 'More romantic tales of journeys out of the mists of Ireland into practical cold Yorkshire? Surely not!'

'No, no: it is not past facts; it is future facts. I may have become a gentleman through my education and ordination . . .'

'You have indeed.'

'But apart from my stipend I have no family money, only my savings, which amount to about thirty pounds. If we marry, were I to die, you would have nothing, not even a roof over your head. Parsonages go with the job. You could be cast into the street with any children we might have!' He stood in front of her, arms extended, such an abject figure she laughed out loud.

'You cheerful Irish peasant! It will not be like that. We shall live long and happy lives and rear a healthy family – how many did you say you were at home?'

'Ten. Five boys, then five girls.'

'And all alive still. My record is not so good, but you'll live to a ripe old age, particularly if you don't spend so much time walking the moor in the dark and the rain.'

'But I have to see you . . .'

'I will write to you, then perhaps that dreadful cough will go and I'll have the chance of a husband who lives beyond forty. And anyway,' she added lightly, 'I have fifty pounds a year of my own . . .'

❧

The next week he sat her down on a grassy knoll near the mount in the woods beyond the house and sang her 'Moll Dubh A'Ghleanna', a sweet ballad which hangs in the air with sadness and a little joy.

'What does it mean, Pat?' she asked. 'It's a foreign language, your Gaelic.'

'You're foreign, too,' he said. 'We're both Celts. I'll sing it again, and it'll bind our foreign souls together.' *Not that there is any need,* he thought with joy. *She has accepted me and we are engaged!*

He was bursting with happiness these days. When her letters arrived he could do nothing until he had been to his room and devoured them hungrily. He was delighted with her style, her sentiments, her humour; he read them over and over again, deaf to Mrs Bedford's pleas that he should come and eat:

. . . neither can I walk our accustomed rounds without thinking on you. I wish to write the truth and give you satisfaction, yet fear to go too far, and exceed the bounds of propriety . . . but have you not been too hasty in informing your friends of a certain event? Why did you not leave them to guess a little longer?

He took the stairs three at a time and landed at Mrs Bedford's feet.

'Come now, Mr Brontë,' she chided, ''appen you'll break your leg or mine. What would Miss Branwell mek o' that? That'll soon put a stop to your walks across the moor!' She pulled the chair away from the table on which she had put his late supper. Mr Bedford shut the door behind him and slammed the bolt into place.

'In for the night, are you, Mr Brontë? No wandering the moor to Guiseley tonight?' He chuckled as he made for his chair in front of the fire. Patrick stroked the dog which had come expectantly towards him, and began his meal.

'Have you thought where you'll live after you're wed?' enquired Bedford. 'If it should suit you both, there's room here and we . . .'

'No, no,' Patrick spluttered on his beef and potatoes. 'That's too kind of you, but we must find a home on . . . I mean, of . . . our own.'

'It's all reet, lad,' murmured his landlord discreetly. 'I know that a young couple need to be on theer own and out of sight – and sound – of ither folk.' He looked towards the kitchen to see if his wife were in earshot. 'This house is big, and you'd be on your own and private, like. I know the wife wants you to stay, and she's got some plan to mek you rooms of your own, like a house of your own.'

Patrick chewed, absently feeding the dog with his free hand. 'I'll ask Maria,' he said. 'She might be pleased as the time is so short before our wedding, and there's not a lot to rent in Hartshead. One day I shall have a parsonage of my own. But I will ask.'

'December's not far off,' replied Bedford. 'You're not one to hang about, are you, Mr Brontë? You'll be wed before we know where we are!'

༄

66

And they were, but not before Maria had made it plain to Patrick that the state of holy matrimony would not be without some drawbacks to her. The letter lay on his bed:

For some years I have been perfectly my own mistress, subject to no control whatever – so far from it that my sisters, who are many years older than myself, and even my dear mother, used to consult me in every case of importance, and scarcely ever doubted the propriety of my opinions.

Pat stared at the letter for some time. He had never met a woman like this before, fluent, reasoning, fearless. In his other relationships he was used to a certain deference on the part of the women, respect for his profession, a desire to learn. Maria had all these, but her forthright independent spirit treated him as an equal. He loved it. It made for real conversation, not pleasantries, real debate rather than instruction. He had always loved the company of women at home, and this was perfection. Almost.

I do not know whether you will dare to show your face here again or not after the blunder you have committed. When we got to the house on Thursday evening, even before we were within the doors, we found that Mr and Mrs Bedford had been there, and that they had requested that you mention their intention of coming – a single hint of which you never gave!

Pat threw himself onto his bed and groaned. She had also berated him for not writing. All his life he had been bad with bits of paper, other than the ones which really interested him: he had missed the day for his degree, he had forgotten to read himself in at Hartshead and had had to dash off a letter to the archbishop. The piles of paper on his desk, private and parish, merged into an untidy pile, and he had indeed found an unposted letter to Maria in the leaves of his poetry. As if he would not write!

He had also forgotten to give Jane Fennell's note to the doctor. Mrs Bedford had found it, soggy and crumpled in the pockets of his best black coat, when she was brushing and scouring it with lye, the flatiron poised to scorch the neglected missive. She had given it to Pat quite crossly, still smarting from their unheralded arrival at Woodhouse Grove.

'You need Miss Branwell to keep you in order,' she had said

strictly, 'for I can't be coping with your papers and all that. I've not polished that desk of yours for two weeks now. It's no good saying leave it – the muddle gets worse and the dust thicker!'

Patrick sighed. He would have to improve, for he would have household expenses and children and servants, and he would have to know about it all. But perhaps Maria would do all that. He glanced at the last line: '. . . *we are walking to Kirkstall Abbey again on Wednesday and I suppose your presence will not make the walk any less agreeable to us.*'

He seized his coat, ran down the stairs, grabbed his hat and shillelagh and was gone over the moor to Guiseley.

☙

'*My dear saucy Pat,*' she had written in response to his abject apologies, '*I really know not what to make of the beginning of your last; the winds, waves and rocks almost stunned me . . . What will you say when you get a real downright scolding?*' He had shuddered at the thought. Today he was hoping to arrange their wedding, proposed for 29th December, at Guiseley parish church. His feet crackled and slid over the frozen undergrowth; he had had to send the dog back to Lousy Thorn, for her enthusiasm to follow him would have ended in exhaustion and frozen pads on her paws. His long strides had developed into a mild canter, and he was breathless from the wind and his own stertorous breathing. He reluctantly agreed that the walking this winter had not been good for his health, but his spirits were in very good order. He was glad that the wedding would have them safe under one roof, and a warm one at that. They had accepted the Bedfords' offer of rooms of their own and assistance with food and washing.

Arriving at Woodhouse Grove, he made for the drawing room and was glad to warm his aching body in front of the blazing fire. Ellen had become a good friend to him, as she prided herself on picking up on the romance even before he had himself, as she put it. She took his outer coat, hat and stick and went off in search of hot food and drink. Soon Maria and Jane came in, arms full of boys' mending, and John Fennell followed them almost immediately.

'You chose well with the new Latin master, Pat,' he said, rubbing his hands and making for the fire. 'He sticks to your curriculum, and the results are most pleasing. Now, what are we to do about these weddings?'

68

'Are we to have two different days?' queried Pat. 'If so, I can marry William and Jane, and then William can marry Maria and me.'

'I have a far better idea,' said Maria from where she stood looking out of the window where the snow was starting to lie against the frame. 'There's clergy enough and to spare – so we can all go on the one day. Uncle Fennell can give away both the brides, being father to one and uncle to the other; Jane and I can be each other's bridesmaids; and William can marry us first, then Pat can marry William and Jane.'

Her uncle laughed. 'Masterly!' he cried. 'Everyone taken care of. You're a clever girl. Do you agree, Pat?'

'Daunting,' said Pat, winking at her over the head of her cousin. 'It seems an excellent plan; a double wedding with the clergy thrown in free.'

And so it was. On December the twenty-ninth he married his beloved Maria. Snow lay on the ground and both brides shivered in their light dresses, but their rosy cheeks proclaimed their happiness. They had a struggle to keep the occasion solemn, as with a graceful choreography they changed places and entered and re-entered the church. At last they emerged into the biting wind and kissed each other – kisses all round as they were now a family.

'Are you still my friend or are you a relation?' said Pat to William. 'I hope I'm married to Maria and not to Jane – although I mean no offence by saying so.' He smiled at them all. 'I think we did it right. This . . .', he held Maria tightly to him and kissed her upturned face, 'is Mrs Brontë, and this . . .', he took Jane's hand and kissed it gravely, 'is Mrs Morgan.'

They returned to Woodhouse Grove in extravagant style: a burgundy and black landau had been sent to fetch them as a gift from William's congregation, whose imagination had been caught by the news of the double wedding. The black horses set a smart pace through the frosty lanes, their white plumes stirred by the wind which failed to reach the four happy people inside the carriage. Warmed by the brass charcoal burner at his feet, Pat reflected that it was the most luxurious journey he had ever had. In the drawing room, the staff were waiting with selected boys; Maria and Jane had insisted that cakes be sent with them to the rest of the school, whom they knew well from tending their bloody knees and mending their torn breeches. Soon the clatter of hooves was heard as the horses were brought round from the stables where they had been rested, fed and watered. Maria and Patrick climbed into the carriage again, laughing and waving, and with Maria's box stowed behind, they bowled away to start their married life.

◌◌

The Bedfords had surpassed themselves in their efforts for the newly-weds. Patrick had purchased in Bradford the best feather bed he could find, and in their bedroom Mrs Bedford had put on new, fine linen sheets as a present for them. The room smelt of lavender she had gathered in the summer, and more faintly of beeswax, for she had polished the big, dark old furniture till it glowed in the light of the applewood fire. The starched lace runner on the table by the bed bore a crystal decanter of warm wine and a glass of whiskey for Patrick.

When he had drunk it, and Maria had more than respectably taken care of a glass or two of wine, Pat sang her 'The Raggle-taggle Gipsies':

> *'O what care I for my goose feather bed*
> *With the sheet turned down so bravely – O . . .*
> *I'm off with the raggle taggle gipsies – O . . .'*

'Not me, Pat Brunty,' she said. 'You'll never get rid of me to the gipsies or the fairies or whatever else it is you have in that misty land of yours.' Her sharp intake of breath, as his hands roamed her warm body, delighted him.

'Please God – as my Catholic mother would say – never. Ever.'

'Do you know, Pat,' she said, 'Stop it, saucy Pat – do you know, I never thought being married would be like this. I thought it would be . . . well . . . er . . . duty. But I could stay in this bed all day with you.'

Done.

◌◌

A month later she fixed him with a determined eye.

'I am *idle*, Pat,' she complained. 'The Bedfords are good friends and perfect servants, the rooms are spacious and comfortable, but what can I *do*?'

'You are my wife,' he replied experimentally, ducking low.

70

'But I do not even order your food! All I have to do is a little mending of beautifully laundered linen. I have polished up my pamphlet on *Poverty* over and over again. There is little I can do in the parish from here. Can't we use my fifty pounds a year to move to a house of our own, so that I can be useful?'

'No,' Pat replied firmly. 'That is your security against my early death.'

'Cheerful Irish peasant!' She laughed impatiently. 'Always looking on the bright side!'

'I have told you before,' he said sternly, 'that your position as the wife of a clergyman without private means is precarious. No husband, no house. We won't touch your annuity. If I die, you will have a good capital sum, and your annuity.'

'And if I die you will get nothing as the money returns to my family. That is not fair.'

'It is perfectly fair. It's Branwell money. I will support us, and we will have a house of our own.' He crossed the room to where she sat on the wide window ledge, catching the last light for her sewing. Picking her up – *hardly an armful,* he thought in wonderment – he placed her tenderly on his desk, little legs swinging. 'I know of a house,' he said. 'Clough House at Hightown in Hartshead. The church has a connection with it. I sold two ash trees last December, and I know it's empty. We'll live there, and you can wear yourself out with housekeeping and visiting the sick.'

She gave him a long kiss. 'I meant to be thankful, not importunate,' she said. 'For this,' – and she reached behind him for a paper he had left that morning before he set out for a meeting in Bradford. 'My birthday poem:

> *Maria, let us walk and breathe the morning air,*
> *And hear the cuckoo sing;*
> *The primrose pale,*
> *Perfumes the gale.*

She glanced over the lines. 'But it's these two:

> *How much enhanced is all this bliss to me*
> *Since it is shared, in mutual joy, with thee!*

'Oh, Pat, I've never had a poem before, and do you really mean that?'

'How can you ever doubt?' he said, pulling her to him. 'Surely you know the happiness you give me. You've made me a happy man, a whole man. There's nothing I can't share with you, nothing I lack.'

'Except, perhaps, a child?' she murmured.

'That would be perfection,' he said, gently unwinding her pretty hair until it covered her shoulders. 'Now – come to bed. We won't get one any other way.'

11

I have . . . been married . . . I know what it is to live entirely for and with what I love best on earth . . . To be together is for us to be at once as free as in solitude, as gay as in company . . . we are precisely suited in character; perfect concord is the result.

Charlotte Brontë, *Jane Eyre*, Volume 3, Chapter 12.

She could see him from the window when he was still quite far away, a black-clad figure taking the hill at a canter, jumping any obstruction like a young boy. Once her narrowed eyes had recognised him, her face glowed, and she ran from the parlour window out into the hall and stood on the step of the open door, waving both arms wide above her head so that he would see her and hurry even more. When he arrived at the railings outside the house, he was breathless and, sweeping off his hat, he kissed her soundly and drew her inside, where he kissed her several times more. When she could speak she burst out:

'I miss you so much, even though you've been gone only three hours!'

He kissed her again. 'And I you! I think about you all the time I'm away.' He steered her into the bright parlour where the stone window embraced the view down the hill towards the church. The fire crackled in the grate. The daily servant-girl had gone leaving them alone as they preferred to be, to eat the dinner she had prepared under Maria's supervision, and talk and read and write until their eyes were tired by the candlelight and they were ready for bed. Pat moved from his chair, *The Lay of the Last Minstrel* in his hand, towards the new shelves where the manuscript of his next book lay. Thoughtfully he placed the Scott next to them, and picked up the papers.

'Not there,' said Maria. 'Well away from your papers. Keep them separate.'

Pat looked surprised at such a suggestion.

'And put the papers on the shelves by the window; I will label them all with the subject – I've started already – look: Parish Finance, Services, Sermons, Future Sermon Material, Bradford Bible Society, Church Missionary Association . . .'

He was aghast at the thought of such organisation. As long as he could find his books and his manuscript, he was quite happy.

'And put your writing on a shelf by itself – I'll label that, too – and then you won't lose your papers inside others.'

'I'll do as you say.' He sighed.

'And Pat . . .'

He held up his hands in surrender, then changed his mind and kissed her.

'Pat, I was going to tell you that we are to have a baby.'

He stood back and surveyed her with a wide smile.

'Well, well,' he said, 'That's wonderful. You might say it's not for want of trying!' And they pealed with laughter as he danced her round the room.

෨෨

The months before the baby's birth passed happily for them. Pat roamed the parish with his dog, worked on his sermons and his book; Maria delighted in her orderly house and copied his manuscript of *The Rural Minstrel* in her clear hand for Hebden, the publisher at Halifax.

He had called the dog Rafferty after all the strays he had fed and all the poor Irish immigrants, including himself, who had ever needed food and shelter. He had found him tied at a cottage gate, ribby-thin, bright-eyed, long-coated and eager to please like the rest of his species. The man had lost his work, and they had given up feeding him; they could scarcely feed themselves. He quickly gave Pat his total devotion and was tireless in his companionship, however far Pat walked and however long he had to sit outside and wait for him. In the evenings he liked to stretch by the fire. Maria had insisted that he sleep outside at night, but as the year grew colder he was found by the kitchen grate, warmed by the dying embers.

'How did that dog get in?' enquired Maria, perplexed. 'I'm sure I put him out.'

'You did, indeed,' replied Patrick, not quite so perplexed. 'Let him stay, Maria – he has walked as far as I have today. And it's good to have a dog in the house in case the Luddites return,' he added coaxingly.

'I thought that was what your pistols were for. The neighbours are very curious as to why two shots ring out early in the morning. I don't think they realise that you have to discharge the pistol you load overnight. In fact,' she said, chuckling, 'I get some sympathetic looks when I go marketing. They seem to think I've a *reet* tough husband! But,' she said sternly, remembering her theme, 'when the baby is born we can't have animals in the house.'

We shall see.

◌◌

When the baby was born in November, Patrick was taken by surprise at the emotion which seized him. There had been babies at home, he had seen them grow; he had baptised babies, even buried little babies in their tiny coffins, but this, this beautiful little girl asleep in her mother's arms, overwhelmed him.

'Look,' said Maria, brushing the tears off his cheeks with her free hand, 'look how the little hand will grasp yours.' He put out his long slim forefinger, and it was taken immediately. She had fingers similar to his, tapering, with filbert nails. Suddenly, she opened her eyes and he gazed back into his own blue ones. He fell deeply in love again: nothing must ever separate him from this tiny being, from his flesh and blood, from Maria's flesh and blood. He imagined all the inherited characteristics she would have from both of them, and then thought of what they would add as they cared for her. He was mesmerised.

'Pat, you're in a dream,' said Maria, touching his hand. 'She's not that beautiful. A bit of a monkey, really!'

'No. She's beautiful and she's ours – our creation. And everything we can do for her will shape her life. What a responsibility!' He took the tiny bundle from her and looked intently at the little face. 'What riches! I never thought I would feel like this.'

'No,' she said with a laugh. 'Neither did I. But I'm tired, so take your lovely daughter and look after her while I sleep.' His startled

75

look amused her. 'Give her to the nurse if you don't know what to do.' She turned over on her pillows and closed her eyes.

Pat walked the bundle round the house, humming Gaelic songs to her, warm inside with pride and pleasure, until she slept and he placed her gently in the lined blanket box near the fire.

∽

The baby was christened Maria ('Why Maria?' she had said, 'it's so confusing.' 'What else?' he had replied, 'You and she are the greatest joys I have.') The ceremony, attended by the Fennells and the Morgans, was a replica of the quadrille of their wedding, with William as godparent and priest, replying to his own questions, and the Fennells and Jane Morgan becoming the other godparents. They returned to Clough House afterwards.

Standing near the window, surveying the great sweep down the hill, already becoming green in the April sunshine, Fennell turned to Pat and smiled.

'Your cup is running over, Patrick.'

'Indeed,' said Pat. 'This lovely daughter, who's as bright and canny as any baby I have ever met; Maria who makes me happy in every possible way, and I am being published. If only our church would encourage imagination as well as morality, I could write novels . . .'

'You have enough, Pat. Don't yearn for more.'

'You are right,' agreed Pat, and he filled his glass again.

By the time the godparents had departed in the fine spring evening, Maria was complaining that Pat had woken the baby by singing too loudly in Gaelic; he was sure he had not, for the baby had woken to listen to her father's fine songs. Maria also thought that Pat had taken a dram too many.

'But we were celebrating, Maria,' he pleaded. 'Come to bed and I'll show you much I love you. Let's celebrate!'

'You're always celebrating,' she grumbled. 'Every night. But I love you too, so I'll come, and we'll celebrate.'

∽

Despite the Peace of Paris and the abdication of Napoleon, the distress among the people of the parish did not abate. Maria was expecting another baby but was tireless in her efforts to relieve the suffering she and Pat saw all about them. The plight of families

76

with hungry children was made all the more poignant by the presence of their own well-fed, warmly clothed baby. Maria made pints of soup and baked quantities of bread daily, distributing it from the kitchen door fairly and firmly. Rafferty and his friends lent a comic air to the tragic scene as they joined the queue, drawn by the meaty smell. Maria attacked them with the broom, declaring that they should not eat while people were hungry.

'All God's creatures, Maria,' said Pat mischievously.

She cast him a dark look as she threw the last of the soup to the dogs, and clouted the healthy Rafferty for joining in the struggle. He and Pat left swiftly on parish business.

Elizabeth Branwell arrived by sea from Penzance towards the end of the year. She had written to say that she longed to see her new niece and would be glad to help when the new baby was born. She was weary after the long journey and somewhat outraged by the Yorkshire climate and its redoubtable people; but Pat thought he would like her. She was small and neat, with a face rather like Maria's, but sharper and less radiant. She asked him to call her Bess as her brothers used to; she was, she said, in need of a brother now.

The evenings were a little crowded, and Pat was unable to tease Maria as he used to, for Bess's ideas of clergymen seemed not to extend to singing, drinking and the telling of Irish tales. So he spent more time writing at the table, while Bess and Maria worked on baby clothes and linen and talked about Penzance, its sunny climate and their friends and family. Pat sat behind Bess, facing Maria; he had the satisfaction, on several occasions, of making her remove herself to the kitchen on some purported errand to avoid choking with laughter at Pat's dramatic mimes of Bess's more seemly statements.

That winter was bitterly cold: the moor was treacherous, and it often seemed pointless for Pat to free the stranded sheep he met if the farmer could not reach them with food. Rafferty and he stumbled about in the snow, guided by the dog's keen nose when the lantern was extinguished in the roaring wind. He had been to a cottage five miles away where a mother and a child had died and the man was distracted with grief and anxiety for his other five motherless children. When he reached home in sombre mood, Bess was still up.

'I sent Maria to bed, Patrick,' she said, 'she's tired by the born and the unborn. Sit by the fire and give me those wet clothes. I have whiskey and hot water ready, and Jenny has left you a good dinner.'

'You're very good,' he replied. 'You're a great comfort to us at this time. I'll fetch Rafferty so that he can dry out by the fire.'

'Do you really think he should come in to the parlour? Surely he'll smell if he lies by the fire . . .'

'Do you not love the smell of wet dog, Bess? One of the best smells in the world.'

'I think not,' she said, frowning a little as she eased Rafferty into the kitchen with her smartly booted little foot. She brought a steaming tray and placed it by him as he hugged the fire.

'You walk too far, you know,' she said with a sigh. 'This climate is ferocious. Maria is not used to such cold and wind, and neither am I. And you need to take more care of yourself. I heard you coughing last night . . .'

I hope that's all you heard, thought Pat, *or Maria will be less willing . . .*

'. . . I have bought more silk for your stock so that when you walk the parish you will at least be warm around the neck. And when you go into the cottages where there is disease you can muffle your mouth a little with it to ward off the infections.'

'Your kindness is overwhelming, Bess,' he said, as he put the tray aside and drank deeply of the warm whiskey. 'Do you not find it dull here with us after the gay life you had in Penzance?'

She folded her work, spectacles glinting in the firelight, silk rustling as she moved about the room, tidying. 'A little, but nothing exceeds the pleasure of doing one's duty and helping one's family. The tea parties I miss, and the soirées, and of course I've had many beaux since I was seventeen.'

'Of course,' Pat said respectfully, 'I can imagine.' *And did you come here, in the hope that there might be another clergyman to marry another Branwell sister? Unworthy thought!*

'I'm fortunate in having my independence like Maria' – she glanced quickly over her spectacles, auburn fringe bobbing – 'so I am able to do as I please.'

78

He drained the last drop from his glass and rose to his feet.

'You're a good girl, Bess,' he said, stretching his aching limbs. 'All the Branwells seem to be good girls, all the ones I know anyway.' He dropped a kiss on her pretty cap, and opening the door for her, handed her a candle for the stairs.

∞

Elizabeth, named after her resident aunt, was born in the front room of Clough House, deemed by Bess to be the correct way of doing things: there was access to the kitchen for hot water (*Why do babies always need hot water?* wondered Pat) and access to friends who wished to see the newborn, and Maria did not need to climb the stairs for a month. Pat, cold in their big bed, wondered how he would survive that lonely month. The new baby had shocked little Maria into speech, and he found that she could understand far more than she could say. To ease the situation at home, he would often take her on his shorter walks, to the church and to nearby parishioners, perched high on his shoulders and quiet and attentive in cottages and gurgling with mirth on the walks. Pat was glad to be seen as a man with children who could understand the difficulties of families.

∞

Emerging from the vestry of his church with little Maria one cold March day, he met Thomas Atkinson as he began the ascent back to Clough House, slowly this time, to accommodate his daughter's willing but tiny legs.

'A fine child, Brontë,' said his fellow clergyman. 'You are a lucky man in your family. How is the new little one?'

Pat smiled with pleasure. 'All is well with everyone,' he said. 'Maria is well, and so is the new baby, and my sister-in-law is with us and a great help. I don't often see you here,' he added. 'What brings you to Hartshead?'

Atkinson blushed slightly. 'I have been to Lascelles Hall to see Miss Walker.'

'Ah,' said Pat knowingly. 'A very fine young woman.'

'I was going to call on you. I have a matter to discuss. But we could do it here as we walk up the hill.' He took the child's free hand, and between them they swung her up the hill to delighted cries.

'The thing is, Brontë,' murmured Atkinson softly, as though

79

Maria could understand, 'the thing is – I love Miss Walker and I have very little chance to meet her when I am stuck over at Thornton. What I was going to ask . . .' He paused.

'Yes?' Pat couldn't work out what was coming next.

'The thing is – would you consider changing livings with me, so that I come to Hartshead and you go to Thornton?'

Patrick was amazed. The living at Thornton was worth one hundred and twenty pounds a year, whereas here at Dewsbury he had merely sixty pounds.

'It would be worth your while,' continued Atkinson, sensing his thoughts. 'I mean a complete change. You would get the entire stipend. I'm not a family man yet, so I can manage on less, and I have money of my own.'

Pat let several swings go by as he collected his thoughts. If Atkinson married Miss Walker, he would not want for money, so in a way he was casting his bread upon the waters. The move to Thornton, and the increased money, would certainly help the growing Brontë family and might enable him to save to offset his lack of private means. As the children came, he was more worried than ever for Maria if he were to die. There was also a parsonage at Thornton; he would not have to rent.

'I see the point,' he said seriously, picking the child up and putting her on his shoulders for the last bit of the hill. 'I will, of course, have to ask Maria. But we will certainly talk about it, and we'll let you know soon.'

They shook hands outside the house; little Maria, too, gave Atkinson her hand from her lofty perch, and he blew her a kiss as they turned in at the gate.

❦

'Who was that, Pat?' asked Maria from her sofa as father and daughter entered the parlour with a swirl of cold air. She was nursing the baby and looked better: rested and smiling, content and proud. Maria minor flung herself into her mother's arms and played with the baby's fingers.

'Atkinson,' replied Pat. 'He had a proposal for me, but not one that would interest you, my love.'

'Why, Pat? Why would it not interest me?' Maria was her old alert self; her hand, previously stroking the baby's downy head, was momentarily suspended.

'Simply that it is about money and therefore not of interest to the author of *The Advantages of Poverty in Religious Concerns*.' He positively smirked as he walked towards the window, adopting his characteristic pose, feet apart, hands in pockets, back to the room.

His hat, which he had thrown onto the table near the sofa, suddenly hit him in the small of the back.

'Stop it!' she cried, 'It's not fair to treat a nursing mother like this. Whatever do you mean?'

He picked up his hat and, still grinning, sat on the end of the sofa, where the child immediately struggled to sit on him. Disentangling his rather shaggy red locks – usually Maria's province for trimming – from her little fingers, he looked into his wife's luminous eyes with his own laughing ones. 'It is merely that Atkinson wants to catch the wealthy Miss Walker and is willing to give up Thornton to come here so that he is in a better position to do so. But knowing your views through reading your pamphlet, my love, I told him it was impossible.'

Maria's eyes widened. 'You might have asked me! We could do with a change. And with two children it is reasonable to want a little more money. Pat! You are teasing me, aren't you? We always talk about everything!'

Pat burst out laughing. 'Of course I haven't made a decision without asking you! It's just that I thought the money might embarrass you . . .'

'You're laughing at my writing,' Maria said quite forcefully. 'Just because you've been doing it for years . . .'

'With very little success . . .'

'With quite a bit of success, but you can't expect mine to be perfect when I've only just started. I . . .'

'It's just a joke, a joke,' he said, smoothing her hair back from her brow. 'I'm not laughing at you. I'm proud to have a wife who can set down her thoughts so clearly, and wants to. If we can both write, think what the children might do!'

'Well,' said Maria, 'that's all right then. Now tell me properly about this proposal.'

By the time Bess came to put little Maria to bed, it was decided that they should go to Thornton.

12

I need not tell you how happily my Helen and I have lived and loved together, and how blessed we still are in each other's society, and in the promising young scions that are growing up about us.

Anne Brontë, *The Tenant of Wildfell Hall*, Chapter 53.

Patrick hated the move to Thornton more than he could have possibly imagined. Not the prospect of their new life, but the process of putting their goods in a cart and setting off with them and his family on the road. He had often pitied poor people who had to shift, as they called it, usually on foot, with every human being in the drab procession necklaced about with pots and pans, bundles of clothing and bits of precious food wrapped in cloths; or the more prosperous with a horse and cart, but still with their whole lives exposed to curious eyes for the duration of the slow journey. The three carts he had hired were at least covered, but his proud, private soul rebelled at the sight of even a pot handle poking out for the eyes of the inquisitive world.

He walked at the first horse's head, Rafferty and Thunder at his heels, and little Maria on his shoulders or in his arms whenever she became impatient inside the cart she shared with her mother and aunt.

'A great journey, Papa!' she cried, 'we are going to another land!'

They had waited until May to do the change with Atkinson; Maria had taken longer to recover from the birth of Elizabeth, and they both felt that warmer weather would be better for them all if they were settling into a new and unknown house. When the horses finally clattered to a halt outside the parsonage in Main

Street, he lifted the little girl off his shoulders and kissed her cold, bright cheek.

'There!' he said to her. 'Your new house. You, me, Mama, Elizabeth, Aunt Branwell, Rafferty and Thunder. What a number we have become!'

'Aunt Branwell says there is room for chickens here,' piped the child.

'We'll see,' said Maria, easing herself from the cart as Pat took the baby from her, 'It's our house,' she whispered to Pat, 'we'll decide things like that.'

'She means no harm,' he whispered back. 'But there is certainly room for chickens.'

They wandered through the rooms of the new house: three downstairs and the same upstairs; a good kitchen at the back with backstairs leading out of it. Outside there was a cottage, a barn and space for a horse and a cow.

'It's good,' said Maria. She turned to him, putting her arm into his and encircling him and the baby with her other one. 'We'll be happy here, I know it. Come on, we'd better help Bess; she's already organising the carter and bringing things in. I get lazy with her around.'

They had soon made beds for the night, and Patrick thought he would be well employed reading the children to sleep. He found his books in a box and took out the Milton he had borrowed from the Bradford Library and Literary Society, a subscription to which had marked their new prosperity. The children were restless with the excitement of the long, unusual day, but by the time he had reached 'But O the heavy change now thou art gone' in his reading of *Lycidas*, the pearly dark-veined lids had drooped, and a soft Gaelic lament finished them off. As he crept from the room the sisters Branwell appeared at the top of the stairs.

'Pat,' said Maria, 'why can't you read them a fairy story?'

'Yes,' said Bess, 'that's what children like.'

'No,' said Pat. 'Rhythm and soft sounds for sleep. It has helped me all my life to sleep. I will defy you both.'

With a couple of leaps he was gone down the stairs and out on the moor with the dogs to explore their new kingdom.

෨෧

Social life in Thornton got off to an auspicious start when Miss Elizabeth Firth, returned from a visit to her cousin Miss Walker of Lascelles Hall, called on the Brontës. Freshly packaged by Miss Richmal Mangall at her Crofton Hall school, she walked up the slight hill from Kipping House in her sprigged muslin frock, pretty face shaded from the sun by a lacy parasol; she was a delightful sight to Maria and Bess, who could see immediately the social possibilities and a life similar to that in Penzance. No one had called at Clough House except old friends and clergymen. Miss Firth came with an invitation from her father, the doctor, to dine at Kipping House.

('That's so right,' purred Bess later, 'that's just how it should be for a man in Patrick's position.'

'You bet it's right,' whispered Patrick to Maria, 'Dr Firth is a widower from a recent carriage accident!')

Miss Firth wanted the girls and women to go the next day to Kipping House for tea; she was sure they would like the garden. They walked down in the sun, leaving Patrick to his visiting and writing. He said he might go to meet them on their way back.

☙

Patrick had been deeply immersed in the progress of the war and was ecstatic at the victory at Waterloo. As soon as the news came, he summoned the Firths to dinner to celebrate and announced that henceforth the anniversary of the battle, the 18th of June, should be honoured in the Brontë household. Knowing his penchant for missing deadlines, Maria thought it would probably be approximate.

The drams slipped down the throats as toast after toast was drunk to the duke, and the Peninsular battles were also remembered. Dr Firth was as assiduously patriotic as Patrick, and when he and his daughter departed in their carriage, Pat was a happy man.

'Every year,' he said contentedly to Maria, as they climbed the stairs to bed, 'every year we will celebrate this victory thus in our house.'

'Not thus,' replied Maria, as she peeled off his clothes. 'You never know when to stop, Pat. One minute you're the sober parish priest, the next you're a wild – leprechaun do you call it? – stirring up the children with frightening stories and drinking yourself into this state, all because the duke has won a battle.'

'Not a leprechaun,' sighed Pat, 'but I can't for the love of God think what it is. What a battle, what a man!' he continued, pursuing the bedpost, which seemed to evade his grasp. 'Maria, I would have been a great soldier if I hadn't been a peasant. I'd have been a great writer, too, if I had not had to please my evangelical brethren . . .'

'You're a great man, Pat, but at the moment you're a great drunk man. I expect your sister-in-law will have a few words to say on the subject tomorrow.'

'If she can remember,' giggled Pat. 'I filled her glass as often as I filled my own.'

'Of course you didn't. Now move yourself over a bit so there's an inch left for me.'

൭൦

The official thanksgiving for Waterloo at Thornton was conducted by Pat in the Old Bell Chapel. He had a big job ahead of him to restore the building to comfort and dignity, but for this occasion nobody seemed to mind the damp and the people streamed down into the valley in the sunshine as the single bell rang out. However poor they were, their imagination had been caught by this soldier and his army. *Like the Duke of Brontë caught mine,* thought Pat.

In the evening the Firths came, and the Morgans from Bradford, and they toasted the duke again. When they had gone, and Bess was asleep in the little dressing room, well separated from the main bedroom, Pat murmured to Maria:

'Let us conceive a very special child on this special night.'

'Your arrogance is unchanged,' she whispered. 'Why should we have a special child?'

'Both our children are already special,' he whispered back, 'the product of our Celtic imaginations. Let's just try to make this one very, very special.'

Maria held him tight. 'I love your flights of fancy,' she laughed softly. 'Yes, this one will be very, very special.'

൭൦

September was enlivened by Dr Firth's marriage to Miss Greame in Halifax. ('Sad,' said Pat, 'Bess had hopes there, I think.' 'Nonsense,' replied Maria, 'she's longing to quit this climate and get back to Penzance.') When Miss Firth returned from the festivities

85

and told all the details to Maria and Bess, the socialising began again.

'You'll like her,' said Miss Firth of her new stepmother. 'I certainly do, and she will love your children.' Picking up little Maria, she whispered in her ear, 'How could anyone not love a Miss Brontë? You and your sister are my dearest little friends.' Maria chuckled and pulled at her bonnet.

'May we come to your house again?' she asked.

'Certainly. Come tomorrow, and we'll have tea in the garden as it's still warm and you can meet the new Mrs Firth and pick apples.'

Patrick returned from Bradford just as she was leaving. He was hot and tired from his walk, and his face glowed. He bent to kiss her hand and then sat, at her command, to drink what was left in the teapot.

'You can come too and pick apples if you want to,' she said and departed, raising her parasol against the September sunshine.

That night, Maria was busy copying Pat's new manuscript for the printer. He had called it *The Cottage in the Wood.* Suddenly she glanced up, pausing at the title page, which she had left until last.

'Do you mock me, Patrick?' (Always 'Patrick' when it was serious.)

'Mock you, my love?'

'This subtitle – *or, The Art of Being Rich and Happy* – seems to be a parody of the title of my pamphlet – you may remember it?'

Pat feigned a lapse of memory and then clicked his fingers. 'Of course, my dear. Isn't it called the *Advantages of Poverty in Religious Concerns?* It just struck me how similar our minds were, even if we express things differently . . .'

She threw him a sharp look over the spectacles she shared with Bess. 'You'll do your own copying in future if you invent any more titles like that,' she said, 'and you always lose the papers and make omissions so a fine mess you'll be in.'

ை

On a cold day in January little Maria insisted that she, Rafferty and Thunder should accompany Papa on his visits.

'It's too cold, Pat,' said Maria. She was by the fire, frowning at her book. She sounded very tired.

86

'It will make a restful afternoon for you, Maria. Bess will take Elizabeth and you could sleep.'

'I don't need to sleep in the day, Patrick,' she said sharply. 'There is always work to do. Even if Jane does everything in the kitchen and cleans the house, there is always work to do.'

Were there tears in her eyes? Pat knelt beside her and kissed her hands. She smiled. There were tears.

'It's just this baby,' she whispered, glancing towards the half-open door. 'Perhaps it is very special. It's not that big but it kicks all night, lies awkwardly and I have scarcely any sleep.'

'Perhaps it's a wild boy,' he joked. 'And all the more reason for Maria to come with me, then you can sleep as you need to.'

She leaned back in the chair and closed her book. 'I'll soon nod off,' she said. 'Ask Bess to play with Elizabeth in the nursery. She'll love to have her all to herself!'

Pat wrapped the child in the biggest shawl he could find, from head to toe, and heaved her up onto his shoulders. She was no light weight now.

'Flying, Papa!' she cried, chuckling with delight at the snow-covered moors.

'What is it for, Papa? Who makes it? Why is it now and not always? Does your God do it?'

'Your metaphysical questions perplex me, my dear,' he shouted back, holding her tiny hand in its woollen wrap, her little fingers firmly grasping his.

'Met-a-fizz-i-cal,' she replied, 'That's nice sounds. Raff-er-tee is nice, too. Why is Rafferty called Rafferty and Thunder Thunder?'

'Because Rafferty was once as alone and hungry as I was when I came from Ireland (*How easily I can say it now*), so he has an Irish name.'

'Poor Papa!'

'No, not poor Papa – Papa has a lovely wife and special children and has a wonderful time with them now.' He threw her up in the air and caught her, as she shrieked with delight. 'And Thunder is Thunder because the Greek word for "thunder" sounds like Brontë.'

'So I am Maria Thunder, and he is my brother?'

'You can be Maria Thunder if you wish, but Thunder is not your brother. But you will have a brother one day, I'm sure.'

When they arrived at Hill Farm, Mrs Greenwood reached up to take Maria.

'What a day to bring the child out, Mr Brontë,' she exclaimed, 'but I do love to see her!'

'She wanted to come,' Pat smiled. 'I see she never sets foot in the snow. Sit her by the fire while I talk to your mother.'

When he returned to the kitchen from the bedroom where the old lady lay, Maria was by the fire with milk, scones and a cat, to whom she was telling a story.

'She's a forward bairn,' said Mrs Greenwood. 'She talks like a grown woman, nay, better than some. And her laugh! It does me good.'

'She's a great companion,' Pat told her, 'even though small. She takes after her mother.' He waited until the story ended, then wrapped her up again and tucked her into the crook of his arm.

ⅆⅆ

The moor at the back of the house was loud with birds when the new baby was born, but despite the spring sunshine Bess had a good fire going in the dining room where she had prepared for the lying-in. The shutters were closed against prying eyes and the noise of the street. When Patrick returned from his walk across the moor to his chapel of ease at Denholm, he came out of the bright sunshine into a glowing nativity picture.

He saw with a shock that Maria looked exhausted: she was lying against the fresh white pillows which had replaced those used in the birth, and her face nearly matched them. He sat on the bed and took her hands in his.

'She's beautiful,' he said, looking at the tiny bundle in her arms. 'Like all of them – beautiful. But you – are you all right?'

Maria smiled weakly. 'The noise she made! I should think the whole street heard. She came out shouting. This one will have plenty to say!'

He kissed the little wrinkled face and Maria's tired one. 'Perhaps she's extra special,' he whispered. 'We did try . . .' They put their heads closer and laughed.

'Tiny she may be,' sighed Maria, 'but it was like giving birth to a giant. I thought it would never end. The last one was so quick.'

Pat took the bundle from her and looked intently into the half-opened eyes. 'Perhaps you have a lot to tell us,' he said to the baby. 'Look,' – he held her up to the light of the nearest candle, and her little head moved towards it – 'she can't see clearly but her eyes are everywhere.'

'For goodness sake put that poor baby down, Pat!' exclaimed Bess, entering with a tray of food for them both. 'She's supposed to be sleeping not having an examination!' She arranged the food, replaced the baby in the cot and sat in the nursing chair with a contented sigh.

'What a family you have. You have re-created my childhood for me. Maria, Elizabeth and Charlotte, Branwell girls. This is such a happy house, I shall find it difficult to leave.'

Maria dropped her eyes to her plate, then slid them sideways to Pat and back again.

'You've been here over a year, Bess,' she said, 'and helped us with two babies. We can't ask you to do more. We wouldn't have managed these last two months without you. But we can't expect more.'

Bess sighed again. 'I do have to return to Penzance. There are things I should do, people I should see. I'll wait until July when the weather is warm and the seas calmer. If only it were not such a long way. But this house and these girls – and you – I shall miss . . .' She faltered.

'But you will return,' said Patrick gently, putting his hand on hers. 'These girls need to know their aunt and greatest friend.'

'I will return, yes.' She sniffed and blew her nose neatly. 'Most certainly I will return.'

തെ

Bess's departure was finally fixed for July. The previous week was spent in farewells and visits, and on the Sunday Patrick preached a sermon to help her bear up: 'Jesus Christ, the same yesterday, today and forever.' Even that brought a tear as they filed out of church, Maria carrying Charlotte and Bess taking little Maria and Elizabeth by the hand. Outside the Old Bell Chapel the valley was beautiful in the summer sun, and Patrick, doing his clerical greetings at the door, was full of happiness as his eyes wandered to his family. *O Praise the Lord,* he thought. *For his merciful kindness is ever more and more towards us.*

Bess had been part of the social scene all the time they had been in Thornton and was much liked at Kipping House, where her strong sense of social obligation had endeared her to the Firths, who enjoyed dinners and teas and outings and visits. Patrick often teased Bess that her Methodist background had rendered her even more frivolous than the Anglican Church – notorious for its sporting parsons who kicked off their hunting boots in the vestry – had made him. Miss Firth gave a great tea party for all the children and ladies of Thornton; keepsakes were exchanged, bonnets and slippers, handkerchiefs and gloves, all worked with affection and care. They had been splashed with a few tears when Patrick came in from a Church Missionary Society meeting in Bradford. He sat amidst the spoils of tea and piles of presents.

'Mr Brontë,' said Miss Firth, 'you will surely miss Miss Branwell after all this time. We certainly shall.'

'Deeply,' he replied, taking the cup she offered him. 'I have a household of lovely women, and she is among the loveliest.'

Bess's ringletted fringe shook with emotion. *I shouldn't say these things*, thought Patrick, *but she loves it and it does her good.*

'You flatter me, Patrick,' she murmured, 'but don't you sometimes wish for another man in your house?'

'I've got Rafferty and Thunder, who are ideal as they never disagree with me. We think alike on walks and food and other dogs. I love the company of women and my own more than others. I shall miss you, Bess.' He felt in his pocket and took out a slim volume. 'Here, Bess, take my book – it is all I can make, for you know I can't ply a needle well.'

She took the book and gazed at the inscription inside: ' "To my dear friend Miss Branwell." ' Tears welled up again. 'I shall keep it all my life, Patrick,' she sniffed. 'Oh dear, how I shall miss this family and these friends!'

'Will Aunt Branwell come back?' asked little Maria, as her nose was blown by Miss Firth, 'For I do need her to come back!' And she flung herself on Bess's lap, who cried even more.

As they said their farewells at the gate of Kipping House, Miss Firth said to Pat:

'With Miss Branwell gone, Mrs Brontë will need help other than Jane. Why don't you try the Bradford School of Industry for a trained girl? They are taught to read and write as well as sew and clean, and,' she added slyly, 'I know you will want an educated girl to help raise your clever children.'

'Thank you,' he said, inclining his red head towards her curly one, 'I'm sure you're right, and I shall act on your advice.'

'Pat,' said Maria as they crossed the street and walked towards the parsonage, 'you are an old flirt. Don't upset that nice girl.'

'Flirt! I was hearing how you need a nursemaid. I never flirt, Maria. You know that. What need have I to flirt with a wife like you?'

'It's just that the older you get the handsomer you are,' she laughed and took his hand in her free one, for all to see.

༄

Maria was soon back to the soup-making. Despite the Peace of Paris, the people around Dewsbury and Bradford were without work and hungry, and the Luddites seized the opportunity for further protest. Pat carried his pistol by day and kept it loaded at night. He tried only to be out when the moon was full and it was possible to see what was going on round the house, but still he made Maria keep a loaded pistol, and he taught her to fire it.

'Don't try to hit anything,' he instructed. 'Just fire it out of the kitchen window up in the air if you hear anyone about.' He felt better now that Nancy Garrs had joined them as nursemaid, although a thirteen-year-old was not a match for desperate men. He always left Thunder behind, taking only Rafferty with him. Thunder, by virtue of his new guard dog status, insinuated himself into previously forbidden places, the children's bed and Pat's chair, in his absence.

One dark afternoon a man came to the kitchen door, begging bread for his family. Pat had just returned from the moor and invited him in. He would not enter. He refused the offer of milk for his children, content to put the loaf in the cloth he carried and disappear back into the darkness. He was ashamed to come. Later, as they sat in the kitchen for the children's tea, Pat looked at the alert faces, bright eyes and answered the constant questions. *What would I feel if they were crying with hunger, grey and listless, and prone to the diseases that poverty brings?* He always made sure the collection for the poor in Ireland came only from those with comfortable incomes and regularly sent money to his mother.

He was more conscious of his happiness because he could remember times which were not so good. Every stroke of good fortune, whether a new baby or a new book, stirred enormous thankfulness in him. He felt quite guilty when William Morgan wrote such a kind review of *The Cottage in the Wood* that the publisher wanted a reprint.

'Shall we celebrate, Maria?' he asked, as the candles burned low and he poured her a second dram, to his third. She looked at him with her lovely, glowing eyes, pretending incomprehension.

'Indeed we will,' she replied, raising her glass. 'Congratulations, dearest and most clever husband!'

'I was thinking Maria . . .'

She looked up innocently.

'I was thinking I would love a son . . .'

'Are your daughters not good enough?' she asked, hiding a smile as she bent to reach the fireguard. 'Do you want to disturb the peace and harmony of this house with wild male behaviour?'

He looked straight into her beautiful eyes.

'Our daughters are the best in the world, and you well know I think so. Maria is as much a friend to me as any son I will ever have, and Elizabeth and Charlotte are becoming so. But I would like to teach a boy to shoot and fish, and perhaps he could go in the army. He could write if we keep him out of the church. He could do all these things better than I have done.'

'There's no need for him to do better than you, Pat. You're everything your women want. Teach the girls to shoot as you've taught me, and they say Miss Austen writes a good novel, Mrs Radcliffe, too, although I've never read them. But I assume the celebration is to be as usual?'

'Correct,' he said, draining his glass and gently removing her hemming from her lap. The candle threw their tall and short shadows on to the staircase wall as he led her upstairs, past the room where the children lay spread about their big bed, as if they had dropped asleep in mid-sentence. They paused at the door and looked in before reaching their own room.

'Just one more,' she said, as she uncoiled her hair and slipped out of her chemise, 'just a son for you, and then perhaps we should stop.'

'Never!'

'No,' she murmured later, 'no, certainly not.'

ᎶᏙ

Pat's stomach was screwed into a constant knot. Maria had been sick for months, losing weight, unable to keep anything but the plainest food down. Her pallor and her wasted flesh reproached him every time he went to sit with her, although she did not. Even her beautiful eyes had lost their glow.

'My desire for a son has made you so ill,' he whispered. She pulled herself up on her pillows and took his hand.

'No,' she said. 'Not yours. Ours. This is the way for women. So many of us have an easy time with the early babies. I suppose I'm getting old.' She laughed and smoothed the counterpane with her small, fine hands, then sighed. 'We are lucky, Pat, compared with most families. Think of the women and children you've buried!'

He shuddered. 'I think of it all the time. I always thought a big family was an easy thing. My mother had ten, and she and all her children are still alive today. I thought it would be the same for us. How stupid I am not to learn the lessons I see all about me.'

'No,' said Maria again. 'It will be the same for us. I shall soon be well, and the children are thriving. All they ever have is coughs and colds, in fact your chest gives me more anxiety than all their ailments.'

'My chest is nothing. I had coughs in Ireland, and the doctor there said that they were good protection against consumption as they seemed to shield you later on. It's you – you who must be well; you who have warmed me and who are so precious because you have tamed me.'

'Tamed!' chuckled Maria. To convince her, he told her about the bell ringers at Dewsbury.

'I can't believe it,' she gasped. 'Were you really hanging on the bell with your feet swinging?'

'It's not funny,' he said. 'It shows what a fool I could be without your love and reasonableness. They were only practising for a competition! I was always looking for slights and ways to assert my authority.'

'I think', she said when their laughter had subsided, 'that when I met you, you were quite stern. You didn't like being crossed. You weren't willing to suffer any more the insults and slights which had been your lot when you first came to England. Now you're more content.'

'Content! If you were well I would be the happiest man on

earth.' He pressed her hand to his lips. 'Don't ever let me be like that again.'

'I've never had a cross word from you, Pat,' she said softly. 'A kinder husband there has never been.'

13

Like as the arrows in the hand of the giant: even so are the young children. Happy is the man that has his quiver full of them.

Psalm 127, verse 5.

'It's you, Pat,' said Maria happily. 'Look at the red hair and strange pale blue eyes.'

'Strange? Why strange?'

'Like the fairies in Ireland. I'm sure they have pale blue eyes . . . But he's too small. We shall have to keep him swaddled and feed him whenever he asks. I couldn't bear to lose a child. I've seen grief in women here, and I wouldn't manage, I know.'

The little boy had been born at the end of June. The lying in arrangements were less rigorous without Bess, but Maria was still in the dining room, devotedly waited on by Nancy and her newly recruited sister Sarah.

'We won't lose a child,' he said quite sharply. His heart was thudding and his stomach ached. 'Sleep now, and let Nancy take the children.'

Little Maria, who had been deep in a book at the other side of the room, ran across and jumped onto the bed. 'There's no need for Nancy to come,' she said firmly. 'I will take Elizabeth and Charlotte upstairs. I read better than Nancy.' She went into the hall and made her way to the kitchen.

'Charlotte won't be able to climb the stairs,' whispered Maria. 'You'd better ask if they need help!'

Pat stepped in to the hall. 'I am Pegasus, Madam,' he stated, pawing the ground with one foot. 'May I help you by flying your sister up the stairs?'

Maria looked at him gravely. 'Just this once, until Charlotte grows longer legs.'

He put Charlotte on his shoulders, and the others staggered up in front of him. He left them in their big room, overlooking the street, perched by the window and ready for the reading.

⌒⌒

The harvest moon was full when Pat returned from Bradford and the Literary Society, where he had been giving a paper on Scott. A bit of a risk to be seen to worship this Romantic novelist, but his enthusiasm had overcome his judgement. Maria had left the shutters partly open and was reading by moonlight as well as by her candle.

'I don't like that,' Pat said sharply when he came in. 'You know I don't like it.' She looked up, startled at his tone. She was about to speak, but he blew the candle out before she could. 'I'm sorry. Please don't have a candle near the bedclothes. If you fell asleep . . . You know I fear fire. It's not just the children I bury round here, but the memory of my father's kiln when I was as little as ours are now. It took the thatch from the cabin and the burns Billy had scarred his hands forever. Please don't.'

She folded the letter she had been reading. 'I'd forgotten,' she said amiably. 'I had started to read Bess's letter downstairs and thought I would read it again now. Of course, you're right. It's a good rule for a house full of children.'

He sat on the bed by her and pulled at his neckcloth in a sawing movement to loosen it. 'I can't get rid of that fear,' he sighed. 'All the others you've banished. But fire and children – no.'

Maria, who had become used to hopping between the small rugs he allowed to avoid the cold floors, nodded at him. 'You're right, Pat', she said. 'If more people did without carpets and used their shutters for privacy there would be fewer accidents. I really don't mind.'

He smiled at her, silvered all over in the moonlight. 'Who else would put up with all my oddities?' He took her long plait in his hands and wound it round them. 'Tell me what Bess says. She suffered from my eccentricities when she was here. She said the only way to get through the winters here was thick curtains and carpets to keep the draughts out.'

'She's ecstatic because we have a son, and delighted that he is called Patrick Branwell. She . . .' – she peered closely at the page in a shaft of moonlight – '. . . hopes that we'll call him Branwell, not Patrick. She implies that one Patrick is enough for any household. Is that for convenience or a comment on your personality?'

'Me, I suppose,' Pat said ruefully. 'She wasn't used to pistols and singing and the odd dram. She . . .'

'She loved this house and the children and the fun you make for them – she'd never seen children like ours. So don't get into an Irish gloom about Bess – she loves us all.'

'By the way, Pat,' she said a little later, when the shuttered windows had made the room pitch black, 'I've heard that a woman does not conceive if she is nursing a child.'

'And where in the world would a respectable clergyman's wife hear such thing?' he queried.

'At Kipping House, would you believe.' She twisted her tiny body so that it was enclosed by his big one. 'At Kipping House no less. At tea! We were, of course, speaking in a general manner about poor relief and the women of the parish with their large, hungry families.'

'Naturally.'

'But as I don't feel strong enough for another baby yet Pat, so you must love me only when I am nursing Branwell. Which is now.'

Pat, who had been drifting off to sleep, woke with a start. 'Now?'

'Yes, now.'

༄

As Pat paced the kitchen floor he could not believe that he had been so stupid as to listen to old wives' tales, or let Maria believe them. During the last six months he had watched Maria like a hawk until she complained that he was harrassing her. She had been quite well but nothing would restore his appetite until the birth was over. Outside, the rain of a summer storm fell in torrents and rushed off the moor, pushing against the back door and nearly flooding the kitchen. He had dammed the door with sacking and paced alone, as Nancy and Sarah were with the midwife. Pat left the house abruptly and borrowed a horse from his farrier neighbour to ride for the doctor.

'Please come,' he shouted against the roaring wind, when the sleepy man had poked his head out of the window. 'It's our fifth child, and the last was difficult enough for her.'

97

'It's not usual,' said the doctor, as he let him into the house. 'Babies are the midwife's business. There's no need for me to be there. What can I do? Babies just come.'

'Please,' beseeched Pat. The doctor seized his bag and followed him out into the wild night. He would go because he liked the Brontës, and Pat in particular. There were not many parsons in these parts who would provide such a good evening's entertainment. They rode together in the rain, Pat setting a fast canter which the doctor had trouble keeping up with.

'Slow down!' he shouted to Pat's disappearing back. 'Either the child will be already born, or it will keep us waiting. It needs a father, so don't break your neck.'

Ignoring him, Pat pressed on, and they soon clattered up Main Street to the parsonage. A fierce little cry greeted Pat as he fell into the hallway, and Nancy handed him a baby with a shock of black hair. As he took her, a great crack of thunder shook the house.

'Poor child!' the midwife said. 'Poor little bairn! Cover her head.'

'She doesn't mind it,' said Maria faintly from the bed. 'Look, she didn't even stir. She's looking round as if she likes it. Pat, Mrs Fox has been so good with me. I don't think we'd have managed without her.'

The doctor was examining Maria and the baby. 'This was not an easy birth,' he said, stroking the child's head. 'I'm glad you fetched me. But Mrs Fox is an expert. She's done a wonderful job.'

The colour was beginning to return to Pat's face, and his breathing was more regular. 'Thank you,' he said. 'Perhaps I should have stayed and not gone for Dr Richards. But I was desperate. What's your Christian name?' he enquired.

The midwife looked surprised. 'It's Emily, sir.'

'Then let's call her Emily, Maria,' he said. 'Thank God she was here and delivered you both safely to me.' He flopped into a chair, still holding the baby against his shoulder. 'Nancy, bring the whiskey and glasses for us all. We all need it, except for this fearless little Emily, who doesn't turn a hair for rain or wind or birth or anything.'

Maria smiled at Emily Fox. 'That's just what I want,' she said. 'You've been so good to us. I hope you'll like your namesake.'

'I'm greatly flattered, madam.' She beamed with pleasure. 'I hope she enjoys her life as much as I have mine. I really love my work, and this family gives me a great deal!' She laughed, handing Maria a glass as Pat poured the golden, warming liquid into the glasses. The room glowed in the firelight as the weather raged outside.

14

They are Yorkshiremen. The fact is that the people of
Haworth are unique, a race apart. Their nobility is without
equal; their faults, bad beyond belief. They make the most
loyal of friends, the most inveterate of foes ... nothing is
sweet and simpering. Everything resembles the millstone grit,
tough, sturdy, independent, defiant ... Haworth is beyond
the realms of compromise.

J. Lock and W. T. Dixon, *A Man of Sorrow* (1965).

Pat's head thumped with every step he took; he screwed up his
eyes to clear his vision and breathed deeply. It was downhill to the
Bell Chapel, and the bright August sun was merciless. It had been
such a good evening: Emily christened, and all the friends of the
family there; the Fennells as godparents and Jane Morgan a
godmother; William performing the ceremony and doing his dual
role again ('You'll have to find some new friends, Pat,' he had said,
'I don't have time for all these duties. Talk about a quiverful'). Pat
smiled at the thought; they were so lucky; William and Jane were
childless, and Maria was reluctant to ask William to christen in case
he felt the contrast between their fertility and the Morgans' barren-
ness. But Pat had a sure instinct about feelings: he knew that not
asking William would wound him more. And so it had been the
usual Brontë christening: the amber liquid flowing and Pat singing
late into the night. They had also been to the Firths the night
before the christening, so Patrick was suffering a double hangover.
He shook his head hard, and it cleared a little. He stopped, sitting
for a moment on a stile, and looked with satisfaction at the Bell
Chapel.
  Rising from the green flanks of the Pinchbeck Valley, the chapel,

restored, complete and very handsome, stood confidently in the sunshine. It was seen to its best advantage in this bright light, the bell tower clearly etched against the green of the hills and the light glancing off the new stonework. *Dear God,* he thought, *it has taken a long time.* Built in the seventeenth century, the chapel had gone without repair for years, and Patrick's task when he came to Thornton had been awesome indeed. He was often puzzled that God required him maintain buildings when the message of the Gospels was so much simpler and the surrounding hills a fine enough setting to worship in; but then he had remembered the honeyed stone of Cambridge and the delight and inspiration it had given him. Gradually he had raised money and persuaded builders, and the damp and decay had given way to order, warmth and dignity.

Except for the organ. He sighed as he inserted the key into the freshly painted door and breathed in the smell of new wood and cleanly sanded stone. He would have dearly loved to install an organ to replace the musicians who scraped away on their fiddles and windily blew their serpents, but the money would not extend to that. When the gallery had collapsed and the musicians had to sit under Pat's stern eye there had been quite a rumbling, in the tradition of Yorkshire congregations, but he had fixed them with his pale blue gaze week after week until the mutterings subsided into a reluctant pact: they would play in their fairground rhythms and Pat would have their attention during his sermon. Their rustic sounds reminded him keenly of the music in Drumballyroney church, hurting his ears but tugging at his heart. He remembered hot days like this in Cambridge when the music of the organ in King's College had pealed out through the great open doors and reached him as he walked in the shade by the river with his book. He had grown to love the great oratorios, but concerts in Bradford and Halifax were all too rare treats for him and Maria; he nevertheless cherished a dream that one day he would have a church with an organ and recitals for the congregation. Music, after all, did not require men to read and write to feel and understand it: it reached the soul directly without the need for tutored filtering.

He left the door open; the sunlight poured in as he busied himself in the vestry, with his list of confirmation candidates. He could not help but feel pleased that there were so many this year; surely he was having some effect on the poverty-stricken popula-

101

tion, with their big families, tiny cottages and grim lives bounded by poverty and disease. He felt grateful that they put their children into his care in such numbers; the growth of his own family while he was in Thornton, the modesty of the parsonage in Market Street and Maria's attention to the needy had made him a trusted parson and friend.

Wiping his pen as he finished his list, he locked the top of the desk (it was Maria's idea that as many church papers as possible should be kept in the new vestry, an idea proposed after little Maria used the back of a letter from the archbishop for a story) and cast a last look at the bright interior as he stood with his hand on the huge cool handle of the door before he locked up. Suddenly he dropped the ring with a clang and sank to his knees in a pew in a sudden rush of emotion. He thanked God fervently for his good fortune; his wife, his children, his friends, his church, poetry and music. What a joy he had in all these things. What a road he had travelled to have them.

∾

Emily was nearly a year old when the confirmation took place in Bradford; the Firths had insisted that Maria accompany them in their carriage; she had protested mildly, feeling the Garrs girls should not be left with five children for such a long time, but the prospect of a visit to the town and adult company had tempted her. They had started early, done some shopping for muslins and haberdashery, lunched in the Talbot, Mr Firth's favourite hostelry, and were now waiting for the children and Pat to arrive from Thornton. She stretched her toes in front of the fire and thanked the Firths for her day.

'I feel almost like a normal person,' she laughed. 'We have lovely days with the children, but it's hard work!'

'We'll do it more often,' replied Elizabeth Firth. 'You know how I love your company – it's made such a difference having you and Mr Brontë here. Mr Atkinson didn't have a family, and I do so love your family!'

Suddenly there was a sound like bees buzzing and unshod horses. Sixty Thornton children had arrived in Bradford, and Pat's voice was heard in the hall. Maria and Elizabeth turned to see him talking to the landlord.

'Sixty,' he said, 'that will be enough. Just a simple plate of hot

102

food. The weather's turned, and I don't want them catching cold. In about two hours.'

'Whatever are you doing?' asked Maria as he joined them. 'Ordering sixty dinners!'

'It's cold,' he said simply, rubbing his long stiff fingers and stamping his feet. 'By the time they've sat through the service they will be even colder. They're all skinny children, and many are without shoes. If they were ours we'd do it. And they are ours, in spirit if not by blood.'

'But the cost, Pat!' whispered Maria. 'I know you should, but whatever will it cost?'

'The landlord is a good man,' Pat whispered back. 'He'll see it's not a fortune.' He took Maria by the arm. 'Take no thought,' he said with a wink. 'We always get by.'

At the end of the long service the children fell upon their food ravenously and then lined up to start the journey back to Thornton. Pat walked with Maria back to the Firths' carriage.

'After you left this morning,' he said, 'money came in for *The Maid of Killarney*. I knew we could afford to feed the children. It has made the day memorable for them.'

Maria sighed. 'I know you're right. But I'm glad it's extra money. We really are getting a bit tight with five children, two adults and two servants, not to mention your – *our* – dogs. Everyone has to be fed and clothed.'

'I can see Rafferty in a fine black broadcloth,' speculated Pat, 'and Thunder, I think, would be best in dark blue linen. Remind me to place the order the next time I send for myself to Mr Wright at Cambridge.'

She squeezed his arm hard. 'I do love you, Mr Brontë! Sometimes I worry a lot, and you just don't – about money, anyway.'

'That's not entirely true. But we'll be able to save on the publisher for my future work.' He laughed. 'Mr Inkersley put in a note with the banker's order to say he had reduced his charge slightly as we had provided our own excellent proofreader.'

'You mean Maria? Did she really find the mistakes? I thought you were joking to please her when you told me.'

'No, no. She sat on the counter and read the sheets upside down and still found the mistakes. Not bad for five. But here,' he said, 'here's your carriage, madam. In you get, and I'll see you in about three hours, when we've seen them all home.'

She leaned out of the window and caught his hand. 'If you do the story tonight, leave off the Milton, would you, just for a bit? Charlotte has such a literal mind and starting off for Bradford on her own in search of paradise scared me a little. It might not have been Mr Greenwood who found her and brought her home.'

He smiled ruefully. 'I'm not as sensible as you. It's the difference between the Irish Celt and the Cornish. We're just hopeless.' And he shrugged helplessly and blew her a kiss as the carriage rolled away.

ᏆᏆ

The weather was much warmer when the Morgans came to dinner and stayed the night in May. They were sitting in the parlour, candles just lit, Maria busy with the blue and white teacups and Jane tidying the last books and toys which were evidence of a busy afternoon for everyone. The children had gone to bed with a soothing story from her. They had come because Pat had sensed that William was feeling solitary since the Fennells had removed from Bradford; he had worked near his father-in-law for many years and had become used to the older man's company and advice.

'I hope he likes Cross Stone,' Jane said, winding the twine of a whipping top. 'He and my mother have done such a lot of moving in their lives. I suppose this will be his last post, but they seem a long way away.'

'Where is it?' asked Maria.

'North of here, towards Haworth,' William said, gesturing vaguely as he put *The Maid of Killarney* down reverently on the table. He folded his glasses. 'Haworth's the place where the vicar of Bradford nominates the minister, but the trustees choose him and pay his salary.'

Maria's eyes widened. 'That could be complicated,' she said with interest. 'What if they don't like the bishop's man? What then?'

'It hasn't happened,' put in Pat. 'Charnock has been there for about thirty years. Imagine it! The same place for thirty years!'

'Pat's really an Irish tinker,' said William, throwing his stick at him, which Pat, as usual, caught deftly. 'He never stays in one place for long, but moves on with his tribe of children, peddling his anonymous wares' – he brandished *The Maid* – 'to unsuspecting buyers.'

104

'We shan't be staying here for thirty years.' Maria's voice was soft. 'We can scarcely squeeze us all in now – imagine what it would be like when the children grow.'

Jane sighed. 'Five is a lot for a house this size. But I'd live in the smallest space there was if we had a child; I just wouldn't care.' She stopped, blushing at her outburst. It didn't matter. These friends knew how she and William longed for a child.

'We'll have another in January.' Maria's eyes met Pat's over the heads of their friends. They had agreed that the Morgans must be told; there had always been total frankness between them.

'How do you two manage it?' Williams round rosy face shone with enthusiasm for another baby. 'You are quite amazing!'

'We've found what causes it now.' chuckled Pat. 'We've always got something to celebrate. I think this one was for John's promotion.'

∞

Maria could not get over it.

'But we were only speaking about him yesterday!' she said in amazement.

'That sadly is what nearly everyone says when someone dies,' said Pat. 'I deal with it all the time, and that's what they all say: "But I was only speaking to him yesterday." '

'Thirty years. They will surely miss Mr Charnock at Haworth.'

'They're missing him already,' replied Pat, raising his greying eyebrows to peer more closely at the pen he was sharpening. 'When our esteemed friend the vicar of Bradford turned up to take the services on Sunday, they shut the door in his face. But he was never as diplomatic as dear old John Crosse.'

'How can he shut the door in his face? Did it squash?' enquired Charlotte from the fireside.

'Be quiet,' said Maria. 'I want to hear this. What happened, Pat? Stop it, Branwell. I can't hear if you bang that drum.'

'He went over to take the service on Sunday, which was the first day after Charnock's death,' repeated Pat, 'and the trustees and the wardens wouldn't let him in. They'd got wind that he wanted to appoint his own man to be the perpetual curate of Haworth, and they were telling him that they intended to choose the man they would be paying.'

'Dear Lord,' Maria said, blowing out her cheeks. 'What sort of people are they, and whom does he wish to appoint?'

105

'They're Yorkshiremen of the kind I met at Dewsbury – and dealt with – which is fortunate as the man he intends to appoint is me.'

'You! Really? But that's unbelievable! Why would God want you to go to a place like that? It sounds wild to me.'

'He might have heard your prayers for more space and more money, my love. It's a big, quite new parsonage, with five bedrooms, well set back behind the church away from the village, and the stipend is one hundred and eighty pounds a year, which, with all the bits and pieces, makes nearly two hundred. Could it just be the answer to a harrassed mother's prayer?' His eyes were laughing.

'But not if the people are wild enough to shut out a clergyman from his own church! That is not seemly!'

'Possibly we might be expected to take the rough with the smooth, dear one. It's a fact I have often found in life: beautiful Ireland, damnable politics; exciting Cambridge, dire poverty, lovely wife and children, never a moment's peace . . .'

'Well then,' she said, putting away her work, 'then go we must. When is it all to happen Pat? We still have a baby due in January. Before or after?'

For a moment a shadow passed over his face. 'I want you to be well,' he said quietly. 'I shall speak to Heap and try for the best time for you. Leave it for the moment. I want it to be right for you. Come, Elizabeth,' scooping her from the floor into his arms, 'come and help me with my sermon. Your calm presence soothes me. Bring a book to read and call the dogs.' He stepped over Branwell. 'Let's leave the demon king and his cronies.' And they were gone to the peace of his study.

꠵

Pat was travelling rapidly over the barely tracked moor towards Haworth; overhead the skylark's incessant optimism occasionally lifted his anxious mood. He had started early, and the mist was still clinging to the hillsides. Midsummer on the moors was beautiful, fresh and green: budding heather and the sun blazing down on a landscape whose only shade was intermittent clouds patterning the hills, and today there was little of that. Before he came to Yorkshire he had heard of the severity of the winters and the hard lives of the moorland farmers. Today it was a picture of gentle beauty, softly rounded hills, sheep in a wavering blob ahead of him,

106

bleating and trotting in their usual panic. To his left he noticed a single green acre which had been resolutely reclaimed from the unrelenting moor. Usually this kind of thing fascinated him; today he scarcely noticed it, as he strode along, rehearsing the words he would say to Stephen Taylor.

He had talked at great length with Maria and thought long and hard about Haworth; it would suit them as a family very well, and to be the vicar of Bradford's perpetual curate at Haworth would give them security and an adequate income. Their present house had become cramped with the birth of three, soon to be four children, since their arrival from Hartshead; if it was possible to afford more help for Maria in Thornton, the additional body would make the house truly overcrowded.

But Haworth? Pat's five years in Thornton had laid to rest the fears he had of the truculent grimness of the Yorkshire people he had clashed with in Dewsbury and Hartshead. He had also mellowed with Maria's gentleness and the absorbing task of bringing up their bright, companionable children. He skimmed the grass with his stick, and his face broke out into a broad smile at the thought of his family. He really longed to install them in the more spacious, grey house behind the church at Haworth. He could hardly confess, even to Maria, the satisfaction he would get from living in what was almost a gentleman's residence. A long way from Pat Brunty.

The tales which were now coming out of Haworth had prompted him to cross the moor to see one of the trustees of the church whom he had met socially in Thornton. He increased his pace as the sun rose higher in the sky. He took Kirkgate almost at a canter, hat well down to avoid the curious stares, and, skirting the wall of the church and parsonage, he left Hill Top Farm above him as he descended to Stanbury, almost running so that he could get to grips with the problem more speedily. He found Stephen Taylor in the yard of his farm.

'Good morning,' he shouted against the noise of the pigs being rounded up into a cart. 'They're fine and healthy. How are you, Mr Taylor?'

Taylor, a strongly built man with a fine head of hair almost the same colour as Pat's, turned and smiled at the tall, hot clergyman. 'You don't waste any time, Mr Brontë. I didn't think you'd be here for an hour yet. Come into the house; you could do with a drink,

I'm sure.' He led Pat into the cool, thick-walled interior of his ancient house, and they sat at the table, black with age and brilliant with beeswax.

'How well you'd fit in here, Mr Brontë,' remarked Taylor a few minutes later when they had finished the farming talk. 'You know all about our problems and harvests and animals. I met Bedford a while back at the market, and he was saying you were a strange parson!'

'You think I would fit in?' Pat was eager.

'Given the chance, yes,' replied Taylor. 'But the problem is not you but the vicar of Bradford. They don't learn, you see. We had trouble about Grimshaw, and even dear old Charnock. All because they will be so high and mighty and not stick to the terms of the trust. We have to agree to the nomination. It is not to be thrust upon us.'

'So it's not personal?'

'Certainly not. But I'm afraid that the other trustees and the people of Haworth – the last thing they are thinking about at the moment is the suitability of the parson. It's battle lines drawn between them and the vicar of Bradford. And you must admit, he's not a diplomat.' He pronounced each syllable of his final word separately, eyebrows raised.

'So what's your advice?'

Taylor took a deep breath. 'That's difficult. Until the vicar backs off, I can't see us accepting Jesus Christ himself.' He looked at Pat apologetically. 'If you see what I mean. It's that bad. Half the villagers aren't interested in the church until this issue comes up, but when it does . . .' – he blew his cheeks out and whistled – '. . . they think of nothing else. There's something in the people hereabouts which meks them extra sensitive to those who think they're superior.'

'I'll remember that,' Pat said quietly.

'That's not your reputation, Mr Brontë, far from it. Folk know you're a Tory because you can't abide violence, but they know you're good to children and families, and help men when they're out of work, and you're always in and out of their cottages. Those aren't the actions of a man who thinks he's superior.'

'And so?'

He sighed. 'It's hard to tell. It's not really anything that your suitability or goodness can change. It's the vicar of Bradford imposing his choice. They'll never budge as long as that's the issue. But' – and he scratched his head thoughtfully – 'if you resigned, it would then leave it open to the trustees to nominate you themselves. My three sons are trustees; it would be easier to work at it in that way.'

'Right.' Pat's tone was decisive. 'I can't fight with any of the weapons at my own disposal. I'll resign from the nomination and get on with my job in Thornton. I'm glad you talked to me. At least I see the plain truth now.'

'It's a great shame,' said Taylor, rising and walking back into the sunlight with him. 'I'd have enjoyed working with you. But I can't see it coming this time.'

They shook hands in the yard, and Pat began the ascent to Haworth at a more reflective pace. He hardly noticed the new cloud formations which changed the moor's mood. The deviousness of his action had plunged him into memories of Drumballyroney.

15

We regret to learn from a correspondent, that scenes scarcely possible in a heathen village, have been witnessed on three successive Sundays, in the church of Haworth ... the house of God, and the hallowed ground of a churchyard, are not proper places in which to allow, by disturbance and howlings, the loudest and lowest marks of irreverence and insult.

The Leeds Intelligencer, 22nd November 1819.

'You're *what?*' said Maria, cutting her thread with her teeth; her puckered lips made her words nearly incomprehensible, but Pat got their meaning only too clearly. 'You're going to *resign?* Are we made of money, then? Are we going to live off the sales of a few volumes of poetry and hope for deaths for the funeral fees? What ever are you up to, Pat Brunty?'

Pat flung himself into a chair close to the window where Maria was sitting to catch the light as she sewed a shift for one of the girls. He ran his hand through his damp hair and gratefully took the glass that Nancy Garrs had brought when she heard him open the parlour door.

'It's strategy, Maria,' he replied wearily. 'You know – like the Duke of Wellington. You remember how he had to plan a campaign and do things to prepare the ground before a battle. This is the same.'

'I don't see it, Pat. Perhaps you would explain how resigning from Haworth is a strategy to be appointed.'

'Is the Duke of Wellington coming to Thornton?' asked Charlotte, rising from the hearth rug and closing Foxe's *Book of Martyrs*. 'Because if he is I'm going to see him.'

'No he is not.' Maria responded quickly. 'So don't go wandering off again trying to find him. Go on Pat; you were telling me how the resignation would help us to Haworth.' Her voice was tired now. She wasn't finding it amusing at all.

'The plan is,' said Patrick, reaching for Charlotte and putting her on his knee to stem further interruptions, 'the plan is that if I resign as the vicar of Bradford's nominee the Haworth trusteees can nominate me themselves, which will make it acceptable to them. Stephen Taylor thinks he can influence his sons and that the others will go along with it if he says I am a suitable candidate. He thinks I am as I know a lot about pigs and farming.'

Maria looked at him, her humour restored. 'It suits you, this strategy,' she said. 'I didn't think that you were going to throw away our chance of a decent house and extra money really. Can you believe that Maria will be seven this year? She and Elizabeth almost need a governess.'

Pat hooted with mirth. 'A governess? They would be teaching her! Some poor girl who is barely literate using her meagre skills to keep a roof over her head and a hot meal a day in her stomach! Their education will be better if it comes from us; I'll never agree to an inferior education for my girls, will I, Charlotte? You'll learn from Papa, Mama and each other, not from some pale young girl with a smattering of writing and ciphering. Sad as it may be for her.'

'Why is she sad?' asked Charlotte with interest. 'How could we make her happy?'

'But you won't have the time, Pat,' interrupted Maria, 'and I have only a smattering, as you call it, of Latin . . .'

'There is no need at all to worry about the education of these children. That's the very least of our worries. Think what I did with no schooling but in the hedge-schools until those good men Harshaw and Tighe took me up. And most of our children are cleverer than I am: Maria reads the newspapers and tells us about the politics in London, and Branwell soaks up anything I have time to teach him. And he's only four. They're surrounded by books, and we talk to them all the time. That is their education.'

Maria seemed relieved. 'So the five bedrooms at Haworth parsonage will be all for us except one for Nancy and Sarah. That's good. You're a clever strategist, Pat.'

౧౪

111

But not clever enough for the archbishop of York, who, feeling he had to maintain the authority of the Established Church and support the vicar of Bradford, ordered Patrick to care for Thornton and Haworth together until tempers cooled. Pat was unable to refuse; his family would always need a parsonage, and if he defied the archbishop they could all be on the road tomorrow. Reluctantly he steeled himself to walk the six miles to Haworth again and take the Sunday service.

As he passed New Hall at the bottom of Kirkgate he could hear a rumble of voices in the distance and the braying of donkeys. Resolutely he walked on, his step losing its spring as his stomach tightened. This unusual gathering of people on a Sunday could only be connected with the church and the service. *Play the part*, he thought desperately. He was glad he was on his own. No one else to consider in what ever he decided to do.

At the top of the steep cobbled street was a huge group of men and women. With them was the biggest band of donkeys Pat had ever seen gathered together. Disliking the waiting, they were braying and stamping. The highly charged atmosphere made them restless with fear. As Patrick came into view catcalls and whistles filled the air.

''Ere comes 't parson!' came the shout. 'Or so 'e thinks 'e is! Coom on, Mr Brontë! We want to hear what tha's got to say. Coom into the church, and tell us all about it!'

Pat swallowed but kept his regular pace.

'Certainly,' he said. 'I've come to preach. Go into the church, and I'll be with you all in five minutes to start the service.'

'Start the service! Start the service!' came the derisive reply. 'You'll start no service in our church. Our trustees will choose who starts the service, won't they, lads?' A great roaring cheer went up. 'And they've not chosen you, Mr Brontë.'

Pat stopped at the wall of the Black Bull. 'The archbishop of York has ordered me to take the services in Haworth until a minister is appointed.' He stood stock-still, a tall black figure alone in front of the multitude. He tried his usual trick of finding a pair of eyes to fix with his, but none would look straight at him.

'I have, therefore, to preach in your church and take the service. I'd be obliged if you would let me through.' He took a step forward. The crowd surged towards him.

'You'd be obliged! He'd be obliged, my friends,' shouted a big

112

man with tattered clothes and a black beard. 'You'll not get past us, Parson.' And he stepped towards Pat and raised his fist in his face.

'I take it you are a regular worshipper at this church, that you feel so strongly about the trustees' rights?' enquired Pat mildly. There was a hoot of laughter from the crowd.

''E's not bin in a church since 'e was baptised! That right, Jed? Or did they not tek you for the row you'd mek?' And they all laughed.

Seizing the moment of light relief, Pat shouted, 'I'm going into the church now. I'll be glad to see you all inside.' He moved forward, and a pathway opened up. He didn't hurry. He smiled at individuals and thanked them as he went. He made it to the church door. Shut. Would it be locked? Praying silently, he turned the handle. The crowd was at his back and almost pushed him in. He braced himself against them in order not to fall. There could be no pause in this drama. He would have to go straight to the chancel.

When he reached it and turned to the congregation, they were arranging themselves comfortably in the pews for the entertainment. He caught sight of Stephen Taylor's face. The man shrugged, embarrassed. He knew that Pat thought of him as a gentleman. This was not what he should be doing.

Pat was now alone at the front of the church, surveying the most outrageous scene he had ever beheld in England or Ireland. The donkeys had been brought in and were braying desperately. He became angry at their exploitation in the house of God.

'Sit down!' he shouted. 'Sit down! You are a disgrace to the church of Jesus Christ!' There was a silence; he was just about to seize this advantage when one of the terrified animals relieved itself on the floor. The congregation whooped and banged on the pews.

'That's what 'e thinks of what you're going to tell us, Mr Brontë! A load of shit!' It was Jed, back to claim his position after his humiliation. But silence followed his outburst as the people came out of shock at hearing this word in church.

'You are a blaspheming heathen,' Patrick roared. He actually ran down the aisle. He was taller but not broader than the man. He took a risk. He seized him by the rag tied round his bull neck and the broad belt at his waist and pushed and shoved him to the

113

door. He kept pushing forwards so that Jed could not turn and hit him. The door was shut but, seeing his objective, Stephen Taylor swiftly opened it, and Pat propelled the man through it and slammed it shut behind him. The crash echoed through the church.

He stood with his back to it, holding the handle with his arm behind his back.

There was absolute silence.

'We will sing hymn number 46,' he said quietly. ' "Oft in danger, oft in woe, Onward Christian, onward go." '

Taylor took the door handle off him. Jed was shut out. The congregation was shut in.

A few faint voices started the hymn. Gradually others joined in. By the fifth verse there was normal harmony. Pat was shaking. For one terrible moment he thought he would vomit. It passed.

He reached the end of the service without further mishap. There was a little muttering from the prisoners, but he fixed each one with his furious eyes, and each stopped, even if another started. He said the blessing, walked to the door, picked up his hat and, raising it to the congregation, made his way at a brisk pace towards the Black Bull and down Kirkgate. When he was a mile away from Haworth, he lay down in the heather and wept.

⟲

'I agree,' she whispered that night, as the moon sent sticks of light through the shutters. 'You can't possibly go there. No house, no money is that important. You cannot be treated like that. If it were not you telling me, I would scarcely believe it.'

'Oh it happened all right.' He put his hand over her swelling belly, stroking the new child within. 'I could have killed the man Jed. I was almost relieved when I saw him alive in the graveyard when I left. But I want so much a better house for you and the children.' He patted her lightly.

'Not at that price, Pat. We could build a bit on here, at the back, use the money you make me save for my widowhood.' She giggled. 'Two more rooms would be a greater comfort now than luxury when I'm an old lady. But what sort of people were they, Pat? I can't imagine that happening in Thornton.'

Pat turned onto his back and stared at the ceiling, striped with the moonlight.

114

'They look terrible,' he said. 'Dirty, ragged, half-starved a lot of them, although hunger is not the motive here. Do you remember how the duke described the men who won Waterloo? – "The scum of the earth, enlisted for drink." The people today were not the people I would normally meet in the congregation. We attract the ones who like order and duty and are reasonably content with their lot, even if they're hungry and poor.'

'But where did these people come from?'

'They're Haworth villagers, and from off the moor, without a doubt. Not many regular churchgoers. There's a feeling of desperation among them. They've lived through the war and the promises; they've lost their jobs to machines; they're tired of prices which rise and fall and make it impossible for them to raise healthy children. Some are angry with grief. The business with the trustees is just an excuse to vent their feelings.'

Maria leaned on one elbow. 'You sound sympathetic.'

'I suppose I am. So are you – remember all the soup and bread you've made and given away? I can't see where this country is to go unless something improves their lot. Some of the more thoughtful among them want to vote in the running of their country.'

'But that's not possible. Voting is for landowners and gentlemen. I've heard William talk about this, and he is adamant that things should stay as they are.'

He kissed her tenderly. 'He and I do not think alike on this. He has never lived in a society where injustice has made men break the law. We don't want that here. Stroke my head, Mrs B.,' he said. 'Get those awful images out of it. I think I'm really quite a violent man, but I feel terrible afterwards. I'll write the letter tomorrow, and we'll go back to a calm life, and improve this house.'

'With two more bedrooms and another privy?'

'With two more bedrooms and another privy.'

◌

But the calm life was elusive. Patrick's resignation spurred the trustees in exactly the way Stephen Taylor had anticipated. No sooner had they received his letter than they sent one winging across the moor saying that they would nominate him if he cared to give then a sample of his preaching. He almost choked on his oatmeal porridge.

115

'Another performance for the entertainment of the village! Can they really think I would go to Haworth after the welcome I had?'

'Of course not, Pat.'

'But should I close my mind entirely to the house and the stipend, and might not God want a man whose experience of life makes him suited to survival among revolutionaries?'

'Revolutionaries were in France,' said little Maria, leaning on Pat and leaving crumbs all over his waistcoat. 'All the papers say they must never be allowed to come here. Are there really revolutionaries so close, Papa? Are there Frenchmen in Haworth, like General Humbert whom you told us about in Ireland?'

'No, no,' laughed Pat. 'You're right about General Humbert, but I was exaggerating. It's hyperbole, you remember that? What do you think, Maria? Shall I risk life and limb again?'

'No,' she said firmly, putting the knives and spoons back from where Branwell had lined them up for a battle. 'No,' she repeated, less firmly. 'Do what you think you ought. What is best for you. For all of us.' She looked round the six faces she loved more than anything else in the world, and at her own round form. 'Do what you think is right.'

Pat rose from the table and went to his desk. He took much longer to arrange his writing than usual. New quill, carefully sharpened, sand at the ready, paper, wax. Still he paced the room. Suddenly he sat down:

My conscience does not altogether approve to a circumstance of exposing myself to the temptation of preaching in order to please . . . I really am of the opinion that the best way by far is for the Trustees and some others of the people of Haworth who are good judges of preaching to come and hear both me and others in our own churches when we do not expect them. It is an easy matter to compose a fine sermon or two for a particular occasion but no easy thing always to give satisfaction . . . believe me, the character and conduct of man out of the pulpit is as much to be considered as his character and conduct in.

He sat back, scattered the sand and read his words. *That leaves it open,* he said to himself. *Let God do the rest.*

⚬

116

When the news of Peterloo reached Thornton in August Maria remembered Pat's words after he had taken the Haworth service. The fifty thousand people who had gathered in their Sunday best to listen to Henry Hunt had ended up fleeing for their lives from the horses and swords of the Fifteenth Hussars who had to rescue the pompous, incompetent Manchester and Salford Yeomanry. The number of dead and wounded was deeply shocking. Manchester was only forty miles away, but the moorland people heard the news with varying degrees of excitement, fear and foreboding. Pat was more cynical.

'This government is inept,' he said, when little Maria had finished reading the account of the tragedy to both her parents and all her siblings. 'Tory as I am, something needs to be done about reform. It's wrong to let the Whigs do it all. Lord Liverpool is without ideas and Castlereagh!' He spread his hands hopelessly.

'But he is from Ireland, and County Down, and your old college,' chipped in Charlotte. 'You must like him!'

'No I mustn't,' replied Pat. 'He is arrogant and unfeeling. Not like the greatest living Irishman.' His eyes twinkled.

'THE DUKE OF WELLINGTON!' shouted all the children

Maria raised a hand to her head. 'Off you go,' she said. 'Go and find Sarah, and let's have less noise. Sorry Pat,' she said, as they hurtled out of the room, 'I'm feeling grim today. It's the heat.'

'Go and see Elizabeth at Kipping House. She's back today and loves you and you'll have a cool day in her garden. It's good to be free of all the Haworth stuff. Let's forget it all and enjoy the good weather.'

He was, however, far less sanguine than his words implied. He still wrestled with the loss of Haworth and the benefits it would have brought them all. He was worried about Maria who seemed to be less well than in any of her other pregnancies. She had unrelated pains, and the doctor could suggest nothing except to wait until the baby was born in January and see if that solved everything. He longed to be able to say, 'We have a fine house and income, and all will be well!' but his realism made him honest and his Irish glooms made him suffer. He ate little and slept badly, but tried to keep outwardly cheerful.

The final straw came in October when the archbishop of York, presumably finding the unresolved problem of Haworth at the bottom of a pile of paper, irritably ordered Pat to take the services

117

in Haworth. Dreading what he would face, he walked the six miles on the tenth of October. The churchyard was packed with a jostling, shouting crowd. When he appeared, the noise died as he reached the church. No one spoke. He entered, expecting the rush from behind him. No one moved.

In the church was Taylor, alone, to greet him. Pat raised his eyebrows. Taylor shrugged back, baffled. 'I don't know what they're up to,' he said.

They soon knew. Pat started the service, in an empty church except for Taylor. Outside the noise grew from shouting to banging on tins, banging with sticks on the door, the singing of raucous songs normally only heard at the horse races on the moor and the occasional crunch as badly maintained tombstones gave way under the excessive weight of the demonstrators. They howled and chanted, rattled and threw stones at the windows. Inside, Patrick, dry-mouthed and shaking, repeated the order of matins, skipped the hymns, gave the blessing to Stephen Taylor and prepared to leave. The moment he turned the handle of the door, silence fell outside. He opened it. A roar went up from the crowd.

'Well done, Mr Brontë!' shouted an old man. 'Tha's up to it! A mind of your own is what you've got. You'll do for us!' Another cheer burst into the air.

Pat looked straight at him. 'I'll not do for you,' he said quietly. 'I'll never do for anyone who suffers disgrace to be brought upon the church of Christ. I want to preach the sermon I have prepared on the order of the archbishop. You'd oblige me' – there was a faint whistle from the crowd – 'by entering the church to listen to me. Otherwise I shall leave and never return.'

Like sheep after a shepherd they followed him in; heard him in silence; noted that he understood the position of the trustees and had no intention of offending anyone; were appraised of the fact that he would brook no disorder or violence in any church of his; bade him a sullen 'Morning' as they filed out and watched him disappear down the cobbled street to Thornton. What they had heard about him from Dewsbury was undoubtedly true. A rum sort of parson.

This time he did not weep when he reached the safety of the moor. He beat the ground with his stick and yelled into the wind.

◌◌

'After all that Heap has appointed Mr Redhead! This is high farce, Pat!'

'I can think of less polite ways to describe it. It's the same old story: because the trustees were on their way to accepting me, Heap won't have it. So he's appointed Sam Redhead.'

'Have you told him what happened to you?'

'No; I haven't seen him since the Bible Society Meeting in Bradford. He knew the basis of it, but I didn't dwell on the details. I'm not exactly proud of what I did.'

Maria's face went into a grimace unconnected with the trustees of Haworth.

'Are you all right?' asked Pat anxiously. 'Are you in pain again?'

She rubbed her groin. 'I don't know what it is,' she said faintly. 'It just isn't like a baby pain. Goodness knows I've had enough to know.' She smiled up at him as he hovered anxiously. He went to the oak settle where he kept the whiskey and poured her a good inch.

'It usually solves my problems,' he said encouragingly. 'Drink it, my love, and it will take the pain away. Just don't go breathing on Mrs Grimshaw if she calls, or the parish will be told you're a drunk.'

She took it gratefully. Nancy, coming in to make up the fire, noticed Pat's concern as he left the room and asked if she could do anything.

'No, but thank you,' said Maria gratefully. 'You do so much anyway. What we'd do without you and Sarah! I never go through a day without thanking God for Miss Firth's idea of asking at the Bradford School of Industry. And there you were!'

'We all work together here, don't we?' replied Nancy, dropping wet tea leaves on the ash to prevent the dust flying over Maria's cambric. 'That's what me and Sarah like about being here, we feel we're family, not just servants. And Mr Brontë's a lot better than most of the masters I hear about, I can tell you,' she added knowingly. 'I reckon he's one of the kindest men who ever lived.'

Maria looked radiant all of a sudden, free from pain. 'You're right,' she said. 'He is. And I'm one of the luckiest wives in the world. Give me that log. I can manage it now, Nancy.'

◌

Jane Morgan's face was ashen. She almost forgot to hold onto Emily, who was lurching from her knee towards Rafferty and Thunder, feeding them with the remains of the tea tray.

'But it could happen to any of you,' she cried. 'No clergyman is safe if such outrages are committed.' She looked at her William with anxious eyes. You could see what she was thinking: all right for big Patrick and confident Samuel Redhead to stand up to the heathen rage of a Yorkshire congregation, but her little round William might get into real difficulties.

'Haworth is not typical,' said William reassuringly. He was pleased with Jane's reaction. Sometimes their childless marriage was hard-going, and he liked this display of concern.

'Pat had two services,' Maria said proudly. 'When he came home, after a twelve-mile walk as well as the awful service, he was a drained man.'

'My experience is nothing to the courage Sam has shown.' Patrick spoke quietly from the corner of the room where the older children sat around his feet with books, little Maria poring over her beloved newspapers. 'He's been back three times. He's a real soldier of Christ; no one has done more than he.'

'Tell us what happened; I think it's better to know these things,' Jane pleaded.

'Well,' said Pat, shifting Branwell from his lap and leaning forward, 'he went the first week, and they had assembled a huge congregation for him, from farms even across the Lancashire border. The moment he started the service, at a signal from the warden, they rose to their feet to a man . . .'

('How can they if there's women there,' muttered Charlotte. Pat tapped her curly head.)

'. . . they rose to their feet and left the church entirely empty. They'd all come in clogs with the purpose of making a great row. Sam conducted the service to an empty church, as I once did.'

'And then?'

'And then the next week, when the brave man returned, they'd persuaded an idiot to ride an ass into the church the moment the service began, so that they could scream and shout at its antics. The fear in the animals almost makes me more angry than the idiotic behaviour of the people.' He scratched Rafferty's ears and chest. 'And then, finally, because he had the courage to turn up a third time, wisely bringing some friends from Bradford, they put on a real performance: they'd got a sweep, well wrecked with the drink to get his courage up, covered him in soot, and he sat beneath the pulpit and nodded sagely as Redhead preached. After they'd enjoyed that to the full, they pulled Sam down from the pulpit, thrust him outside into a pile of soot until he, too, was thoroughly blackened, and chased him round the graveyard yelling and cheering. The poor man fell several times trying to leap between the tombstones.'

'How did he get away?' asked William, anxiously.

'They'd left their horses at the Black Bull. Sugden, fearing for his property, let them in and locked the mob out. He had the horses taken to the bottom of Kirkgate, and he let Sam and the others out of the back door, where they ran down the hill to get their horses. The mob was at the front and didn't realise what was happening.' He paused. 'It has its funny side: the door they escaped from was the same one through which many had fled from Parson Grimshaw's whip when he lashed them into the church.'

'It seems to me that Parson Grimshaw knew how to deal with Haworth,' Maria reflected grimly. 'You children must never mention this out of this house. The less said about it in Thornton the better.'

'Grimshaw didn't improve the reputation of the clergy in Haworth, though he gathered souls to Christ in his own way. I doubt the whip is appropriate in this reforming age.'

'Who will be the next parson at Haworth?' asked Jane.

'God knows,' said Pat. 'Who would dare to go into that lions' den?'

When Anne was born on the 17th January 1820, Patrick was miles away on the freezing moor, returning from a funeral he had no wish to take at Haworth but which was his duty. He hated the desperate cries of childbirth, but liked to be the first to see the baby. He arrived back in Thornton to find she had been born quickly ('I get better at it every time,' murmured Maria to Emily Fox, who was once again in competent charge). Nancy brought him hot food, and he sat with Maria, thawing out gradually and nursing the baby.

'She's the prettiest one yet, don't you think,' said Maria. The little girl was pale-skinned, dark-haired with tiny thin eyebrows and dark blue eyes.

'They're all lovely,' said Pat proudly. Maria and he produced such a good pattern; he thought of the others with their quick wits and companionable intelligence; screwing up his eyes he brought this new face into focus. 'What will you be to us, my love?' he said to the baby. 'Will you have Maria's intellect? Elizabeth's goodness? Charlotte's imagination? Or Branwell's creativity? Emily's love of the moon, sun and stars? What will you do to put your poor old parents in the shade?' He laid her gently back in Maria's arms and went to find his helpers.

'Is Mrs Brontë well?' he asked Mrs Fox as she sat in the kitchen with Nancy and Sarah, enjoying the dram he had just poured them.

'She's well in herself,' said Emily Fox deliberately, 'definitely well in herself. She's pleased with her baby and happy it's all over. But there's something not quite right.' She paused and looked squarely at Patrick. 'In a day or two ask the doctor to come in. I can't put my finger on it. He may know.'

Patrick's heart was thudding. His words came slowly.

'I will,' he said. He went back to Maria: her eyes were closed as she lay against the immaculate pillows; her tiny hands were spread on the sheet, very still. He stood looking at her, stomach clenching, heart still banging in his head. She opened her eyes and smiled. He breathed again. Sitting on the edge of the bed, he took her little hand and enclosed it in both his.

'We have to get you better,' he murmured. 'We must find out if there is anything wrong now that we know it can't be the baby. Anne, did you want, after your mother? I like that. The doctor will come next week. And Maria . . .'

'Something is bothering you,' she said slowly. 'I've known it for a week or two. Come on, Pat, we don't have secrets.'

'Indeed not. It was only that the time was wrong. The truth is . . . The truth is that the trustees of Haworth have asked Heap to appoint me.'

'So you're to be Daniel Brontë after all,' said Maria wryly. 'Thrown to the lions. It's a pity that this one isn't a boy. Daniel Haworth Brontë. It would have made a fine name. But seriously, Pat, what do you feel?'

'I feel very apprehensive, but I want the best for us all. I know

122

now that if I was the minister at Haworth I could cope with those people. There's a procedure I learned in Ireland to keep out of trouble – the arm's length.' He stretched out his right arm, the palm of his hand upwards. 'They're not bad people – opinionated, rude, truculent, but among them there will be some real gold – and they have asked for me, and agreed with the vicar of Bradford at long last. It is me they want to succeed Charnock. Perhaps God means us to go at last, and the easier living would be a reward for you. That means everything to me.'

She was moved by his concern. 'I think I want it, too,' she said. 'I haven't seen that house, but in my mind's eye I've furnished and arranged it over and over again. No,' she said, laughing at his surprise, 'if you didn't want to go I could just as easily forget it; we've been very happy here, but what contained us and two very little children is now impossible. We're like an over-stuffed pillow with the feathers bursting out.'

'But not until you're better. We'll go in the spring when the sun will warm the house and the roads will be easier.' He clasped her hands again. She drew herself gingerly up in the bed so that he could give her a long, loving kiss.

'Stop it!' Pat said in exasperation, abandoning his principles of non-violence as he smacked Branwell hard on the leg. 'I put those in there to go to Haworth. Mama and I agreed that I would pack my books and papers and your things. That's the third time you've been in the box and taken things from the bottom.'

Branwell pulled a furious face. 'But I want my soldiers! How can I manage without them. Charlotte needs them, too. We always share!'

Pat picked up the squirming child and sat down. 'Now take a deep breath, Branwell. You know that's what we decided you'd do if you felt really angry. Papa will do the same. I'm sorry I smacked you.'

'Those whom the Lord loveth, he chasteneth,' intoned Branwell, with an Irish inflection. Pat stared at him.

'Where did you get that from?'

'It's you,' said Branwell, giggling. 'You talked about it in church. You stared hard at Mr Braithwaite. But that wasn't about smacking, was it?'

'No,' replied Pat seriously. He was sometimes perturbed by Branwell's memory and understanding. All the children were very intelligent, but Branwell, at three, was precociously aware. He was also highly strung and had the most distressing rages. 'Come on, we'll take one soldier out and you can keep him all the time if you don't get anything else out of the box.'

'But I need . . .'

'No, Branwell. This is what we'll do.' The bottom lip quivered, tears welled; but for whatever reason Branwell decided not to pursue it further. Sarah Garrs came in, took his hand and said to Pat, 'Mr Brontë, Nancy wants to know about the meat jack. If we pack it today we'll be eating cold for the rest of the week. She didn't want to disturb Mrs Brontë as she's asleep.'

'Is she all right?' Pat's face was grey; there were bags under his eyes from late nights finishing off the work at Thornton, and several sleepless ones worrying about Maria. 'Certainly don't disturb her. Pack the jack. Ask me anything, or do what you think is best.'

'She'll be all right, sir, when we get to Haworth,' said Sarah enthusiastically. 'We're going to have such a good time in that girt house with all them rooms. You remember that you were going to ask the gentlemen to get someone in from the village to light the range and open the windows? We can do all the rest when we get there.'

'I will do that. The trustees will know someone who will help. Take Branwell and be kind to him if he'll let you.' He laughed, and so did Sarah. He returned to his book packing and felt very tired. When they had arrived at Thornton they had had little furniture and just two children. Now they were packing up a family of six and two servants. It seemed endless and was exhausting. Clearing the last papers from his desk, he found the letters Maria had written to him before they were married. His tired face relaxed, and a smile spread across his handsome features. What would his life have been without her? He had loved her on sight, and it had never died. And she had given him these children who filled their lives and delighted them. He carefully replaced the letters in the packet and gently placed them in a box with his most treasured books. These he would keep forever.

⁂

124

The carts were loaded, well tied down with canvas to protect the goods from the weather and the prying eyes of Thornton. The children, except for Anne, had spent the day before at Kipping House, and last night Pat and Maria had dined with the Firths. Elizabeth was distraught at the thought of the village being without the Brontës; she loved the children and their parents.

'It's not far, they tell me,' Maria said tearfully as they rose to go. 'You'll come over in your carriage, and it will be just the same.' She kissed them all; Pat shook her hand warmly and was visibly moved as they walked back to Main Street.

'We'll be lucky if we get such good neighbours and friends again,' said Maria with a sigh. 'Haworth sounds a little grimmer!'

'We'll be all right.' He squeezed her arm as they crossed the road and started up the hill. 'Arm's length, remember! They'll be fine when they get used to us.'

In the morning Nancy made porridge, doled it out into the eight bowls she had kept from the packing and hurried them up so that she could wash the pan, the milk jug and the bowls.

'But I haven't finished,' protested Pat as she scooped up his bowl.

''Appen you haven't,' said Nancy strictly, 'but them horses 'll want feeding again if we keep them waiting. The two they sent from Haworth have done the journey once. Sarah, get the children into the covered wagon, while I wash these pots and sweep out. I don't want folk saying we left a dirty house.'

Maria protested: 'As if they would! ... I'll take Anne, Sarah, if you can manage the rest.' Her words were drowned by the scuffling of feet and scraping of chairs. When Pat emerged from the house he surveyed the seven carts. The horses looked strong and would stand up to the steep, winding moorland road. Faces peeped out of the covered wagon.

'We're going on a journey, Papa! Come on!' shouted Maria.

'Yes, come on, come on!' the others cried. He took one last look at the house, and gravely winking at Maria, gave orders to the carter to start.

∽

Pat walked at the head of the first wagon's horse, with Rafferty and Thunder at his heels, although they had frequent short absences on rabbit business. To relieve the boredom for the children he took one at a time and carried them on his shoulders, and little Maria and Elizabeth walked for short distances after their turn. It was a fine April day which changed as clouds blew over and took the sun away, but then returned it to them with a blazing brilliance. Emily was on his shoulders now: she sang all the time.

'What is that song?' enquired Pat.

'It's the song of this moor,' she lisped back. 'The moor is my friend. Is our new house near the moor?'

'Very near,' he replied. 'If you go out of the kitchen door, past the privy and a few yards, you are on the moor, and there's nothing between you and it for miles. Will you like that?' But his words were taken by the wind and mixed in with her song.

They had at least two stops for food and exercise; they shared their bread and cheese with the carters, and the children disappeared with Sarah to cock their legs, as Branwell insisted on calling it. Refreshed, everyone climbed back in.

'Won't you ride a little of the way, Pat?' asked Maria anxiously. 'You can't walk all the way!'

'I frequently do, dearest,' he replied, laughing. 'I'm the most walked parson in Yorkshire. Without a horse or a carriage, I can go twenty miles at a time. Don't worry about me. You all look excited,' he remarked. He hoped Maria's high colour was excitement. The carts bumped slowly over the track; downhill the drivers got down to steady the horses by holding their heads; uphill they did the same to lighten the load.

Late in the day they reached the bottom of Kirkgate. Outside nearly every house people stood. They nodded at the new parson; few smiled, and there were some pursed lips. They knew him to be a tough man with whom no one should meddle. But these children – chattering and laughing and one on his shoulders? This was a different side to him. He raised his hat to the women as he went, keeping up the conversation with his wife, calling his dogs back, finally passing the child back into the wagon as they turned the corner by the Black Bull and up the narrow lane to the parsonage. Three of the trustees were there to welcome him. Mrs Brown, the sexton's wife, took Nancy and Sarah inside and explained the arcane range. Tea was brewed and given to the carters as they carried and heaved. Maria walked through the house carrying Anne.

'It's a lovely house, Annie,' she whispered, kissing the baby's soft cheek. 'It's a lovely house, Pat,' she repeated when she met him on the stairs. 'We're so lucky! We'll be so happy here.'

'Good,' he said, taking the baby from her. 'Go into the kitchen and have some tea. I'm going to look upstairs, then I'll come, too.'

Maria met little Maria in the hall.

'There's a double privy, Mama!' said Maria excitedly. 'Two people at a time! And Branwell did . . .'

'I don't think I want to know that,' she said, smiling. She put her hands on the little girl's shoulders and beamed down at her. 'Now you can have what you've always wanted. Somewhere to put your newspapers and writing.'

'Where, Mama?' The child's face lit up.

'That little room over the front door. You could have that to work and play in – even sleep if you want to, now we have all this space.'

'A study, like Papa? Oh, please!'

'Just like Papa.'

That night, when Pat and Maria lay in the big room overlooking the churchyard, with the windows unshuttered to catch the moonlight, the breeze blew gently through the house. Their boxes made black shapes all round them. He held her tight, full of happiness and hope. But his heart contracted when he felt her ribs through her thin shift, and the fragility of the rest of her body.

'We'll have to feed you up,' he whispered. 'No more babies now that we're here and life can be calm for a bit.'

'You're a bit skinny, too,' she breathed. 'All that walking, and some days you hardly eat a thing. You're a good man, Pat, to bring us here. You withstood all that trouble and brought us triumphant over the moor to our Zion.'

'A bit biblical,' he chuckled, 'but I know what you mean. Thank you.'

They kissed long and tenderly.

'But no more celebrations,' he said. 'No more babies.' He turned onto his back. 'My mother was a big woman. Ten was fine for her. You're a little thing; you've done enough.'

'But . . .'

'There are ways,' he whispered. 'You'd be surprised at what I hear in the cottages. Some things work, and you don't always have to . . . No,' he said turning her over and hugging her, 'not now. I'll tell you in the morning. Now it's time to sleep.'

127

Part Two

Haworth

16

And when my dear wife was dead, and buried, and gone, and when I missed her at every corner, and when her memory was hourly revived by the innocent, yet distressing prattle, of my children . . .

Patrick Brontë, letter to the Reverend John Buckworth,
21st November 1821

He pressed his fingers lightly on her eyelids, drawing them down to hide her beautiful eyes, so disturbing in their lifeless stare. Taking her gently by the shoulders, he kissed her damp grey cheeks, over and over again. His eyes rested on the empty laudanum bottle at her elbow. '*Drunk all,*' he thought, '*and left no friendly drop to help me after?*' When he stood up, his posture betrayed the nights spent in a chair at her bedside, and the days at the grind of parish work. Exhaustion was imprinted in his body. 'Goodbye,' he whispered, lifting her hand to his lips and letting it drop limply onto the counterpane.

He took the candle out onto the landing, standing still at the top of the stairs, the silent house breathing to the tick of the clock. The wind was wuthering from the moor, and the flame shuddered in the draught which rattled the window. In the rooms around him the children slept; he pushed the door opposite, and the candle's flame fell on the faces of the four little girls in two beds. Their breathing was easy; the beauty of their perfect skins, dark lashes resting on smooth cheeks, moved him, and he felt the tears start to well up. Quickly he shut the door and briefly glancing in at Branwell, who lay as if he had been catapaulted into sleep, he passed the door where Anne would be sleeping with Bess. That door was closed.

His footfalls on the stairs were slow enough to match the clock's pulse. When he reached the stone-flagged hall he stopped as if bewildered. For the past three months his life had been in their bedroom: sitting night after night, offering prayers he knew could never be answered, watching her grow weaker, thinner, enduring the terrible pain which was beyond the apothecary's drugs, holding her hand as she screamed and tried to muffle it for the children's sake. He had lost God, but for her sake he prayed. She had lost God, but for his sake she prayed. They were as close as ever, but their faith, which had been spontaneous and joyous, became a burden of the deception they practised on each other. Every new doctor was a further deception.

Choosing his study, he was surprised to find Bess there. The fire was burning brightly.

'She's gone,' he said flatly. Bess, as tired as he was, for she had borne the domestic burden for him, rose from her chair with an effort.

'Sit,' she said, patting his chair. 'It's better she's gone.' There were tears in her eyes. 'It's better she's gone. Her suffering was the worst I've seen or heard. You must be glad she's released.'

'No,' he said, 'I'm not. As long as she lived I could love her, look after her. How can I be glad she's gone?'

'I know, I know,' she sighed, stroking his shoulder. 'She's my sister, Pat. I've known her since she was born.'

'What am I going to do?' he whispered hoarsely, his elbows on his knees and head in his hands. The fire lit up his red hair and showed the white strands which now shot through it. 'What on earth can I do?'

Bess rallied. 'I'll help you, Pat. You know I'll help you. For the time being you need have no worries about the house and the children. Of course, I will have to go back to Penzance, but not until everything is comfortable here.'

'Comfortable!' he barked. 'We shall never be comfortable again. She made it comfortable – love and joy and warmth and comfort. That's gone forever.'

'Shsh.' She tried to soothe him. 'You need to sleep. Go and sleep in my bed for the rest of the night. You're exhausted, and tiredness brings its own fears.'

'No,' he said, 'you go. I must sit here. No,' he said, anticipating her practical kindness, 'No, Bess, I don't want to eat or drink.'

Her own grief made her sensitive to his needs; she closed the door quietly behind her and stood gripping the banisters, tears brimming in her eyes. The sound which reached her through the closed door was the yelp of a lonely animal in pain; she braced her shoulders, brushed the tears away and, easing herself up on the banisters, went quietly into the sleeping children's bedrooms. Standing at each door, she prayed silently before she kissed their cheeks and closed her own door.

⌒⌒

'Just leave the problem of the beer, will you?' said Patrick as mildly as he could. The grey light filtering in from the graveyard made the lines etched into his face appear even deeper. Bess sighed and fidgeted with her roll of housekeeping accounts.

'You said we had to be economical,' she said. She felt embarrassed; her attempts to run the house smoothly without disturbing Patrick had failed, for here they were in the middle of a discussion about the beer allowance for Nancy and Sarah. 'I was trying to save a little here and there because I know you have all the doctors' bills to pay, and for the day nursing.' She wished she hadn't said it the moment it was out of her mouth.

'There is no difficulty about that,' Pat replied sharply. 'Never let it be said that Maria's care was anything but her right and my pleasure to give. All I meant was that we would have to be careful, but not where it upsets our faithful servants.'

Bess sighed. 'I don't have Maria's gentle touch. She could say anything she liked, and no one would ever take offence.' Her voice trembled. 'Perhaps I do not suit you, Pat. I am very tired. I need to go back home soon.'

He took her by the arm and guided her towards a chair, removing the papers from her hand and laying them on the table by the fire. 'Neither of us is our normal self, Bess,' he said quietly. 'I will never be the man I was when she was alive. That is gone forever. I miss her at every corner. When the children chatter about her I can't bear to listen. I can't bear to sit at the table without her.' His voice was beginning to break, and he stopped.

'You're not eating and you're not sleeping. We'll have to do something about that, Pat. You can't make yourself ill. What would become of the children then?'

'You don't think I ever forget that, do you?' he replied irritably. 'If I were to die the children would be orphans and sent to one of those clergy orphanages.'

'But I would . . .'

'Bess, you can't take care of six children on fifty pounds a year. You don't even have a house of your own to put them in. No, they would learn to sew and teach their skills in anything to the children of the gentry. And I know how the gentry in England can treat those they think are beneath them. They would eventually lose each other, they would forget their life with Maria and me, their lives would be far worse than anything I ever experienced. I always had a family, kind friends, the education Cambridge gave me . . .'

Bess swung round in her chair, silk rustling and fringe bobbing. 'Then you have to do something about it, Pat. Men in your position usually marry again.'

'Marry? I could never marry again. It would betray Maria. I couldn't love anyone as I loved her. It wouldn't work.'

'Then you are lucky indeed to have married for love. Many women – and indeed men – have to settle for a good deal less, in fact would be glad to settle for a good deal less.' Silence hung between them. Patrick shifted from the window and sat beside her. 'I have been very happy in your family, Pat, but there is nothing I would not have given to have my own children and a house I was truly mistress of.' She took out her handkerchief and dabbed at her eyes. 'All I'm saying is that you may have to marry for the children's sake. I can't stay here for the rest of my life, although I'll stay as long as you need me. But you have to decide before you kill yourself with grief.'

Patrick took her hand, the same shape as Maria's, the same neat bones and delicate nails. 'I'm sorry,' he said with real remorse. 'I'm so absorbed in myself that I don't think about you or the children or the future. I get up in the morning and try to reach the end of the day so that I can sleep and forget.'

'Why don't you think about Miss Firth?' said Bess. 'She loves the children, she's godmother to Anne, and she admires you greatly. We're all friends; she knows the Morgans and the Fennells, and there don't seem to be any suitors. Perhaps it would have pleased her father; you were such good friends.'

Pat looked at her hopelessly. 'I know that what you say is sensible. I've always liked her very much. And it's what other men have to do. But I don't want anyone. I don't want to have to talk to them and bother about them. I want to be able to think about Maria all the time and not lose the memories of her. I want to keep the children's memories of her alive. I can't do that if I take another wife. And Elizabeth Firth is part of my life with Maria. But I'll think about it.'

'And will you think about eating again?' Bess pleaded. 'If it upsets you to sit at the table without her, why don't you have your dinner, at least, in your study? Then you can come in to breakfast and tea to talk with the children, and that way there'll be at least one meal inside you.'

'You're too good, Bess,' he sighed. 'God is good to have given you to me now, although I have little else to thank Him for.' He hurried on when he saw her look of dismay. *Clergymen didn't have doubts.* 'I'll eat in here and try to see myself as a single person. And I will be better with the children at breakfast and tea if I do that.' He pulled her to her feet and kissed the top of her cap. 'You're the best friend I ever had,' he added simply. 'The best friend this family ever had.'

⁊

Miss Firth, despite her devotion to the children, genuine admiration and affection for Patrick and her single state, did not see herself as the wife of a clergyman twenty-two years older than herself and the stepmother of six children, however bright, loving and intelligent they were. Miss Branwell, isolated from Thornton news by the demands of the parsonage at Haworth had also failed to notice that that there was indeed a suitor, the Reverend James Franks. In his efforts to please Bess and release her from her dutiful cares with the house and the children, Patrick offended Maria's great friend and appeared careless of her memory. Which was far from the truth.

Every day he dragged himself out of the pit in which he woke, alone in his bed, the day stretching before him, hours of paperwork, visiting, funerals which were every time a cruel reminder of following her coffin to the church. ('Are you sure you want me to take the service?' William had asked. 'Perhaps a stranger would be better . . .' 'You do it,' Pat had replied bitterly, 'there won't be any more christenings for you.') If he managed to forget his grief briefly, it was soon thrust back at him through the diseases he saw,

135

the services he took, the cast of Emily's face and Charlotte's hands. He had lost the joy he had had in the children: he read to them every night, and they chuckled and questioned as they used to, but often he would feel removed from them, and when he sat on the bed with his arms around them all, Maria turning the pages so that he could stretch his arms wide enough, his dark thoughts were frequently on his own death and the consequences for them.

One night, after carrying Branwell back to his bed and depositing Anne in Bess's room, he sat at his table and took out some writing he had begun in Thornton, before the move to Haworth, before Maria became ill, even before Anne was born. He had not touched it since. If he could write and publish, perhaps the money he made would cushion the children against the worst the world could do to them as the orphan children of a poor clergyman. But he would have to write novels, release his feelings and forget the improving messages of the evangelical church. He would have to write under an assumed name. There could be no *Cottage Poems*, no Reverend Patrick Brontë's name on the cover. He scrunched the papers in his hand and threw them on the fire, where the wind whipped them into ashes. Taking a fresh sheet of paper, he sharpened his pen, dipped it deeply in his inkwell and, comforted by the silence and the sleeping house, began to write.

17

A man shall not marry his deceased wife's sister.
'Table of the Kindred of Affinity,'
Book of Common Prayer (1822).

Pat had tried to stop the wind's sobbing by stuffing paper in the gaps of the window sashes; the wailing and wuthering he could bear, but the sobs which rose when the frames were tugged by a particular easterly blow he could not. The sound was almost human, as if someone was trying to get in, someone needing comfort, and he hated it. The shutters masked the sound at night, but by day, when he was tired and nodding after his dinner, trying to tackle the vast amount of paperwork the parish gave him, he often left the room and went visiting to escape from it.

In the afternoons he had started to take the older children out with him; they looked like a line of washing strung out over the moor, pegged by their linked hands, led by the tall black figure of their father. They were popular in the cottages and farms, their motherlessness appealing to the women, who also warmed to their widowed father. Pat was cheered by this contact he had with his poor parishioners; in their own homes they were hospitable, grateful for his help and advice, and quite unlike the congregations he had faced when he had first tried to come to Haworth.

'Mama would have liked this walk,' shouted Maria, as they reached the waterfall on their way back from Stanbury. The three children splashed in the stream, little legs scrambling among the stones.

'She would, indeed.' He was always relieved when they spoke about their mother. His great fear was that she would be forgotten completely by the younger ones. Maria and Elizabeth would surely always remember her. 'She and I used to walk in beautiful woods before we were married, when your great-aunt Jane lived at Wood-

137

house Grove. She loved the birds and flowers, the streams and copses.' It was painful, but necessary. 'Come on,' he said, a bit abruptly, 'Nancy will have tea ready, and the others will be waiting.' They raced their way back across the moor, past Hill Top and entered the kitchen door with a rush of cold air.

'You've been a long time!' cried Branwell, jumping down from his chair. 'Why couldn't I come?'

'Legs too short for long distances,' replied Elizabeth with satisfaction. 'Only for big girls.'

'You've had a good walk with me and Sarah and the others,' said Nancy, removing the bowl he had licked clean of cake mix and had clung onto as he got down. 'Now just get up again, and I'll bring your tea. How was Edward Feather, Mr Brontë? Better?'

'A bit. Still weak, and not really eating properly since Mrs Feather died.'

You're a fine one to talk, thought Nancy. Aloud she said, 'Next time you go I'll give you something to take with you that he'll like.'

'That's a fine idea. Now come on. Who will start the story today, or shall we do the capital cities for you to learn for tomorrow?

'No, no,' shouted Charlotte.'I'll start the story!'

'No,' shrieked Branwell, 'Me!'

'Too young,' said Maria with finality, 'Elizabeth will start, and then I shall say who goes next.'

Bess, who had appeared at the door during this exchange, raised her eyebrows at Patrick. 'I can't decide whether to have my tea upstairs in peace and quiet or here with noise and arguments!'

'Here,' shouted Branwell, 'here, dear aunt. Sit by me.' He scrambled off his chair and, when Bess was seated, quickly climbed onto her lap. Nancy passed her a cup. She would have preferred Bess upstairs, but Branwell always wanted her with them, and the older girls, too.

'Well,' said Pat, 'you'd better get started on that story, as I have to walk tonight to Keighley to the Auxiliary Bible Society.'

'What's auxiliary?' asked Emily, handing Thunder a whole piece of toast under the table.

'Never mind for the moment. Start the story, Elizabeth. I have to go.' Kissing little Anne on the top of her fair curls, he left the room with a low bow to the others.

∞

Taking a lantern for the return journey, Pat whistled for Rafferty and started across the moor for Keighley. Rafferty's eagerness was not these days matched by his stamina. His back legs, which used to be a liquid blur as he chased rabbits and put up birds in the heather, now worked together in a hopping motion. But his tail never stopped. *When that tail stops*, thought Pat, *I shall know he must stay behind.* Avoiding the road, they arrived in Keighley in less than an hour. The meeting, chaired by the vicar of Keighley, Theodore Dury, had the Reverend William Morgan of Bradford billed as its main speaker. Pat couldn't have stayed away on such an occasion.

He took a seat by Jane Morgan and pushed Rafferty under the seat, where he would lie without a murmur until it was time to go home.

'You're looking well.' He smiled at his cousin-in-law, taking her hand, unable to prevent himself searching her face for Maria's features.

'But not you, Pat,' she replied, concern in her eyes. 'You're still thin. I know Nancy feeds you. Do you not eat?'

'It's still hard. You know that anything in my heart upsets my stomach. I eat with the children at breakfast and tea, and your good cousin Bess makes me eat quietly in my study at dinner if I can't face the table then. She even checks my plate!'

'I can imagine it,' smiled Jane. 'Is she going to stay with you?'

'What else?' sighed Pat. 'I feel terrible that she is trapped in Haworth when she longs to return to the warmth of Penzance and all her friends. You know the kind of pleasant life she led – sociability unimaginable here. But without her I would have only the Garrs sisters, whom the children love, but the whole household is too much of a responsibility for girls of such tender years.'

'You could marry, I suppose,' said Jane gently, voicing the thought of all his friends and acquaintances. 'The vicar's sister is a nice girl.' Glancing over to where the young woman sat, she added, 'She's always seemed very intelligent and pleasant.'

'I'm forty-seven, Jane, and I've got six children and no money other than my stipend. Few young women are that desperate.'

'You're a good man to women, Pat, and that is a great recommendation in a husband,' whispered Jane. 'All those who know you well would give you a testimonial!'

'If I marry it will not be for love. Bess told me sternly that I couldn't expect it and that most people did without and got along quite well with respect and kindness. That's not my idea of marriage. Maria and I were quite romantic in our own way; I'd never get that again. I'd rather be alone with the children and put everything into bringing them up well. But meanwhile poor Bess is trapped.'

'It's a pity you can't marry her,' said Jane thoughtfully. 'But the Prayer Book is quite clear. I expect you could have come to an arrangement with her, and she loves the children. It would have been a good compromise.'

'But not possible,' said Pat. 'No deceased wife's sister. William's about to speak. Stop speculating.'

∾

Rafferty kept very close to Pat on their return journey: the lantern picked out his black and white shape, and at times he lagged, pausing to look at Pat in the wavering light. Suddenly, as Pat turned to urge him on, he fell to one side and lay trembling. Pat raced back and held him in his arms; his bewildered eyes sought Pat's, and he felt the struggling beat of the little heart.

'Come on, old man,' Pat whispered to him. 'I'll get you home. Don't leave me. Come on, come on.' He picked him up; he would have to abandon the lantern and fetch it another day. His warm burden got heavier as he walked, and he stopped more frequently the further he walked. 'Come on, Rafferty. Come on, come on. You'll be all right when we get home.' The dog rested his head in the crook of Pat's arm, and his trapped hands were unable to brush away the tears which irritated his cheeks.

When he reached the parsonage everyone was asleep. He took the key from its hiding place, as he always preferred Bess to lock up if he was out late. With careful use of his teeth and half a hand, he managed to open the door without putting the dog down. In his study he placed him in front of the fire, wrapping him in a shawl which Bess had left on the banisters that evening. He fetched milk from the kitchen, poured a tot of whiskey into it ('This is the best I'm giving you, old lad') and carefully spooned it between the remaining teeth. The dog seemed to relax, and the tail thumped gratefully.

'That's better,' said Pat. 'As long as that tail's going we know you're all right.' Usually he liked all fires extinguished before they went to bed; tonight he added more coal and moved the little bundle nearer. He bent down and kissed the feathered top of the dog's head, which was resting on the hearthstone. Taking the candle, he closed the door and went to bed with a heavy heart.

Next morning Rafferty did not wag his tail on seeing Pat. He sat down on the floor by him, stroking the domed head, looking at the upturned eyes which had never been so dull.

'Is this it, Rafferty?' His voice was a whisper. 'Are you telling me you've had enough?' He rose abruptly and went out to find the sexton. 'Not people, this time, John,' he said brusquely. 'Rafferty. His heart's gone. He doesn't want to go on. Will you dig him a grave on the moor, just outside the yard?'

Later on, when the children were with Bess and the grave was dug, Pat took his gun and shot one of his best friends clean through the head. He had placed him in the grave, where the dignified old dog had lain unprotestingly. He covered him with the wet earth using the spade Brown had left for him. There were men too poor to own guns, or too miserly to use the powder, who hanged their dogs from trees. At least this was quick when the dog had had enough. Would that it were as easy for him. Brushing at his eyes, he straightened his back and made for the kitchen door in the cold moonlight.

That winter was hard, cold and long. Sarah added layers to the children's clothes and, with their daily walks on the moor and the strenuous games they played round the house, they got by without a single chilblain. Bess, however, uncomfortable in the village and unable to bear the wind and rough walking of the moor, endured the cold in her room with fast-shut windows and a well-stoked fire. Every time she left her room for the privy she was chilled to the bone, and she no longer ventured to Keighley for tea with the Durys and trips to the haberdasher's. The children sweltered in her room when they sat with her. She felt the swirling cold of the staircase and the breathtaking chill of the stone-flagged floors. She rarely visited the kitchen unless there was little work going on and she could be sure of an undisturbed seat by the range. Nancy planned her day so that this rarely happened. Bess took to wearing her clicking pattens in the house to keep her feet raised off the numbing floors, and the children dodged round corners when she sought them for their lessons, calling 'We can hear you!'

Patrick, while amused at the capering children and the games they played, was concerned by his sister-in-law's enforced loneliness. He removed his waistcoat in anticipation of the heat in her bedroom and sat down by her fire when the children had left her and gone for tea.

'Bess, this is no life for you. You rarely go out, and endure the cold of this climate and this house most heroically. What can I do to help?'

'Nothing.' Bess was firm, uncomplaining. 'I do not expect doing my duty to be without hardship. I'm quite able to put up with the privations it requires.'

Oh dear, thought Pat. *Where has that nice woman who came to Hartshead gone? What have I done to her?* Out loud he said, 'My dear, I don't want us to be your duty, or for you to endure hardship. If it is really bad for you, I will make other arrangements.'

The candlelight caught the tears which appeared in Bess's eyes. She blew her nose sharply on a handkerchief Elizabeth had hemmed. 'I didn't mean that,' she said when she had settled herself. 'There's nothing I would not do for you and the children. I love them; it's not duty; I love you, too, Patrick, as a sister-in-law should, only it is no duty either.' She blushed faintly. 'When Maria married you and I saw the kind of marriage you had, I knew that even if I married I would be unlikely to achieve the meeting of souls that you two had. I would have settled for less for the sake of having my own children. But it was not to be. I count myself fortunate to have this family. I do want to return to Penzance, but you musn't mind my chilly complaints.' She smiled. 'Things are more difficult for you than for me, Pat. That I do understand.'

Pat leaned forward in the firelight and took her dry, cold hands between his own. 'It is a pity we cannot marry, Bess,' he said, very carefully. 'We have so much in common: our memories of the past, the children, our religion, our shared attitudes, our love of reading . . .' He paused, keenly desiring to express his genuine affection for her, honestly needing to exclude romance. 'But that's how it is; and I cannot expect to keep you here to help me when you have a good life waiting for you in Penzance. I have been thinking again of finding a wife. I can't bear the thought of seeking fresh pastures. I am going to write to Mrs Burder, the mother of Mary to whom I was once engaged, and see if she is still unmarried. She used to love me.'

142

'But did you love her, Pat?'

A silence. He shrugged. 'I loved her in the way I thought of loving then. We had common interests. I didn't love her in the way Maria and I loved each other. That won't happen again. But I'm older now; I don't expect to fall in love. I need to let you go. I need a mother for the children. Don't despair. I'll try again, and maybe you'll soon spend a winter warmed by the gentle air of Cornwall.'

He patted her hands and kissed the top of her head. As he went to the door with Thunder, she realised she hadn't noticed the dog was in her room. She pulled her chair nearer to the fire. What a good man he was. But she was greatly troubled that he felt compelled by her to seek out Mary Burder.

He had misplaced the letter from Mary Burder among the pages of his manuscript (*Oh Maria, this would never happen if you were still here, either the muddle or the letter*) and for a moment he reread what he had written the night before. Pursuing his idea that he would protect the children by creating an additional income from writing, he had decided he could only write from his experience and so began a tale set in Hartshead about the time he had seen the Luddites attack Cartwright's mill. It comforted him to write about that time, when he was happy at the Bedfords' and his life and love with Maria were about to unfold. He found characterisation difficult, but he had created an independent, strong-minded young woman, based on Maria. He was, however, so weary when he had time to spare in the evening that his tale dragged. He had not achieved what he wanted. He sat for a long time with his head in his hands, listening to the wind which buffeted the outside of the house and wailed in the chimney. Eventually he rallied, made a more systematic search of his close-written sheets and found the letter.

From a recent perusal of many letters of yours bearing the date eighteen hundred and eight, nine and ten . . . this review excites in my bosom increased gratitude and thankfulness to that wise, that indulgent providence which then watched over me for good and with held me from forming in very early life an indissoluble engagement with one whom I cannot think was altogether clear of duplicity . . . your

143

confidence I have never betrayed strange as was the disclosure you once made unto me, whether those ardent professions of devoted lasting attachment were sincere is now a matter of but little consequence . . .

He let out a long sigh and pushed the page away from him. Despite the cold room with its dying fire, his whole body flushed hot with shame. In his desperation to help Bess he had been crassly, insanely insensitive. He should never have approached the girl he had abandoned all those years ago. His petrifying fear of the future had made him importunate. He took a clean quill, sharpened it meticulously as if in penance and wrote an apology.

ᕙᕤ

That must be the end of it. He would have to ask Bess to stay with them: he would try to make her life better; he would treat her as an equal partner in the upbringing of his children; those things he could share with her, he would, and he would make sure everyone knew the affection with which he and the children regarded her. He had to admit she was the only mother Anne could remember; Branwell was exuberantly affectionate towards her; and all the others, in varying degrees from respect to affection, were happy in her company. This was how it was to be.

He mounted the stairs to her room; it was late, and she had fallen asleep in her chair by the fire, the book she had been reading to the children lying in the folds of her black silk skirt, a copy of her ladies' magazine on the little rug where one of the girls had left it. She started awake as he entered. Whatever the changes, he still saw Maria dying every time he entered this room.

'I shouldn't be sleeping.' She had jolted awake as he entered. 'If I do, I lie awake half the night, and that's not a good time.'

'Bess,' he said, perching on a child's chair and winding his long legs around it, 'I received a great slap in the face from Mary Burder. I didn't dare tell you. I felt so ashamed. I must have taken leave of my senses. I'm not very rational still. I worry about what will happen to the children if I . . . I don't think I can ever marry again.'

'Pat,' she said gently, 'I knew you never would.' She folded her spectacles and placed them precisely on the table beside her. She was choosing her words with care, ignoring his surprise. 'I really knew you never would. In my mind I have been resolved to stay in Haworth for as long as you and the children need me.'

The room, the memories, her kindness and her Branwell hands spread on her skirt rendered him speechless. All he could do was take her hands and put his gratitude into the chaste kiss he had always given her since she first came to Hartshead.

∽

The next day he tempted Bess out of her room and into the brisk air of the moor. He did not suggest she braved the moor itself, but that they kept close to the packhorse trail which went past Hill Top. They walked about half a mile, she leaning on his arm, quickly out of breath, he slowing his pace to her slow gait. Their talk had been of the long-term domestic arrangements: Bess would have to have her preferences considered if she was to become the mistress of the house, although the domestic arrangements had been created by Maria and were the practices of their Penzance home. Patrick wondered how long Nancy and Sarah would stay with Bess as mistress, but he put this thought aside and the many problems which loomed and threatened to overwhelm him. Sufficient unto the day.

'But do you not think they are remarkable, Pat?' Bess's question broke into his reverie. 'They're all intelligent and wise beyond their years. I feel I have little to teach the girls any more, now that they read and write and cipher. Sewing I can always improve upon; but you need to teach Maria – the quality of her mind is beyond me. You teach Branwell, which is good, as he feels so much that he has to show off in front of the girls, but you really need to teach the girls, too. They will soon be bored with me.'

'Surely not . . .' Pat had never repeated the girls' complaints.

'Yes, they will. My dear sister was unusual; she turned our simple education into real learning. You spotted that. But, apart from the reading I have done, I have little to offer these children except my theology, which is well developed.' She raised her head proudly and looked him straight in the eye. 'There is little I cannot tilt with you about, Patrick, in politics and theology. But the children have all that already. They need more.'

Her cheeks had become rosy with the unaccustomed effort of the walk, and they turned back at the fork which led down to Stanbury. In the distance they could see above them, outlined on

145

the horizon, little figures running and jumping in the company of Sarah Garrs. From the Stanbury road came a brisk body, weighted with a basket but moving at a rapid pace.

'Good afternoon, Miss Branwell, Mr Brontë,' said the woman, smiling at Bess. Her face was open and fine-boned, cheerful and determined. 'It's good to see you out in the fresh air.' Tabitha Aykroyd liked Bess; they were similar ages, similarly bound by family duty.

'Mrs Aykroyd.' Bess bowed. 'How is your mother? I haven't seen her passing down the lane to your chapel; she's well, I hope?'

'She's been badly with the cold; I thought it best she stays in for the time being. How are the bairns, Miss Branwell?'

Bess pointed to the top of the hill in explanation. 'They're all well. You know you're always welcome to come and see them whenever you want.' Patrick smiled. She glowed with pride as she spoke of them.

'I could always come up when the Miss Garrs are off to see their mother in Bradford,' said Tabitha quickly. 'You mun need a hand on those days with the bairns. Just let me have word by Nancy, and I'll be there.' Her fine eyes smiled her eagerness. She nodded to Patrick, apologised for her hurry and was gone towards Haworth with a light step.

'I know exactly what you mean.' Pat resumed the conversation. 'I'll teach them all in the morning, as well as Branwell, but you know any routine will be disrupted by the business of the parish. I do more baptisms, and more funerals of those same baptised children, than I ever thought possible. It's an unhealthy place.'

Bess shuddered. 'We need to keep ours apart if possible. But there's something else. Did you see the advertisement in the *Leeds Intelligencer* for a school for clergy daughters?'

'I did. It's being run by Carus Wilson, and Wilberforce and Simeon, my old patrons, are subscribers. Theodore Dury is a trustee. That surely indicates the quality. I believe the subscribers pay for the teaching and the parents only for the board. I have to admit I saw it and put it from my mind as I don't want them to go away. I would miss them,' he added simply.

They had reached the beginning of the lane that led to the parsonage and were joined by the children, muddy and red-cheeked, helter-skeltering down the hill. Bess looked at them in mock horror.

146

'Do we know these urchins, Reverend?' she asked Pat.

'No, no, Miss Branwell, nothing so muddy was ever in our house. Pray draw away from the contamination!'

'No, no,' shouted Branwell. 'You do know us! You do! You do!'

Pat picked him up and swung him round in the air. 'Perhaps we do after all. Is this not the demon king himself? Off with your crones to the kitchen.' As they raced away, he said to Bess, 'I will write off about the school, although it will be a very still house if they go.'

Bess took his arm for the last few yards. 'Those children are your life,' she said quietly. 'They simply are your life.' He didn't answer, accepting her perception, his stomach telling him about decisions he had to make.

18

I shuddered as I stood and looked round me: it was an inclement day for out-door exercise . . . The stronger among the girls ran about and engaged in active games, but sundry pale and thin ones herded together for warmth and shelter . . . Amongst these, as the dense mist penetrated to their shivering frames, I heard frequently the sound of a hollow cough.

Charlotte Brontë, *Jane Eyre*, Chapter 5.

Bess had checked the church accounts and replaced them on the shelf, which was still labelled in her sister's handwriting.

'I'm going up with the girls now, Pat,' she said over her shoulder. 'I'll take Branwell, too, he can do some writing with Emily. Goodness knows she needs it. Lots to say but won't be bothered to spell. Did you hear what I said?' she asked.

'Yes, yes, of course, my dear,' he replied, rising from his chair and removing his spectacles. 'I'm looking at the Cowan Bridge advertisement. I just can't make up my mind.' He moved to the window and gazed out across the graveyard to the church. He used to be able to see the marks he had made on the tower when he discharged his pistol in the morning. They were less clear now. Dragging himself out of his inattention he turned to Bess as she went into the hall.

'I will make a decision. I know it worries you. It's just that . . .'

'You can't bear to be without them?' She finished his thoughts. 'I know, Pat, and I shall miss them too, but their education is important.' He looked at her in disbelief that she should feel it necessary to say such a thing to him. It was a result of his indecision.

Her voice softened. 'Their life here is good; you've done so

Patrick as a young man, attributed to J. Bradley   Photo courtesy of the Brontë Society

Elizabeth Branwell
Photo courtesy of the Brontë Society

Maria Branwell
Photo courtesy of the Brontë Society

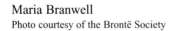

The parsonage at Haworth

Emily Brontë painted by Patrick
Branwell Brontë

Portrait of Anne Brontë by
Charlotte Brontë
Photo courtesy of the Brontë
Society

Medallion of Branwell Brontë   Photo courtesy of the Brontë Society

Photograph said to be of
Charlotte Brontë
Photo courtesy of the Brontë Society

Arthur Bell Nicholls
Photo courtesy of the Brontë Society

Entrance Hall of Haworth Parsonage

Photo courtesy of the Brontë Society

'Keeper - from life' by Emily Brontë   Photo courtesy of the Brontë Society

Patrick Brontë in old age
Photo courtesy of the Brontë
Society

Miniature books of the Brontë children

much to help them get over Maria's death, but we have to think of their future. Training for something will be a great help to them, much as we would like it not to be necessary.'

Charlotte came flying down the hall.

'You know you said Nancy was getting married,' she said breathlessly to her father, 'Well . . .' – she paused dramatically, eyes wide – 'his name is PAT!'

'Kitchen gossip!' frowned Bess.

'Is that a fact?' said Pat, amused. He walked down the hall with the excited child and put his head in at the kitchen door where Nancy was baking surrounded by eager mouths. 'Why, Nancy, is it true that you are engaged to marry a Pat?'

'Yes, it is, sir,' Nancy replied, her good-tempered face pink from the warmth of the baking, flour powdering the air from her immersed hands. 'And if he proves only one-tenth as kind a husband as you have been, I shall think myself very happy to have made a Pat my choice.'

'And that's another reason for Cowan Bridge,' Bess said quietly when he had closed the door. 'Whatever we shall do when those two leave I don't know. Despite the slackness you would expect from their youth,' – and she gave a brisk sniff – 'they have been with the children all their lives and are greatly loved.' *A bit too much, in some ways,* she thought.

'Another loss for them,' said Pat. 'Perhaps they really need a change.'

๑๏

Pat, after all, knew about schools. From Glascar and Drumballyroney he had learned about the differences between and needs of children, and in Woodhouse Grove he had seen John Fennell create a boarding establishment. His own Maria had helped her aunt with the domestic arrangements, and they had often laughed together about Aunt Jane's struggles with the accounts and her exertions to keep the boys clean in their sparse clothing. He himself had examined the boys and knew the academic side. But it was his very experience which told him that his own children would be better off with him teaching them, just as he had said when Maria had raised the subject of a governess. Schools were narrow, the regime strict, and he was convinced that his own education, gathered through omnivorous reading and the influ-

149

ence of educated men, was far better than any offered in a formal school. When he had reached Cambridge, it was not the academic side which floored him.

He took up his customary stance at his study window, hands in his breeches pockets, eyes searching the graveyard, testing with one eye and then the other for his worsening eyesight. His children would have to be prepared to work. He might die, and there were five girls for whom he couldn't expect to find husbands; his mind rebelled at this being the only safe and secure option. They would obtain employment in respectable families as governesses more easily if they had been to a recognised school. Otherwise they might be scratching a living at millinery or sewing, and the seduction of Lord Nelson's sister, unprotected after her parents' death and working in a millinery shop in London, was still whispered about, and it horrified him.

And then there was the money. Despite his skill with money, honed at Cambridge and practised assiduously ever since, there were hardships he had been prepared to suffer himself but would not impose upon his children. With a hundred and ninety pounds a year, and Bess insisting on contributing to her keep, he could manage, and save a little for the children. But five girls kept and trained for fourteen pounds a year each would make their capital sum even bigger.

He sighed with exasperation, turning his back on the window, jingling the coins in his pocket. He took his bottle of whiskey from the shelf next to his books and poured himself a large dram. *I used to celebrate and sing with this,* he thought, *now it's for comfort.* The pride that Maria had tamed was edging in again; this he had realised when he nearly sent back the money his friends in Bradford had collected after her death. It was only when he thought of how she would have received their kind and gracious gesture that he stopped himself. Bess's contribution to the housekeeping irked him, but her comments about being a kept woman finally made him laugh and accept it. At least there were no problems with Branwell: he would educate him himself, delighting in their reciprocal passions, send to him to St John's and then the world would be his oyster. Nothing to worry about there.

Choosing his best paper he sat down and started to write to Carus Wilson and his banker. Soon the door opened, and Maria and Elizabeth, armed with a two-day-old newspaper, came in. Elizabeth curled up on the fire rug with Thunder, and Maria settled herself in Pat's chair, newspaper spread, her shining hair falling into her eyes.

'What are you writing, Papa? Do you want help? Or shall I read?'

He paused, leaning back in his chair. 'We've talked about this school, my dear. I really think you ought to go. You and Elizabeth to start with.' He smiled at his younger daughter, who had turned Thunder over and was stroking his belly from breastbone to tail. 'Elizabeth, what do you think?' His eyes sought theirs, trying to read their faces.

'Mama used to say we needed a governess,' said Elizabeth, 'but you said we'd be teaching her. Why school?'

'Things change, Elizabeth. If Mama were alive, it would be easy to educate you all at home with the help of tutors. Aunt Bess feels she cannot do as much as Mama could. It's just . . . different now.'

Maria got down from the chair and bunched Thunder's paws in her hands. 'If you think it's right, Papa, we ought to go. We don't want to really because we shall miss everybody and home; we did when we went to Crofton Hall for that short time. But as you say – things are different. But who will read to you and the others if I go?' She puckered her smooth forehead.

'Aunt Branwell will read to me, and if Charlotte and Emily join you, then Branwell will read to Anne. I will see it's all done properly.'

'Then that's it,' said Elizabeth. 'We shall go. It's not very far, is it? You will come to see us, and we will be able to come home. Is there anything we have to do?'

There was heavy footstep in the hall, a brief knock. John Brown stood there, hat in hand, damp hair tumbling into his eyes, his arms full of a wet, trembling spaniel.

'Sir, he was on the moor, tied to a stone by the water. I thought you might . . . after Rafferty . . .'

Maria rushed towards the sexton. 'Oh yes, he will, Mr Brown; he will certainly take him, won't you, Papa?' She took the dog in her arms and put him close to the fire. 'There you are, Papa, you'll need him if we go, even more!'

Pat put out his hand to the little creature, who crawled on his belly towards him. 'Not a substitute for you, dear girls, but a needy

151

little dog. Think of a name, Elizabeth. And you're the best one to tell Aunt Branwell that there's another dog in the house!'

⚮

The coach bumped and rumbled towards Kirby Lonsdale, muddy water showering the door glass as it hit holes and troughs. With each lurch he could feel the tension in the stiff little bodies close to him, arms entwined in his. Usually when they sat close to him for stories and reading their bodies were warm and soft. His heart sank, knowing the anxiety which must be consuming them.

They had tried to make a celebration out of the departure for Cowan Bridge: Nancy and Sarah had prepared a great tea which they had served in the parlour: Bess's gifts of books and pocket money had added a festive air, and Charlotte, Emily, Branwell and Anne all had gifts to give. Mrs Aykroyd had been asked to call in, and the Browns, and Pat had offered John a dram and ended up singing his favourite Gaelic songs to an astounded sexton. At bedtime he had told them endless stories – Finn and Oonagh on the Giant's Causeway, the Little Weaver and Devil Daly for a few. Then he stopped, kissed them goodnight. There was cold fear in his stomach as his slippers whispered down the stairs to his study.

The Cowan Bridge buildings hugged the road, newly white-washed, windows gleaming in the afternoon sunlight. A pile of builders' rubble stood against a barn wall. (*Wilson certainly is not sparing any expense,* thought Pat with relief, *and the teachers are paid for by the subscribers, so it should be very good.*) The coachman had undertaken to stop at the school as it was on the main road. Pat received from him his own small bag and the bigger ones belonging to his daughters. He tipped the man generously: he would be returning soon with the other girls, and eventually they might travel unescorted. No harm in making a friend for them.

Miss Evans had hurried to the door when the coach's rumbling was heard in the distance. She smoothed her dress and tucked two stray blonde curls behind her ears. Carus Wilson had told her about Patrick Brontë; a man of strong principles and academic brilliance, he had said, and with five daughters and no wife. She already had other clergy daughters from the Bradford area under her care; Mr Wilson wanted the school to expand quickly, and here was a good stable. She smiled up into Pat's handsome, worn face; his short-sighted blue eyes smiled back.

152

'Mr Brontë,' she said pleasantly, taking his hand. 'And Maria and Elizabeth.' Her hands rested lightly on their shoulders. (*Good,* he thought, *she's not afraid to touch them. They will miss their hugs and kisses.*)

The low-ceilinged hall still smelt of fresh paint and scrubbing. Maria and Elizabeth, reluctantly dropping Pat's hands, went with Miss Evans to see their dormitory and meet the other pupils. Pat stood alone in the hall, listening, absorbing, seeking assurance.

'You're staying with us tonight, Mr Brontë?' Miss Evans had returned, her skirt swishing on the sanded floor.

'Yes. It's very kind.' He bowed slightly. 'Otherwise I would have had to find an inn. I shall feel much easier, too,' he said, a blush suffusing his drawn features, 'if I have spent a night with them.' He felt a little foolish. 'It's quite hard to let them go,' he added apologetically.

'You have no need to worry, Mr Brontë.' The young superintendent was warm and kind. 'I understand that Mrs Brontë died two years ago and that her sister helps you look after them?'

'Yes. She is a most affectionate mother to my children. I . . .'

'Don't worry,' she repeated firmly. 'Parents on their own are understandably anxious when their children first leave home. We will be aware of their needs and be sure they are happy. Let me show you our guest room. We shall eat together in about an hour.'

He followed her neat figure down a dark corridor to a little room: bed, chair, chest of drawers, washstand. He lay down on the bed and closed his eyes. He had only his small edition of Milton in his pocket, but the light was too dim for him to read. His stomach felt like lead and his head ached; without the distraction of his book his thoughts whirled. Why did he feel so grim? He knew himself well enough to know that his physical symptoms were caused by anxiety and the grief of parting from the two little girls he had been protecting for so long. He must believe it was quite rational to send them to school: they would receive a structured education, and he had paid the extra fee for Maria to take the governess's training. Much as he hoped she would never need it, it was a security. The school was excellent of its kind, his colleagues had already sent their daughters here; it was run by committed Christians, it . . .

He jumped off the bed and washed his face and hands to stop his thoughts. He wound a clean neckcloth around his neck, brushed his hair and sought the dining room. Maria and Elizabeth were already there, perched on benches: the colour had returned to their cheeks, and they both smiled at him. He slid in beside them.

'Papa, this is Margaret and Harriet – do you remember we met them at the Durys' in Keighley?'

'I do, indeed,' replied Pat, smiling at the girls. 'Both your fathers have helped me out many times when I have needed it.' His tense body relaxed in a wave of relief. They would be all right. The food, when it came, was plain and plentiful. When he had kissed them good night, he went to his room and prepared for sleep. What a pretty woman Miss Evans was. But real desire had fled with Maria, and he was soon in a dreamless sleep.

∾

Pat repeated the journey with Charlotte in August; the same coachman was driving the Leeds to Kendal road.

'Another little girl to add to the others,' he said, good humouredly, recognising Pat. 'You must have a basketful!'

She had been apprehensive when the packing had started at the parsonage; Pat had carefully described the school, the superintendent and the domestic arrangements. Gradually her suspicions had disappeared, and the journey had passed pleasantly, watching for landmarks and making stories to go with them. When he got her to lean out of the coach window to see the approaching school, however, she gripped his hand and snuggled closer.

'You'll like it,' he whispered. 'You'll be with Maria and Elizabeth. You'll love that.'

'I will love that,' she said, choosing her words with care. 'But I don't know if I will like the school. I'll tell you that when I've been there for a bit.'

He smiled to himself at her usual reserve of judgement. When she had made up her mind she would be very passionate, one way or the other. Her reserve vanished when she climbed down and found her sisters and Miss Evans waiting for her. He watched them disappearing out of the main house towards the dormitory chattering like morning birds. He talked for a pleasant hour with Miss Evans, dined with the girls, slept soundly and was back in Haworth early enough to continue the preparations for the archbishop's visit.

Nancy was in a rare flap.

'I thought I'd just slide along to Christmas, preparing for me wedding, without any girt stir,' she gasped, slapping the dough round the table, pumelling and pulling. 'And here I am cooking for a multitude, and a right grand multitude at that.' She straightened her aching back and dragged a brown curl out of her eyes.

'Never you mind.' Tabitha Aykroyd had dropped into the kitchen with extra supplies Nancy desperately needed, with no time to go into the village. 'I'll help. You have only to ask. It will do Mr Brontë and Miss Branwell good to have some company in the house. He's looking better, lately and Miss Branwell is well settled.'

'She is that,' said Nancy darkly, rattling the range furiously, 'Looks like she's here for ever, and Sarah and I are both off at Christmas. Has he spoken to you yet?'

'Aye. He said that with the four children at school in November, and you and Sarah gone at Christmas, would I like to come as housekeeper.'

'And would you?' Nancy threw the dough on the scrubbed table with a satisfying thump.

'I would,' said Tabitha. 'I love these children.'

'And Miss Branwell?'

'I get on with her. I know you don't, but you knew Mrs Brontë all those years, and it's hard to change a mistress. Miss Branwell and I are of an age. We understand one another. She's never had bairns and neither have I, so we both understand why we love the little ones here so much. We shall get by.'

'They're grand childer,' sighed Nancy. 'I shall miss them. You realise that they're no ordinary childer,' – she glanced sharply at Tabitha – 'these are none of your work-in-the-mill, school-once-a-week childer, or even sit-and-sew childer. These are very clever childer.' She dropped the dough expertly into the tins. 'I know that, and I can read and write. That's why they wanted me at first – because I'd been trained and taught to read and write. The master and mistress wanted nurses and housekeepers what would bring them on.' She smiled proudly, and Tabitha looked apprehensive.

'You've no need to worrit,' went on Nancy quickly. She didn't want to lose this good woman for her treasured children. 'They're well on now. The master tested them out one day as he thought

they were reet clever beyond their years from hearing them prat-
tling to each other.'

'What did he do?'

'Ah was cleaning the grate in his study at the time, and it was
wonderful to behold. First he went down into 't cellar and fetched
up a mask he had with all the dressing-up clothes they use in their
games – allus playing they are, and you'll have to join in – Sarah
broke the branch off the cherry-tree in some daft game they had
her play – and he made them put on the mask and answer the
questions he asked them. They had sich clever answers, and very
sharp were Emily and Branwell. But I shall be easy if you're here.'
She placed the tins neatly in the mouth of the oven. 'That's very
good. I shall rest easy if I know you're here.' She took the kettle
from where it sang over the fire and poured boiling water into the
teapot. 'Sit down, Mrs Aykroyd; you mun learn that this is the time
of day when you can snatch a quiet brew. The children are on the
moor, the master's out visiting and she' – Nancy raised her eyes to
the rooms above – 'is dozing by her fire. It's the only rest you'll get
all day!'

'I shan't mind that,' laughed Tabitha. 'I was niver one for sitting
about. But tell me,' – and she dropped her voice needlessly – 'is it
a happy house? It always seems so.'

'A very happy house.' The statement was unequivocal. 'I should
know. Ah've been here nearly all their lives, and when you live in
the same house as folk you know what they're like. Even though
she' – she nodded her head to the ceiling again – 'can be a bit of
a tyke, there's nothing bad in her. And Mr Brontë – a kinder man
never lived.'

Tabitha hesitated, closely inspecting the pattern on her pretty
blue teacup. 'It's just that I heard he had rages and cut t' sleeves
out of Mrs Brontë's dresses, and he allus shoots his pistol out of
the window when 'e's in a bait . . .'

'Ah know well what you've heard,' said Nancy exasperatedly.
'There's folk in Haworth who're no better than they should be.
Gossipin' theer lives away on their dirty doorsteps. The woman
who nursed Mrs Brontë' – and she leaned forward and looked very
straight and square into Tabitha's eyes – 'had to leave when Miss
Branwell came from Cornwall to help. Mr Brontë did all the night
nursing and Miss Branwell the day. It worn't a matter o' brass, it
wor because they felt she'd be 'appier dying with them that loved

156

her. The nurse wor expecting to stay until Mrs Brontë died, and she was well put out. She lingered around in the village for a bit and blethered to anyone who would listen. And as for that dress – he did cut the sleeves out. It wor a dress Miss Firth had given her, and it made her look a reet wrong 'un. She wor a little, dainty thing and always turned out sweet and plain. He didn't like her to feel she had to tek Miss Firth's old clothes. The sleeves were girt and floppy and reet daft for a lady like the mistress. He walked over to Keighley and bought her beautiful silk for a new frock, and then cut the sleeves to see if they could be remade. And that's it.'

'I'm sorry,' said Tabitha, 'I shouldn't have asked.'

'Nay, lass, you do reet to find out what you're coming into. And he does fire his pistol – every morning when he gets up. He loads it the night before and fires it in the morning. Where we all came from,' she said proudly, 'where we came from there was allus trouble from the Luddites, and Ah've seen him teach the mistress to fire a pistol hersen when we wor alone. That's what it's all about. Nowt else. You'll not work in a better family. 'E brings them up to treat us well, and so did the mistress. So does she,' she added, nodding to the ceiling, 'whatever else she does.'

Tabitha rose from her chair and put her bonnet on. 'I'll be back in the morning early,' she said. 'I'll be here by six so we should be well on by the time the party gets back from blessing the church-yard. Don't you fret. We'll get it all done.' As she left by the kitchen door, she thew a backwards glance at the square grey house which was to be her new home: it was just what she needed, a good big house to take up her energy and children to love and care for.

19

The snares of death compassed me round about, and the pains of hell gat hold upon me: I shall find trouble and heaviness, and I shall call upon the name of the Lord. O Lord, I beseech thee, deliver my soul.

Psalm 116, Book of Common Prayer, verse xx.

The house was silent except for the gentle ticking of the clock on the stairs and the steady snoring of Paddy in front of Patrick's fire. Elizabeth had decided she wanted another Irish name, but she could not call the dog Pat as it would cause a scandal in the village if she or her siblings were to be heard shouting on the moor for what might appear to be their clerical parent. Pat rubbed the dog's chest with his slippered foot and stroked Thunder's velvety ears. The afternoon had been fine and still, but now the air had quickened and the wind was worrying at the windows. He was in the middle of preparing an address for the Bible Society, but his attention wandered as he realised that the silent house, shrouded in twilight, meant that the children were still out with Nancy and Sarah.

Unable to continue with his task, he took the stairs two at a time and went into Branwell's bedroom, which overlooked the moor. Picking his way over the soldiers, paper, pencils and pens, he stood at the window, his eyes straining in the poor light for the little figures he hoped to see roistering along with the Garrs sisters. There was nothing, only the bare moor, a movement here and there as birds and animals shifted in the heather. He ran down the stairs, into the kitchen and was about to go out of the back door when he remembered Bess upstairs. She would probably be asleep after the rigours of teaching in the morning. Bounding up the stairs again he burst into her room. She jumped awake.

'The children are still out.' His voice was sharp, agitated. 'There's no sight of them. It will soon be dark. I'm going out to look for them.' At that moment there was a deafening crash of thunder which made the house jump; the lightning which followed blazed on their fearful faces. A great rumble followed, and the floor shook.

Bess looked at him with terrified eyes. He shook his head and plunged headlong down the stairs and outside where the rain now fell in sheets. He scrambled over the wall onto the moor, unaware that both the dogs, sensing his terror, had raced out of the house and were with him, waiting for commands he was too distracted to give. He ran on and on, dust grating in his eyes, stumbling over the heather and slithering into holes, calling, calling until his voice was hoarse. There was nothing, nobody. He sat on the ground and put his head down between his knees in an attempt to restore his breathing. Thunder and Paddy circled around, eyes fixed on him, desperate to please, unsure of the problem.

He got up and began to run again. The air roared, the sound unfamiliar, terrifying. Suddenly, in the distance, his poor eyesight picked out dots, haloed dots, which grew legs and arms. It was his family. They were sheltered in a sheepfold. He thanked God whom he frequently ignored these days. He kept running on and on towards them, the figures becoming clearer and clearer, the strangling in his chest receding. Finally he was with them.

Drenched to his skin, he took the bedraggled creatures in his arms and hugged and hugged them. 'Nancy, Sarah,' he shouted against the wind, 'are you all right? It was an earthquake! I thought I had lost all of you!' The tears ran down his face as both the danger and delivery hit him at once. Nancy held his hand, and her tears were flowing too.

'Such a terrible thing, sir,' she panted. 'The bog has burst and there's mud and water flowing down the valley. I thought we'd all be killed!' She wiped away tears and hugged her sister, who was holding Branwell, still screaming with fear or delight. 'It's all right now, childer. Your father's here, and we shall all be home soon and in the warm.' She put her cloak round Emily and carried Anne; Patrick bore Branwell on his wet shoulders, the little boy still shrieking.

'Quiet now, Branwell,' he called up to him, 'we're safe now. Soon be home.'

'I didn't mind it, Papa,' shouted Branwell, 'It was a giant's noise. He must be after us!'

'No, Bran, there's nobody after you. God has protected you. We must thank Him.' *I must thank Him,* he thought. *I must love Him and trust Him more than I have been doing since he took Maria. He has shown me His goodness now, and I must respond.*

'I liked it!' sang out Emily. 'I thought the whole world was whirling round!'

They reached the parsonage, and Bess, face stark white against her black silk, was standing in the yard, unaware of her clinging-wet clothes. She threw up her arms as they came into sight, and by the time they were inside, the kitchen was full of dry clothes and a kettle bubbling. When Patrick sat down at the table he was shaking uncontrollably, and Bess failed to notice the pungent smell of wet dog rising from the fireside. They were both in shock.

☙

He could scarcely bear to take Emily to Cowan Bridge after the shock of the bogburst, or, as Patrick insisted on calling it, the earthquake. It had shaken him to the depths of his soul, realising how close he had been to losing his children; their escape had raised theological questions, theology he had pushed aside in the years since Maria's death. His grim devotion to duty was a need to provide a home and a roof for the children; the joy of the faith he had shared with Maria had departed with her, and had been replaced with a practical Christianity which was appreciated by the motherless families, the sick and dying of Haworth. Deeply frightened by the bogburst, he preached a sermon which transferred his own guilt at his recent neglect of spiritual matters to his unfortunate parishioners: God had sent them a timely reminder of their mortality; God had rescued them, and they must love and repay Him, with virtuous lives and preparation for the after life. It was even published and sold for sixpence by Thomas Inkersley of Bradford.

When Patrick and Emily finally boarded the coach for Cowan Bridge, they had with them, carefully folded in Emily's box, a copy of the *Leeds Intelligencer* for Maria. Emily knew she would miss the newspapers and would be excited to see the archbishop's visit to Haworth church, and to her very own home, reported. She clung to Pat when she got out of the coach, and his heart lurched at her six-year-old vulnerability, but she was soon happy to borne off by her sisters and their friends, her bright little face framed with its dark curls, her eyes watching every word and movement.

Pat was sad to find that Miss Evans was ill; his conversations with her were the only ones he had had with an attractive woman since Maria died. The acting superintendent, Miss Andrews, was a small, dark, thin person, lacking her predecessor's charm and warmth.

'We have all four of your girls now, Mr Brontë,' she said briskly. 'They seem bright and interested.'

'I have another daughter at home,' he replied. 'Anne. She is too young for school yet. Yes, they are bright,' he continued enthusiastically, 'they were great companions to their mother and still are to me, despite their tender years.'

'When I say they are bright, Mr Brontë, I do not mean they have achieved what they should.' She looked quite severely at him. He moved his eyes to the ground. 'For such potentially clever children they seem to have had remarkably little systematic teaching.'

Patrick bridled. 'You will find my children can read and write well and have had access to books and newspapers, as well as always being allowed to talk with adults about important things. I do not think you will find them uneducated. They have had a superior education in our home. Education is more than ciphering and spelling.' His face was flushed.

'I simply mean,' said Miss Andrews, drawing her little frame together until it seemed ready to snap, 'that they need to do the basics. All their knowledge of Parliament' – she paused, sniffing slightly, and Pat imagined that Maria had put her right on some basic error – 'will not compensate for a lack of skill in spelling. We shall have to put that right.'

'By all means,' said Pat. He had subsided for the sake of the children. 'I shall be grateful for all the effort you make for them.' He picked up his bag and bowing to her, went to the now familiar guest room. Somehow, without the comforting presence of Miss Evans, he was irritated and worried. When he ate his dinner with the children, there seemed less of a spark in the place; the girls were subdued, and he wished that Maria's cough was not so persistent. The next morning, as the coach rumbled into sight, they flung their arms around him, disappearing into the folds of his cloak, and he kissed them fervently. Miss Andrews shepherded them away, and the last he saw, as the coach turned the bend in the road, was Emily hopping up and down the steps by the door before a hand seized her and pulled her inside. He drew his cloak around him and shivered in the frosty morning air.

⌒⌒

Bess survived the winter with great cheerfulness. Until Christmas the weather was sharp, frosty and bright, and she clattered, patten-shod, around the parsonage, helping Nancy and Sarah leave everything in good order for Tabitha. ('You've no need to wear yoursen out cleaning everything as if the archbishop were coming again. It's only me, and I shall have time on me hands with but two bairns at home. Leave off.' 'I'll leave it when it's done,' muttered Nancy from somewhere beneath the range, 'and not before. Nobody shall say I left a dirty house.' 'But I wouldn't,' protested Tabitha. 'There's them as might,' came the muffled reply. Owing to her position, Nancy was unable to raise her eyes to the ceiling.)

Patrick, sure as he was of the absolute goodness which shone from Tabitha's ruggedly pleasant features, was nevertheless appre-hensive at the changeover. The Garrs girls had been with him since the children were tiny and had seen many of their births. They had been real friends with Maria, and it was that relationship which was a wrench, another part of their life together disappearing. Nancy talked to the younger children about their mother. Tabitha would be unable to do that.

The letter was lying on his table when he came in from a meeting with the trustees; he had been urging them about their responsibilities in poor relief and trying to edge them towards the practical Christianity he found inspiring since his loss of faith. He was tired and cold and enjoying sitting by the fire listening to Branwell's account of the battles his soldiers were having. The boy had set up the opposing forces with his worn-out infantry on the rug and was competing for space now that the dogs had returned and were reclaiming their territory by the fire. Pat dozed a little in the warmth; his nodding head slipped suddenly and startled him; he caught sight of the letter which he had forgotten to open. Pressing against the wax with his thumb, he unfolded the thin paper and carried it to the window to catch a better light. Sud-denly, he dropped it and was out in the hall and calling for Bess.

'Dear God!' he shouted. 'Maria is ill! I must go to her! Will you get me some clean clothes while I find my money and see John Brown about my absence? Dear God, Bess, what shall I find?'

Bess rustled out of her room and held him by the arms. 'Pat, be calm: let me see the letter – it will only be a precaution – schools always prefer sick pupils to return home. It will be a precaution . . .'

Tabitha, who had heard everything from the kitchen, came bearing the clean linen she had taken straight from the fireguard. She handed it to Bess. Pat grabbed it from her as he ran up to his bedroom, looking for his bag.

'It's in the cellar, Pat,' called Bess. 'We'll fetch it up. Be calm, we'll . . .'

'Give it me now,' he barked, clearing the stairs three at a time, scattering Branwell's soldiers with the force of his re-entry to his study. The boy looked up alarmed, his face contorting with anxiety. Pat saw it and stopped, reining in his distress.

'It's all right, Bran,' he said, taking a deep breath, 'I have to go to see Maria. She's not well.'

'Why? Why do you have to go? When will you be back? I don't like you to go . . . I . . .'

'It's all right,' he soothed him, 'I will be back, and Maria will get well. Go to Aunt Branwell, and she will tell you all about it.' He unlocked his drawer and took out his money, slamming it shut without bothering to turn the key. Tabitha and Bess hovered in the hall. He grabbed the bag and pushed his money and papers into it, spiralling into the coat which hung from Tabby's shaking hands. She seized a linen cloth which she had dropped on the floor and thrust it towards him.

'No food,' he said, stumbling on the steps outside the door, his fearful face turned from them, the wind fracturing his words.

'Pat, get the carrier to take you to Keighley,' shouted Bess.

But he was gone, boots clattering on the cobbles on his way to the fields which would shorten his journey to the coach at Keighley. He arrived with minutes to spare and flung himself inside. Turner, his good acquaintance now, began the usual affable conversation.

'No little lass today? 'Appen tha's run out o' them.'

'No.' Pat's chest was still heaving, and he felt his side would crack. 'Not today. My elder girl is ill. How long will it take? Will you hurry if I . . . ?' and he shifted on to his left buttock to reach into his pocket.

'Nay, there's no need for that, Reverend,' the man replied firmly. 'It's good weather, and I'll get on reet away. The horses will enjoy it.' And he flicked the whip lightly on the gleaming rumps in front of him, and they were away, heads raised and ears well forward in anticipation of a good run.

Pat counted every mile to make them pass more quickly. The road was particularly bad, and he was thrown about inside the coach. The other passengers, knowing who he was, were reluctant to make conversation for fear of being thought familiar. He was disinclined to talk to them from sheer anxiety. When Cowan Bridge came into sight he already had the door's brass handle in his grip, and he was on the ground before the hooves scraped to a halt. For once his manners deserted him as he ran towards the door, and he ignored Turner whose concerned eyes followed him rather than his horses, who reared a little and had to be spoken to sharply. Only when he heard the coach well on its way did Pat realise his discourtesy, but by then he was inside the hall, his frantic banging on the door bringing a tiny, frightened maid.

'Mr Brontë!' Miss Andrews came out of the dusk as the little girl sank back into the shadows. 'I didn't expect you so soon!' She peered at him in the gloom, disturbed by his evident distress.

'Miss Andrews! Where is Maria? I must see her now!'

'Be calm, Mr Brontë, there is no need for anxiety. Come with me. Jane, bring tea to the sickroom,' and she whisked away in front of him, shoes clicking on the stone floor, her sleek head with its tight bun haloed by the candle she held in her raised hand. They stopped at a door. She turned round, barring the way, pulling herself up, chin to the fore.

'Maria is not well, Mr Brontë.' Her words came like little bullets. 'She is a difficult girl to help; sometimes her own wilfulness makes it imposs . . .'

'Maria wilful? I've never heard such nonsense!' Pat was standing close to the challenging little figure, his whole frame shaking; she opened the door slightly to give herself space in the room from his threatening closeness. She lowered her voice.

'It will do Maria no good to see you so agitated,' she whispered. 'Please be calm – we will go in and see if she has woken from her sleep. Yesterday she was most intransigent when I asked her to leave her bed; there are some things that have to be done, and she is a child who will be untidy if left to her own devices. When I, for

164

her own good, instructed her to rise, wash and tidy herself, she was, as I have said, wilful.' She paused, her hands twisting and punishing her shawl's ends. 'We had already sent for you; I merely wished her to be ready, should you decide to come.'

You unspeakable witch, thought Pat. 'I see,' he said aloud. 'Let me see her now.' And he moved forward, forcing her to step aside and let him enter the sickroom.

A little bed stood against the wall; a single candle burned, softly lighting the small figure huddled under bedclothes, the pallor of her face indistinguishable from the pillow she lay upon. Maria turned her head at Pat's swift entry. Her face lit up.

'Papa!' The smile which transformed her face seemed to devour it completely. He could not believe she had become so thin.

'My dearest girl!' He sank to his knees at the bedside, ignoring the chair he could hear Miss Andrews scraping towards him. He took her in his arms and lifted her up, kissing the wasted face. His hands met skin and bones beneath her shift. His heart contracted at the memory of her mother. She started to speak, but he stopped her.

'We're going home now.' He looked towards the fidgeting acting superintendent. 'I need warm clothes for her to travel in, and a blanket to wrap her in; I'll see it's returned. Please hurry: if we go now we'll catch the coach that gets to Keighley late tonight. No,' – and he raised his hand with an authority that Miss Andrews knew better than to challenge – ' I will not wait. Fetch my other daughters – all of them – and be quick.' His anger banished his habitual courtesy. Miss Andrews fled.

He continued to sit on the bed and tried to talk calmly to Maria, his heart racing with anger and fear. Her face had become flushed with the excitement of seeing him and the effort of speaking. Very soon the little maid entered timorously, leading Emily by the hand, Charlotte and Elizabeth following. On seeing Pat they forgot the illness and hurtled towards the bed, jumping on him and squealing with joy.

'There, there!' He shielded Maria from the bouncing bodies and kissed them all.

'Oh Papa!' Charlotte was breathless. 'We've been so worried! Miss Andrews was so horrid to Maria – I wanted to kill her – and Maria was so good!'

'She's a nasty cruel woman.' Emily, despite her six years, pronounced every word with great emphasis. 'One day God will get her.'

Elizabeth chuckled at her sisters. 'They're right, Papa. She's a bad person. Poor Maria,' but suddenly her beautiful grey eyes filled with tears. Pat made a huge effort to control his anger.

'I'm taking Maria home to get better,' he said, his voice shaking a little. 'I'll make sure she gets better and then I'll see how the rest of you are getting on.' His heart wanted to scoop them all up and take them back to the safety of the parsonage. His head told him that Bess and Tabby couldn't cope without some preparation time. Tentatively he asked, 'Do you still like school?'

'Yes,' said Charlotte softly, looking earnestly into his face. 'We do like the school bit, it's the food and Miss Andrews and that black man Mr Wilson . . .'

'But we'll manage,' interrupted Elizabeth. 'I'll look after all of us, and you take Maria to get better, Papa; that's the best thing.'

Tess, the little maid, entered with clothes and blankets and a bag. *I doubt I'll see Miss Andrews again*, thought Pat. Tess dressed Maria while Pat talked to them all. He wrapped her in the coarse blanket, then picked her up. He was horrifed at her weight. Elizabeth slung the bag into his elbow's crook. As he passed through the hall he could hear the distant sound of hooves, and he was out of the door by the time the coach came into view. His own daughters had been joined by many others, calling goodbye to Maria, stroking her hand, gathering at the coach door. Inside the hallway a black figure rustled; the children were called in. Settling the fragile body into a corner opposite a comfortably snoring old man, he turned and quickly laid his hands on the heads of the others and drew them to him.

'Goodbye,' he whispered, 'it'll be all right. I'll be back.' At the crack of Turner's whip he leapt inside and sat back, shaking in the musty, swaying cab.

‿

Stirred by the cry of a solitary curlew which had drifted from the moor and hovered around the house, mewing in the early morning silence, Pat was finally woken by the pale early sun. He moved gingerly in his chair, testing his back and neck for the usual stiffness and pain which followed a night slumped dozing by the little girl's bed. 'You shouldn't do it, Pat,' Bess had said, quite

166

severely, despite her devotion to the child, 'First Maria, now our little Maria, the lack of sleep will k . . .', but she had stopped before completing the word. She had prepared the little room over the front door with such care, the bed beneath the window, warmed over and over with the copper pan freshly loaded with coals from the kitchen-range, rubbing it up and down the bed as if in a trance, listening for the clatter of the carrier's cart Pat would have to hire from Keighley. The moment she saw the child in Pat's arms on the steps of the house she knew that it was hopeless: the blue tinge to her nearly transparent skin, the rasp of her breathing. She had looked covertly at Pat and saw despair in his face. The little girl would die.

He sat with her every night because he never wanted her to be alone, never to wake alone as she waited for this last journey. He would allow no one else to take the night nursing from him, just as he had insisted with her mother. He was amazed and relieved at Maria's composure: she knew she was dying, and there was little comfort he could sincerely offer, although he could have gone through the motions he used to comfort his parishioners. But she was intent on cheering him: 'Bear up, Papa,' she had said once, 'it saddens me to see you sad,' and she had patted his knee and asked him to read again the account of a debate in the House of Lords. He read to her every evening until she had fallen asleep, often after a bout of coughing which stained the cloths Bess left for her with the bright red of arterial blood; sometimes when he was nodding she would take the book or paper from him and reverse the roles.

He eased himself up and noted the way his body creaked in different places; his eyes were worse than ever, blurred and hazy in the early morning, recovering a little towards noon. His slippers shuffled towards Bess's door; he tapped, knowing she was ready, despite the early hour, to take on the nursing, to wash Maria and encourage her to eat. Later she would read to her and bring Anne and Branwell to play in the room. Anne played quietly, instinctively knowing the reality of her sister's situation; Branwell was unrestrained, noisy, anxious. In the kitchen Tabitha was already busy, reaching for Pat's shaving mug to fill it ready for his return from the privy. One of Pat's eccentricities, which had endeared him to every servant he had ever had, was his refusal to use a chamber pot. Whatever the weather, whatever the time of day or night, whatever his state of health, out he would go to the privy. Once after a celebration for Waterloo, with the rain hammering in a summer storm, he had clung unsteadily to the bedpost as he began the descent to the privy in Thornton. Maria had delved beneath the bed and handed him the chamber pot. 'A disgusting habit,' he had said pompously. 'In Ireland we used the fields rather than pollute the house.' She had heaved with mirth when he eventually returned, wet through and bedraggled, falling back into bed in a heap with the effort of negotiating the stairs.

Closing the door behind him he picked up the mug and turned to Tabby who was appalled at the grim misery etched on his face by the morning light. *Dear Lord, this may kill him,* she thought.

'It will not be long now, Tabitha,' he said flatly. 'I have seen death so many times I know when it's near.' He breathed deeply to steady himself. He leaned on the table, arms folded as though to defend himself, facing the moor which was now bathed in sun. The hot water dripped onto the floor; Tabitha did nothing to prevent it. 'I don't know how to bear it. She's our first-born.' He often spoke as if his wife were still alive. *She probably is in his head,* Tabby thought. 'I just don't know what I shall do.'

Tabitha was shocked by this rare moment of confidence. He must be desperate to speak so freely.

'There now,' she ventured. ' 'Appen we'll lose the bairn, but tha knows that the good Lord will tek care of her just as he teks care of all those tha teks to the churchyard.' She wiped her eyes on her apron. 'We'll miss the little lass more than tongue can say, but tha must bear up, Mr Brontë, for the sake of the rest of the childer.'

He leaned backwards and placed the half-empty shaving mug on the table. 'That's what she says to me,' he whispered. 'I did it when Maria died, for the sake of the others. I sat in my study and rationed my grief to the times when I was alone. I can't do it again. I just can't.'

'God will give you strength.' Tabby spoke without conviction, but what else could she say to a man whose profession was the life eternal? 'Give me that mug, and I'll just fill it up again. Then up you go and wash, and I'll put your breakfast in your study. You might have a little sleep in your chair after.'

'No. Don't let me. There's a funeral at ten and a meeting at twelve, there's visits in the afternoon which I've neglected. Don't let me miss any of these things today.' He spoke as though he wanted the distraction, today of all days.

⟋⟍

When Maria died, Pat was out on a visit. He had spent most of the day on parish affairs, frequently returning to the house, sitting for minutes at the bedside and then departing. The little girl slept, despite the painful rasping of her lungs. When Bess met him at the gate, he pushed roughly past her, straight into his study.

'I know,' he said. 'Did she not die half an hour ago? I was on the moor and I knew. Her soul flew away in the wind.'

Bess was shocked but said nothing, trying to propel him gently to a chair. A minister of religion talking like those poets who didn't believe in God? It was grief; he hardly knew what he said. 'Pat, we must make arrangements for the funeral. You can't take it yourself; will you send to William?'

'Do what you like.' He picked up his stick again, brushing past her in the doorway. 'I'm going on the moor. I'll be back when you see me.'

Bess sat down by the window. His tall figure went by in a blur; there was a desperation in his exhausted energy. In the kitchen she could hear the sounds of Branwell and Anne with Tabby talking about Maria's death. No doubt Anne was on her lap and Branwell standing tight against her, arm round her hips, thumb in his mouth, nestling. She was suddenly appalled at the situation. Never in his life since she had known him had Pat shirked his responsibilities. She would have to send to William Morgan herself. Using his table and pens, she wrote quickly, flowingly, telling of the little girl's death, hinting at Pat's grief and distress, saying that it was most appropriate that he who had baptised her should bury her. She also wrote to Elizabeth Firth, now the Reverend Mrs Franks. Pat needed his friends now, almost as much as he needed his relatives.

Sealing the two papers, she sighed, letting her eyes wander over the grey bulk of Haworth church and its depressing graveyard; if ever she had thought that the schooling of the girls would release her from her obligations, now she knew that her life must be lived in this grey Yorkshire village with its cold winds and independent people. More than ever, Pat needed a familiar friend, a link with the past. God had called her, and she would do his will.

169

The next day Pat appeared calmer, profoundly apologetic for what he deemed an outburst unbecoming to a clergyman, whatever the reason. Maria lay in the parlour, beautiful, calm, but dead. Branwell would not believe it.

'No, Aunt,' he said firmly, 'she is not. Soon she will read to me.'

'She has gone to heaven, Branwell.'

'No, Aunt, she will be back to play with me.'

'Branwell,' she said quietly, 'she has gone to be with God. Just as Mama has gone. She is safe in God's hands.'

'No. No! NO!' His voice rose to shriek, and he banged his soldier on the floor with such ferocity that he split the wood. 'No! NO!'

Bess rose from her chair, full of anxiety for the child. He seemed possessed by something stronger than himself. Gently she took him by the shoulders and propelled him into the parlour, towards the little coffin. 'Look, Bany,' she said, holding him to her, 'look, she has gone to be with Jesus. She's in her coffin and asleep in Jesus. She is safe.'

He turned away and buried his head in her black silky bosom. 'No, no, Aunt,' he sobbed, 'No, no, no.'

❧

William and Jane came to bury Maria on the twelfth of May. The sun shone, lambs were bleating on the moor and every natural thing seemed full of hope and renewal. William was visibly shaken: he had buried the mother with great sadness at the loss of a loving friend and the beloved wife of his best friend; but burying this child whom he had baptised and watched grow shook him to the core of his spirit. On the way from Bradford Jane had held his hand in the gig and spoken of the good times and Maria's assured salvation, but he just repeated over and over again, 'How will Pat bear it? Another one gone.' When they arrived at the parsonage Bess received them in the parlour. She shut the door quickly behind them.

'As you might expect, Pat is not himself,' she said anxiously. 'It's almost worse than when my sister died. He feels, I think, that he's let their mother down by allowing Maria to be ill and die. At least that's what he says when . . .' She paused and looked directly at them. 'I can tell you both, I know, in confidence, that his sorrow is so great that since she died he's . . .'

170

'He's been drinking, has he?' William's voice was warm, his round pink face flabby with grief. He loved Patrick; he knew him as a brother. He admired his tenacity, his intellect, his humour, everything about him. He had always felt enlarged by Patrick's friendship. 'My dear Miss Branwell, if a man cannot have a drink to drown his sorrow at a time like this, when can he?' He leaned forward and patted her hand, overcome with emotion, too, for this good woman whom he had known ever since she became a visitor to Hartshead. 'Don't worry; he'll get over it.'

When the time came for the service, Pat appeared, determinedly upright, immaculate in black, only his reddened eyes giving away his distress. He was courteous, quite affable, gentle with Branwell and Anne, took Bess's arm as they walked through the little gate to the path through the graveyard. In church he was composed, responded to William's exhortations, and wiped Branwell's tears; he held both children by the hand on the return to the parsonage. After tea he kissed Jane, shook Wiliam's hand, thanked him, and it was only when he stumbled as he bowed himself out of the parlour and into his study that anyone realised he was drunk.

20

When the typhus fever had fulfilled its mission of devastation at Lowood, it gradually disappeared from thence; but not till its virulence and the number of its victims had drawn public attention to the school. Inquiry was made . . . and the discovery produced a result mortifying to Mr. Brocklehurst, but beneficial to the institution.

Charlotte Brontë, *Jane Eyre*, Volume 1, Chapter 10.

The drinking continued for about two weeks; Bess commanded Tabitha to bring no more whiskey from the village, but the store in the cellar which Pat had left largely undisturbed in recent times – there being, he had said, little to celebrate – was sufficient to keep him well oiled without being well wrecked. Bess was wiser than might have been expected of a spinster lady of her years; she reminded herself of Pat's essential goodness and dedication to the children and convinced herself that it would pass as his grief ebbed. She was relieved that drinking to assuage his grief had different results from the celebration drinking which she was more familiar with. It would have been difficult to deal with the parish if the minister had been singing his Gaelic songs and reciting his own works; as it was, he became quieter, almost mesmerised, sensible yet distracted. The sexton, John Brown, was the best friend the parsonage had, displaying all the best in the Haworth temperament: his reticence became discretion, his closeness, fierce loyalty. He shielded his parson from prying eyes and wagging tongues with the same unflagging strength with which he dug the graves. If Patrick was not at his best, no one got past the graveyard or the gate.

It stopped dead on the thirty-first of May. Clattering over the cobbles a gig drew up at the parsonage gate, and the driver, tying his horse to the ring on the garden wall, opened the door and assisted a large, plainly dressed woman down the single step and directed her towards the front door. Tabitha reacted to her message with sense and speed: she went straight out to the gig and picked up Elizabeth from the inside and carried her into the parlour. She then knocked on Patrick's study door and told him that Mrs Hardace had brought Elizabeth from Cowan Bridge as the school had been evacuated to the seaside.

Patrick emerged from his study feeling that he was in a dream. In truth he had been dozing after a sleepless night and had not started on the whiskey yet. He went straight to Elizabeth and knelt beside her as she sat huddled on the couch. Her pinched face, quick breathing and pallor struck terror into his heart.

'What do you mean – the school has been evacuated? Elizabeth is here. Where are Charlotte and Emily?' He was brusque in his questioning, a gnawing pain in his stomach beginning to cut him in half.

Mrs Hardacre felt it would be better to be gone as swiftly as possible from this house and this man. As a servant she had to do her master's bidding, but she had not wanted to do the Reverend Carus Wilson's least pleasant errand. She rose and drew her shawl around her, ready to depart. 'The school is evacuated to Mr Wilson's house at Silverdale. It was thought that a change of place might defeat the typhus. But Elizabeth was thought to be too sick of another illness . . .' Her voice trailed away. 'I was instructed to bring her.' She hoped he would see her only as the messenger.

Patrick went out into the hall, calling for Bess; the rarity of his raised voice brought her bustling from her room, pattens clacking on the stairs.

'Go into the parlour and look after Elizabeth,' he said, ignoring the surprise on her face at hearing the girl's name. 'Madam, will you step this way, please.' He ushered Mrs Hardacre into his study. Without asking her to sit down, he shut the door. 'Tell me in Heaven's name what has happened at Cowan Bridge.'

'The whole school has been affected by typhus fever. Mr Wilson called a doctor who advised that the conditions there would make it impossible to defeat the disease. All the girls have been taken to Silverdale to recover. Except Elizabeth, whom the doctor thought was too sick and should be brought home.' She didn't meet his eyes. In the long silence which followed she took a covert look at him. He was standing with his eyes closed, swaying slightly. A minute went by.

'It is not your fault. I'm sorry if I appeared rude. Please go. Let me take you to the gig.' He offered her his arm, and as he shut the door he pressed the catch home with a desperate finality.

୭୬

They put Elizabeth to bed, bathed and warm in a fresh shift, with milk and oatcakes. Anne wanted to read to her, her slight hesitations merely adding to Elizabeth's delight at being home, and clean and loved. Bess had a hard evening with Pat. He thumped his breast and paced the room until Bess thought she would swoon.

'I had said to them, when I fetched Maria, that I would be back. I wanted to bring them all home at the time but . . . I failed to care for them. I should have gone back immediately.'

'But Pat, you were nursing Maria, and had the parish . . .'

'The parish? *The parish?* Since when does a good father put his children's lives beneath the needs of a parish?' He thumped the table; the candlestick jumped, scattering the wax across the table and making the flame flare. 'I should have gone back straight away.'

'The girls were being educated. That was the plan. You were caring for Maria. That was your correct priority. And when she died you were . . .'

'Too drunk to notice? Is that what you were going to say? You'd be right there. What a wreck of a man I have become, to neglect my children for the drink. What would Maria think of me now? How would she feel about the way I treat our children?' He stopped and Bess realised that he was close to tears. She thought quickly.

'You have done everything possible for the children. They have a happy home; when they were all here there was not a happier house for children anywhere. You gave them your time, your interest, your companionship. Many children scarcely know their fathers. Your children lacked a mother, but so do many others. Maria would have approved of everything you did. I approve.' She stopped. She always knew when to stop.

He ran his hands through his thick hair where the red still lingered. 'Is there no end to what God will do to me?' He sat down heavily in his chair, leaning his elbows on his knees. 'That child is going to die – it's in her face. Will he really take three of them

174

from me? After Maria's death they became my whole life – you know that. I should never have sent them to Cowan Bridge.' He spat the last words out as if they were poison. 'I was impressed by the sponsors; I thought a clergyman of the Church of England would care for little children as if they were his own. Well' – he rose – 'I shall see the Reverend Carus Wilson. Ask Tabitha to pack me a bag while I see Brown about my work tomorrow. I'm going to this seaside place to fetch Charlotte and Emily. He's not having my children any longer.' He swept out of the door, seizing a sheaf of papers to take with him to Brown's cottage. Bess heaved a sigh and went back to Elizabeth.

⋄⋄

Running and walking over the fields to Keighley in the pale morning sun, he knew he had little time to catch the first coach to Kendal. His anxiety was such that he had not worked out how he would proceed from there. Turner, seeing him arrive in an exhausted state, and remembering Elizabeth and Mrs Hardacre the day before, didn't attempt any pleasantries: he opened the door, saying, 'You'll have it 't yersen' till the next stage,' and mounted the box swiftly, cracking the whip as he did so. When they stopped to pick up more passengers in half an hour, Pat was sufficiently outwardly composed to enquire about the route to Silverdale. The best way, apparently, was to stay on this coach as far as far as Kirby Lonsdale and then pick up the coach which ran from there to Carnforth. There was one due soon after the Keighley one arrived. Pat was thankful for the excellent network of predictable coaches which ran around the north of England. Sometimes his conscience was tugged by the strain on the horses, but this coachman was kind and Pat's daughters in desperate need of rescue.

He cursed Carus Wilson's ample means which allowed him to live well off the route of public coaches. He had to hire a gig for the remainder of the journey, and he would need it to make a swift escape with Emily and Charlotte. The driver had no difficulty locating the house. The Reverend Carus Wilson was well known and his holiday house frequented by his wife and daughters. Pat could imagine their feelings at having a typhus-ridden school evacuated to their pleasant retreat; presumably they were miles away. Perhaps Wilson was, too. That would be a pity, as Pat particularly wanted to see him. He had not felt so angry for years.

175

The sort of feelings which were coursing through him had been tamed by Maria, the feelings which had left him hanging at the end of a bell rope in Dewsbury and had sustained him as he faced the hostile crowds in Haworth. The sight of the sea, which should have been pleasure to an Irishman long exiled from the Mountains of Mourne, left him largely unmoved.

The house was large, well screened from the road by rhododendron bushes. He told the driver to wait, for a long time if necessary, and the man was happy to as the afternoon was fine and he could graze his horses by the roadside. As the gig drew away, Pat gave the iron bell pull a hard tug and waited as the sound echoed and died away within the house. The maid who opened the door was clearly not expecting callers. Patrick removed his hat.

'I am the Reverend Patrick Brontë. I have come to fetch my daughters, Charlotte and Emily Brontë. Please have them brought to me, and all their belongings, as quickly as possible. While you do that, I would like to see Mr Wilson.'

The maid, whose normal duties were to wait on the Wilsons if they were in residence, looked dumbfounded at she tried to take in so much information. When she had struggled through it all, she showed Pat to a small parlour, saying as she did so, 'You'd best wait there, sir. I don't think Mr Wilson is seeing anyone.' She closed the door and silence enveloped the room like a shroud. For at least five minutes, nothing happened. His own quick breathing suddenly startled him. Then, in the distance, Pat caught the sound of a door opening, a light murmur, a deeper voice replying 'No' and the door closing again.

He rose from his chair, opened the door and was back in the tessellated hall. He stood still in the middle of it and said loudly, 'Wilson!' Nothing. 'Wilson!' he said more loudly. A third time. He looked at the choice of doors. Where was the man hiding? He chose the most obvious, one which would look onto the back of the house and the garden and would therefore make a pleasant study. Walking softly towards it, he turned the handle and flung it wide open. Right first time.

The Reverend Carus Wilson sat with his black back to the door, his shining, oiled head bent over his papers. As he heard the door open he swung round in his chair and his spectacles fell from his nose into his lap.

'Brontë!' he said. 'I can't . . . I didn't . . . I haven't seen you since we met at the inauguration of the Bradford Bible Society,' he continued more smoothly, as he sensed the situation.

'You will not see me again, Wilson, after I have said what I have come to say. I entrusted to your care my most precious children, my four daughters, with the promise of a fifth. I believed your calling as a man of God and a Christian would ensure that you took as good care of my children as you did of your own, which,' – he glanced around the well-appointed room – 'seems to be fastidious. In return for my trust you returned to me one child dying, whom it was too late to help, and another without warning in the same condition. What they have told me leads me to believe that your school was dirty, the food insufficient, the care negligent and, at times, brutal.' He could not continue, and Wilson seized the break in his voice as a chance to fight back.

'Your daughters had the care which was due to them according to their deserts. By that I mean that we are not running a school for the daughters of gentlemen to gain accomplishments, we are attempting to provide education for the daughters of clergy who are too . . .' – he paused a little, as if even he were embarrassed by the word – 'too poor to bring their children up in the way I would wish my own to be.' He stopped, congratulating himself that he had put it so succinctly, so inoffensively.

The cords of veins in Patrick's head stood out, and as he took a step towards him, the man shrank back. Seizing him by the collar of his fine barathea coat, he pulled him forwards. 'According to their deserts, Wilson? If it were all according to our deserts, who would escape the whipping?' he growled, misquoting *Hamlet.* 'Are you saying that because they were poor my daughters can expect to be cold, hungry, bored and beaten? That their illness can be ignored and their father uninformed because, presumably, his poverty makes him less vulnerable, too? You know well that they have no mother – you know well that I would die myself rather than allow them to be badly treated. You . . .' but he had run out of breath and words and simply pushed Wilson across the room where he landed on a sofa and slithered to the floor.

'I am taking my children now, and if ever our paths cross again, I warn you to keep well away from me. You and your institution are a disgrace.' He slammed the door as hard as he could, not bothering to see if Wilson managed to crawl to his feet or retrieve his damaged spectacles.

Sitting in the gig on the way back to the coach, Charlotte and Emily chirped and squealed with joy. 'You said you would come, Papa, and you have,' shouted Emily. 'And we will stay at home for ever now, won't we? No Miss Andrews' – and Charlotte pulled a face so perfectly like the acting superintendent's that Patrick laughed despite himself – 'and no burnt porridge and no' – they both shouted – 'MR WILSON!'

Pat lay back in the seat, the children secure in his arms. His pleasure at having them safe was tempered by Elizabeth's illness and the knowledge that his outburst to Wilson was the result of his guilt at not fetching them sooner.

୧୬

Elizabeth lingered briefly; her sisters' joy at being at home was diminished by the palpable absence of Maria and the weakness of their second sister. The other four played near her quietly, and even Branwell was subdued and apparently realistic. Pat had again taken the night nursing; each morning as he awoke from his aching doze he felt as if he were climbing out of a black pit. Mostly he wished that he could return to it. Bess and Tabitha, quietly reeling from the increase from two to five children, worked like good-humoured packhorses until they dropped into their beds at night, when their old bones protested at the extra miles they had come that day.

Elizabeth died in the night while Patrick was with her. She was sleeping and woke briefly to cough and gasp; he jerked awake and was supporting her on her pillows when she gave a little sigh and her head dropped on his arm. He wept for several minutes, holding her tightly before he could drop her back on the pillows and close her eyes. Standing up, he looked at her and thought that, however resistant he had become to death in the cottages of Haworth, he would never recover from the deaths within his own house. He drew the sheet over her head and closed the door, returning to his own room where he lay on his bed and let the tears run down his face until his ears were wet.

୧୬

Her funeral took place within three days. Pat and Bess had felt that the sooner the house became outwardly normal the better it would be for the other children, whose grief was stimulated by the sight of the coffin which had to lie in the parlour. William Morgan had

178

known in advance to expect Elizabeth's death, and he and Jane came over again, huddled together, hardly speaking on the journey. 'If we feel like this,' William whispered to her in the gig, 'how on earth does Pat feel?' They soon knew when he greeted them on the steps of the parsonage. He looked like an old man, hardly able to straighten himself to his usual erect posture, his clothes hanging off him as if they were made for someone else, his face white with the deep lines of sleeplessness ground into it. As ever, he was courteous, grateful to see his dearest friends, but scarcely aware of what was going on around him. His eyes were red and his hands trembled. But he was stone-cold sober.

When the Morgans had gone, the house quiet and the children in bed, Pat summoned Bess and Tabitha to his study. He told Tabitha to sit, a thing she had never done in his study, although he often sat in her kitchen. When he spoke his voice still had a tremor in it. The effort he was making was huge.

'We now have Charlotte, Emily, Branwell and Anne at home,' he said, pacing the floor, his hands in his pockets. 'I want them to remain here. I don't want them to go away for any reason. It will mean a lot of work for you, Tabby, and we may need to get extra help. I am sorely to blame for the deaths of my two daughters' – both women made protesting noises, but his upraised hand silenced them – 'and I will never let these four out of my sight, or in my absence, out of yours. Do you understand?' They both nodded. 'I don't want to restrict them for the greatest thing a child has is freedom before the chains of maturity fasten on them.' *He's been reading that poet again*, sighed Bess to herself. 'And I want them to be free in the house and to have freedom out of it, but if they go out they must go with either you or me.' Bess looked a little glum as she was not fond of the Yorkshire outside, but Tabitha cast her a look which said, 'I'll do that bit.'

'I'll take them with me as much as I can,' he continued. 'We'll educate them here, and we'll have tutors for what we cannot teach ourselves. It will be hard to start with, but that's how it must be. Never, never will I lose a child again because I am not there.' It seemed as if he had made a great effort to say all this and was suddenly spent. 'Thank you. I must get on with my work.'

Or with your weeping, thought Bess sadly as he shut the door behind him. *Please God*, she prayed, *let it pass*.

21

I remember the day when the Intelligence extraordinary came
... with what eagerness Papa tore off the cover & how we all
gathered round him and with what breathless anxiety we
listened ... the Great Duke in green sash and waistcoat, the
rising of all the peeresses when he rose the reading of his
speech Papa saying his words were like precious gold ...

Charlotte Brontë, *Tales of the Islanders*, Volume 2 (1829).

Patrick tidied his papers into a shaggy pile and pushed back his
chair. 'There is a little refreshment waiting for you, gentlemen, if
you have the time to stay. Miss Branwell would be very glad if you
would step into the parlour.' He opened the door of his study and
held it for the trustees. They all knew the reputation of Tabitha's
baking and were inclined to linger. As they passed through the
hall there was tremendous crash which shook the house. The men
stopped and looked enquiringly at Patrick.

'Do go through,' he said charmingly. 'I'll just alert my sister-in-
law to your needs.' He closed the door behind the last broad back
and, quick as a hot knife through butter, he was up the stairs with
his lightest step. In his bedroom, which was above his study, four
pairs of eyes turned towards him from the pile of bedclothes which
draped the floor. There was no fear in their eyes, just interest in
his reaction. Branwell was still clinging onto the four-poster bed.

'What . . .?' Pat began.

'It's all right, Papa.' Charlotte sounded reassuring. 'We were
building a boat for the journey to Africa, and Branwell, who is not
our best sailor, fell from the rigging while he was trying to fix the
sail – that's your sheet,' she added unnecessarily, 'but he would
not have been Lord Nelson's choice of rigging boy. You should be

180

more careful, Bany,' she said severely, 'the ship could have gone aground without a properly furled sail, couldn't it, Papa?' She turned to him with confidence born of complete trust.

'Charlotte,' said Patrick, patiently but with some spirit, 'you know the trustees are downstairs. It sounded as if their house was collapsing about their ears. Do you want them to think I am careless tenant and have us all thrown upon the street?'

'They can't do that.' Branwell laughed as he negotiated the bedpost and landed with another thump on the bare boards of his father's bedroom. 'It's our house.'

'I haven't time now to go into the terms of my occupancy as the incumbent of Haworth, but you will kindly be quiet for the next half-hour until they have gone. I'm supposed to be summoning your aunt to pour the tea. Anne, you go and tell her so that I can slide back into the parlour.' And cuffing Branwell's ear affection-ately he made a swift but silent descent in to the hall, slowing his pace abruptly at the parlour door and entering as casually as if he had strolled from the kitchen.

Bess followed him in to dispense tea and Tabitha's baking. She quite enjoyed playing hostess, but sometimes yearned for the sociability of Penzance, even the lighter repartee of Thornton, compared with Haworth chat on the daily grind and the eternally interesting accumulation of money. She had on her finest silk, deep lilac in the fashion of Cornwall of at least twenty years ago, and looked quite radiant. The trustees were impressed by her sophistication and enjoyed hearing her conversations with Patrick, when, as Stephen Taylor had once observed, 'she gives 't parson a good run round. Not that 'e can't tek care of hissen.'

Patrick asked Taylor to remain for a minute, and they returned to the study where he took down a document from the top shelf.

'I've been looking at the terms of my incumbency,' he began, after motioning Taylor to the most comfortable seat. 'It occurs to me that the wording doesn't make my position entirely secure.' He flushed a little. 'You will perhaps excuse me raising this, but the deaths of my two little girls, and the future of my remaining children, have made me sensitive to the future.' He stopped. Taylor nodded encouragement for him to continue. He had liked this man since their first meeting and admired his fortitude. He had been through the mill more than most, with less mithering.

'I had assumed that as the perpetual curate my living was secure

– that the care of the parish, on behalf of the vicar of Bradford, and the house that goes with it, were mine for life. But the deeds of the parsonage actually say that the trustees can rent the parsonage to whom they like, and the terms of my salary allow it to be witheld on any grounds they choose, even if I do a satisfactory job.' He shook his head. 'You may think it's unnecessarily gloomy for me to question my terms, but my recent experience has made me mindful of the fragility of human life and events.'

Taylor spread his well-shaped, practical hands in front of him and leaned towards the fire, which crackled and shifted in the grate, hung about with Patrick's dogs. 'I don't think you have any need to worry, Mr Brontë,' he said. 'The terms of the trustees are, as you've put it, a bit on our side rather than yours, but that's the way of things: too many times the vicars of Bradford have tried to hassle the trustees, and I suppose it's a way to protect oursen. But you're not going to cross us, are you, and we'd 'eck as like put a man and four motherless bairns out o' parsonage onto street.' And he slapped his thigh and laughed good-naturedly.

That's all he can say, thought Pat. *He's not going to be able to change this document, written in God knows when.* Aloud he said, 'Thank you for listening to me. It's just that I've had to take stock of my means recently. I'm not getting any younger.'

'Tha wears thy years better than most of us,' chuckled Taylor. 'No spare fat on thee, and tha strides along the moor like a lad of twenty. Ye'll see us all out!'

Pat accompanied him to the door, watching him out of the gate and raising his hand in a final farewell.

෧ඉ

Later that night, after Bess had taken the children to bed after their prayers, he closed the shutters on the rain and wind and took down the deeds again. What he had found had really shaken him, and his gentle query to Stephen Taylor in no way expressed the terrible anxiety he felt. Perhaps he was still tired, and grief-stricken, but the thought that he could have his salary withdrawn by the trustees on a mere whim, 'however circumspectly he walks' made him wake in the night sweating with fear. The issue of the parsonage, whatever Taylor said, still brought to his vivid dreams himself with his four little ones, trudging along a stony road in Ireland, bog and sheep on either side, bare-footed, blue with cold, the children crying with hunger. These were images he had seen in real life in his early years, and he had to sit up in bed and shake his head violently to banish the terrifying pictures. Sometimes he would creep downstairs and take a dram to steady himself.

He stood in front of the fire and leaned on the wall above it; flames spurted into life as he kicked the smouldering coals with his boot; the flaring stirred the need for action in him. He would never have got to Cambridge if he had accepted that things must stay as they are. Nothing was unalterable. If he had no security with the trustees, he must make his own. As he replaced the trustees' document, his eye rested on his own works; he kept them at that level as the children liked to take them down and trace his name on the cover, sometimes reading bits out to each other. He had little time to read these days, but he knew that the Keighley Circulating Library had novels by all the latest authors because their suitability was often a subject for discussion at clergy meetings.

He rummaged in a pile of yellowing papers at the end of the shelf, hoping to find the story he had started about Dewsbury and the Luddites. Not there; he'd never mastered the tidy systems Maria had encouraged. Too late now. He needed to write a novel that would sell, the usual three volumes; something which would be bought privately and in multiples by all the circulating libraries in England. Wales, too, he supposed, and Scotland, had them; they probably went to India and Australia and New Zealand to keep the transplanted wives and daughters happy. The market was immense! But not the Luddites; he had got stuck with that, and the heroine, based on Maria, had haunted him in his unrelenting grief. He was past the Luddism; too much had happened since then.

He sat down at his table and tapped his thumbnail with the end of his quill. Suddenly he caught a flash of himself: when Elizabeth had died he had sat up all the next night trying to convert his grief into poetry. The bottle of whiskey which accompanied his efforts also considerably diminished them. Suddenly he stood up, opened one of the shutters and gazed out into the black, wild night. Rising within him he felt a surge of energy strong enough to dispel the grief he still felt for the two little girls and the boiling anger with Carus Wilson. This conflict drained him every day, exhausting him for his daily tasks.

There was his story. He felt cleansed and excited. What a relief to write it all down: seizing a fresh sheet of paper, he began an untidy plan, spattering the page in his eagerness to write, ignoring the dry ink flaking from his quill, too hurried to sharpen it. An orphan girl, abandoned to the awful world of Cowan Bridge, unprotected, prey to disease, bad food and the wicked Calvinist doctrines of Mr Wilson. But she must eventually find happiness, not die. She was not to die like Maria and Elizabeth. The candle was on the rim of the candlestick by the time he carried it into the hall, and as he mounted the stairs he felt exhilarated, purged, excited. After a few minutes of the old creative surge spinning in his head, he slept soundly for the first time in months.

＠

'I don't see,' said Charlotte from where she sat by the window in Pat's study, 'why Branwell learns Greek and we do not.'

'You learn a bit of Latin,' said Branwell mischievously. 'Papa thinks that's all girls' brains can cope with. It is,' he said pompously, 'much harder to learn Greek.'

'Did Papa really say that?' Emily shot across the room and tugged at his red curly hair. 'He didn't! I know he didn't!'

'I didn't say what?' enquired Pat mildly, entering the room in his greatcoat and hat, drenched from his walk over the moor to a sick parishioner. 'What didn't I say?'

Charlotte went into battle. 'Branwell says that we don't learn Greek because you think that girls aren't clever enough. Is that what you think, Papa?' Her huge eyes blazed with indignation as she confronted her clerical parent.

'That is not the way of it at all,' he replied. He sat in the chair in front of the fire, and the children eagerly divested him of his outdoor clothes, keen to urge the argument on. 'I teach Bran Greek because eventually he will go to St John's like me and he has to have it . . .'

'But I . . .' interrupted Emily.'

'Not even I could persuade the Master and Fellows that women, that my three daughters in particular, were possibly worth educating more than my flibbertigibbet son – yes, Branwell, I mean it – for your sisters will work far harder than you for longer periods, although I have to admit you show the odd flash of genius when you do apply yourself.' He smiled at Branwell who had crept up to his chair and rested his head on his father's arm. 'Just accept, Bran, that you have clever sisters and trying to belittle them will

184

land you with the most awful rows. I wouldn't want to tangle with them, old man. I advise you not to!'

'I would still like to learn Greek,' persisted Charlotte. 'Even if I can't go to the university, although I don't know why they decide on your sex rather than your intelligence whether you can go.' Pat smiled; he had often pondered this fact himself and discussed it with her mother and aunt.

'One problem,' continued Pat, 'is my time. It is less time-consuming to teach four children Latin when they have the basics of the Roman alphabet, but ensuring the progress of each one into the Greek alphabet before the teaching commences is more than I can do adequately. Besides, there's your history and geography, literature and mathematics. If it seems unfair . . .'

'No,' said Anne, 'we understand that Bany has to earn a living' – and she shot him a naughty look over her father's head; he didn't look enthusiastic about it – 'and may even have to support us in our old age. Do you not think that is a delightful prospect, Charlotte?'

Charlotte grinned. 'I would prefer to be borne off to a castle by Lord Douro himself, to lie in silken sheets and be waited on by a hundred servants, but Branwell slaving away is a good alternative, while we do nothing at all. But really, Papa, what I want to do is spend less time with Aunt on sewing and spelling. It goes on and on.'

Anne sighed. 'It would hurt her feelings if we don't have lessons with her.' Patrick nodded. 'I think she likes our company. She hardly ever goes out.'

'But the room!' exclaimed Emily from the fireside, where she lay entangled with Thunder and Paddy. 'It's so hot, and when we come back from the moor with Tabby and we're hot from running, it nearly suffocates us, with the fire and the windows tight shut.'

'She feels the cold,' said Anne quietly. 'It's because it was warm in Penzance and . . .'

'I had so many beaux there – and the soirées!' Charlotte imitated Bess perfectly.

'That's not fair, Charlotte.' Anne was very quick in her response. 'She loves us. I don't want to hurt her. I shall keep on with my lessons.'

'Yes,' urged Branwell, 'you should go to the lessons. She likes you there. She might think we didn't love her, and we do.'

'Fine for you, Bany, when you have nearly all your lessons with Papa,' cried Emily, 'although I suppose you do read to her, which I couldn't bear to do.'

'Now children,' said Pat, summoning up the strength for an intervention. 'We will not hurt Aunt Branwell; she has given up her life for us, and we will not repay her with harshness.' He raised his hand to stop Charlotte, who was dying to defend herself against such a charge. 'It's time we made a few changes in your lessons and I' – he looked severely at them – '*I* will organise it so that your aunt is unaware of your discontent. You will all do the Latin with me, Branwell will do Greek for the university, although if you want to be writers,' he added slyly, watching their faces carefully from beneath his hooded brows, 'you might as well know that your favourite author, Mr Shakespeare, had small Latin and less Greek.' They all kept their eyes fixed on the dogs. 'I am at your disposal for any additional extras you may require of me, free of charge.' He smiled at them all. 'And we'll get drawing and piano lessons as well.' They shrieked with delight and jumped all over him.

ᘓ

Anne had pricked her finger while she was sewing the tiny book; the blood dripped onto the rough page, and she carefully wiped it off, cleaning it with spittle to make sure the surface was ready for their pens.

'You do these really well,' said Emily admiringly. 'This one's even smaller than the last one. It's only three inches all round, and Branwell's *Blackwood's Magazine* is much bigger.' She put the two tiny books back in the tin box where they kept them. 'Is this for Charlotte and Branwell? We don't need a new one just yet.'

'Mm.' Anne's mouth was busy with the thread. 'I thought I would make a few spares while we had this surplus' – she hesitated slightly over the *s* – 'of paper. Tabby kept all the sugar bags dry behind the fire, and I found a few pages Papa' – she blushed guiltily – 'didn't seem to need.'

'He wouldn't mind anyway,' said Emily. 'He says we can't buy new exercise books all the time because they cost so much. Do you remember when he gave us four new ones and we'd filled them by the end of the week? He didn't know what to say. He said in the end that we must be the most profli . . . prolifli . . .'

'Prolific,' said Anne.

'That's it – writers that he'd ever known. I heard him talking to Aunt Branwell about it. He told her that we were like him and Mama, always wanting to write, but more so. Aunt said,' – and she raised her voice and wagged her head a little – 'that it was all right provided we didn't lose touch with the real world. That was after Tabby got so worried about us acting out our stories that she sent for William.'

'Who found us all sitting quietly reading our Bibles when he came to break up the riot!' Anne put her sewing down, and they fell onto the truckle-bed under the window, croaking with mirth. 'Do you think Gondal is a better country than Angria, Emily? I certainly think our people are better by far than Branwell's and Charlotte's.'

'I heard that.' Branwell entered and bounced down on the bed. 'Our stories are the work of mature genius, illustrated by fine artists who have been taught by the greatest living painters.'

'We're to have lessons next week, too,' said Emily sharply, 'and Anne and I start the piano with Mr Sutherland. And Charlotte can't do that because' – and she made circles of her index fingers and thumbs round her eyes – 'because she can't see the music if she sits on a chair.' She pulled a face. 'That's why she writes so small, too.'

'No it's not,' said Anne. 'We all write small so Aunt can't read it. It's mean, really.'

'But you don't want Aunt reading about the drunken japes of young Soult, do you?' Branwell's eyes lit up. 'It would be all right for Papa, for he's a man of the world.' He leaned back against the window sill. 'After all, he wrote about that prostitute . . .'

'A what?' asked Anne.

'A prostitute,' replied Branwell grandly. 'She was called Maria . . .'

'But that was Mama's name!'

'He wrote it before he knew Mama; it's in *Cottage Poems*, which is 1811.' He stood on the bed and declaimed:

> *'Here, every rake, exerts his art,*
> *T' ensnare the unsuspecting heart.*
> *The prostitute with faithless smiles,*
> *Remorseless plays her tricks and wiles,*

Her gesture bold and ogling eyes,
Obtrusive speech and pert reply –

'I'll show it you next time he's out. And you know about them anyway – it's in the *Leeds Intelligencer* – when they catch them in the street they get sent to prison,' he added darkly.

Charlotte came thumping up the stairs, pink-cheeked from her walk to the village with Tabby.

'I heard all that as I came up,' she said. 'Your voice carries, Bany.' She flung herself down on the floor. 'Why doesn't Papa write like that any more? Do you remember:

'Loud howls the wild inconstant blast,
Deep sullen glooms, the sky o'ercast,
And all the heartless scene –

'Oh I wish I could write like Lord Byron! He has black curls and a white pillar of a neck; I've seen a painting. Papa knew him at Cambridge, did you know? They both loved dogs.' She slapped her fist down hard on the bare floorboards. 'Oh why can't a girl go and meet writers and soldiers as Papa did? He just got himself to Cambridge, and there they all were, Byron and Lord Palmerston and . . .'

'And you can just get yerselves downstairs t' yer tea,' interrupted Tabby, entering on her soft-soled shoes. 'There's apples t' peel and no one's done a thing to this bedroom today. Theer's a job for tomorrow.' Charlotte pulled a face at Branwell, but Emily and Anne were already down the stairs behind Tabby. Kitchen or writing, it was all the same to them.

৩৩

'Do you think he knows?' whispered Emily to Charlotte as they lay in bed that night, the full moon shining on the white coverlet, patterned with the window bars.

'Of course he does,' snorted Charlotte. 'He knows we take his paper and Tabby's sugar bags, and he sees us stitching the books. He never says a word because' – and she giggled with joy and hugged Emily – 'because he thinks we will grow up to be like him and write. And that's what he wants, so he lets us do what we want.'

'You're probably right,' whispered Emily. 'I would like to write

188

like Papa. There can't be any other children in this village who have a Papa who has written books. He must be very clever.'

'He is,' replied Charlotte, staring unblinkingly at the moon, 'He is very clever; he's not like anyone else we know. Not like Uncle William, or Uncle Fennell or any of the trustees' – Emily stifled a giggle – 'or Mr Wilson.' They both shuddered and clung to each other. 'He's not like all the men he is like, if you see what I mean – he's an intellectual.'

'A what?' asked Emily.

'It means he cares for things of the mind very passionately – I think,' Charlotte whispered. 'Now, let's get on with these bed plays. They're quite the best we do. Slip along to Aunt's room, she's bound to be asleep now, and get Anne in here. We must be sure she doesn't fall asleep like last time, for the sleepwalking excuse won't work again.'

⚬⚬

Patrick had drafted the letter twice. It was difficult for him to support Catholic Emancipation when his colleagues were, as Protestant clergy of the Church of England, encouraging their congregations against it. He was Irish and thought that some of them suspected him of being a closet Catholic. But he knew he was right: the misery of a torn society had disrupted his life in Ireland, and although he had few regrets he was adamant in his belief that civil rights were due to a man whatever his religion. Or even a woman. His pen came to a raised halt as he recalled the conversation of the night before. Surely he was not the first man to be consumed with worry about the fate of his daughters after his death? And there was Charlotte right at the centre of it: how could a woman support herself without marriage if she was banned from education beyond school? Marriage was the only safety, and that brought its own dangers – and he shivered – of regular childbirth and abusive husbands, who could render even a rich woman helpless.

He finished his letter to the *Leeds Intelligencer* and added the first draft to a brown folder still labelled in Maria's handwriting 'Letters to the newspapers'. The last one had been about the abolition of capital punishment for anything except murder. Little chance there. It amazed him that in a Christian society the penalty for stealing a sheep was the same as for killing a man. He often tried to draw William and John and Theodore Dury on this matter, but

189

found them puzzlingly unconcerned. The plain statements of the Gospels about forgiveness and the poor were not to be applied here. In the case of Catholic Emancipation, William was totally opposed. But it mattered little to their friendship.

'Are we going now?' Branwell put his head round the door, coat and muffler on, strongest boots. 'I can't wait to see his paintings.'

'Yes,' said Pat rising, folding the letter and pressing hard on the wax, 'we'll start now. 'Is Charlotte ready?'

'I am!' She was standing behind Branwell, also suitably muffled against the cold. 'Papa, I'm so excited. To go to a real artist's studio!' She almost squealed with delight despite her twelve years.

The rain had started again, but the children bounced along beside him as if it were the finest, sunniest day. By the time they reached Keighley an hour later Pat had to slow his immense stride to keep with Branwell and Charlotte, although their breathlessness was the result of their tongues' exercise as much as their legs'. When they arrived at Bradley's studio the skies had cleared, and after mounting a dark, fragile staircase, which creaked ominously and made the overexcited children shiver with anticipation, they emerged into a spacious room, filled with clear north light and looking towards the moors beyond the rooftops of Keighley.

'Good morning,' said Pat. 'We've come as arranged.' Bradley was almost equal in height to Pat, with unruly dark hair restrained by a black ribbon. He had reached for his coat and was putting it on in anticipation of doing business. 'This is Branwell, and this is Charlotte.'

'I am very pleased make your acquaintance,' said Bradley gravely. 'Would you like to look at some of my work?' he asked the children. 'I'll remove the covers.'

Branwell's face was white, tense with excitement. Pat, looking at him, thought he might have one of his excited outbursts. He refused to call them fits as the doctor did. He put his hands gently on the boy's shoulders and propelled him towards the canvases which were emerging from beneath the sheets – portraits, land-scapes, architectural drawings. Branwell walked slowly forward, as if in a trance, peering closely, touching the roughness of the oils, inspecting minutely the pencil strokes of the drawings.

He turned to his father. 'This is what I want to to do for the rest of my life.' He breathed deeply, drawing in the smell of paint, canvas, cleaning materials, everything which made the studio an

190

artist's domain. 'I know it's what I want to do,' he repeated vehemently.

Pat laughed. 'I think I know how he feels. When I was his age I wanted to be a poet. I used to write poetry and read it to the trees.' He laughed. 'You see what I do now!'

Bradley turned to him. He had heard about this man many times before he had met him at the planning meeting for the Keighley Mechanics' Institute. 'You're a published author yourself,' he said, 'and not just sermons like your colleagues.'

'That's true,' replied Pat, 'but a parish like mine leaves little time for writing. I have no curate.' He didn't mention the children and the demands their education made on his time. Never should they feel it was anything but a delight to teach them. 'I scribble a little,' he added, thinking of the story of the orphan at Cowan Bridge, which had given him such release from his grief and anger.

'We all scribble,' put in Branwell, 'we've all got scribblemania!' Charlotte darted him a look from where she was standing with her nose close to a beautifully illustrated book of birds. It said, 'Don't tell him, Branwell. If it stops being secret it breaks the spell.' Pat saw the exchange between them and smiled to himself.

'So you'd come to the house, then, and teach them all together?' he asked Bradley.

'Certainly, sir. I could come once a week if the weather allows it. I would charge an hourly rate for the four of them.'

Pat was relieved. Individual lessons were expensive. Painting lessons, he had heard, could be two guineas an hour, which was a huge amount from his annual income of one hundred and eighty pounds. Eventually it might come to this, but Bradley was cheaper and for that he was thankful. With the Keighley organist, Abraham Sutherland, visiting for the piano, he was stretching himself. But they needed the opportunities he had lacked himself and were ravenous for instruction of any sort.

'I'll come on Wednesday,' Bradley was saying. 'Why don't you take the Bewick's *Birds* home with you and both of you try a copy from it, than I shall know where we're starting from.' Charlotte hugged the book to her and thanked him. As they stepped out of the studio and made for the moor, Pat was almost as excited at the prospect before them as the two children.

෨෨

The soldiers caught his eye before he saw the doll he had been seeking for Anne. Twelve of them, brightly painted, blue and red, muskets at ease; in his head he could hear the tramp of their feet, and he was back in Cambridge, forming the perfect square. Branwell badly needed replacements for his depleted infantry if he was to deploy his troops effectively. Pale and paintless, splintered and unsteady, his overworked troops would have little chance in the teeth of an attack. With these beauties, victories would be assured. He had his hand on the door of the shop before he broke into a smile at his own make-believe.

The clerical conference had gone on for three days, and he had stayed away from home for two nights, enjoying the company of his fellow clerics, but wary of finding himself near Carus Wilson. He had vowed never to be in the same room as him, to avoid hitting him. There were men at the conference whose company Pat genuinely enjoyed, and, although he was often puzzled at the ordinariness of his friends' minds, the change did him good. Nagged by anxiety at leaving the children with Bess and Tabitha, he wanted to make his thanks tangible, and so had set off around the shops of Leeds to make his purchases.

When the coach dropped him at Keighley there was about an hour's light left, so he decided to walk home despite his packages and bag. He found it hard-going with his burdens, but forgot his discomfort watching the pale moon and weak stars turn bright against the deepening darkness. Taking the key from its hiding-place he went straight to his study and removed the soldiers from their box. He crouched on the floor with the overexcited dogs, ranging the soldiers in sixes opposite each other. Would Branwell mix the old and the new? Would he make them opposing forces? Which would be the Great Duke? He changed their positions, squared them off, pushed them into different formations. Paddy, always an instinctive retriever, furtively removed one before Pat had noticed and was surveying it with interest between his paws, preparing for an experimental chew. Gently removing it, Pat wiped it on his handkerchief and replaced them in the box, then scrambled to his feet. He put Tabitha's silk purse in its tissue on the kitchen table, mounted the stairs softly and placed a small packet at Bess's door, opened the girls' door and left the two dolls and the ninepins on their coverlet and finally entered Branwell's bedroom, taking the greatest care not to wake this notorious insomniac. He pushed the box beneath the bed with the end sticking out. Then he returned to his own room and thankfully undressed and got into bed.

His sleep was short. There was a tremendous chatter in the girls' room next to him. Branwell had taken the soldiers in and they were all talking at the tops of their voices.

'Mine!' shouted Charlotte. 'This is the Duke of Wellington!'

'Mine!' Emily, even louder. 'I shall call him Gravey!'

'Look!' Anne's soft voice. 'Mine is Waiting Boy!'

'Oh, all right,' he heard Branwell say, 'you can name them. Mine is Bonaparte, and he will fight your Great Duke. But remember that they are mine. Papa brought you other things.'

There was a silence and rustling as they scrabbled at the dolls and the ninepins. The door burst open, and the bed was suddenly full of children.

'Papa!' 'Thank you!' 'You're back!' 'We've missed you so!' Kisses and hugs rained upon him as he struggled to pull himself up out of the line of fire.

'Oh Papa,' sighed Charlotte softly, 'thank you for our presents, but those soldiers are so magnificent and Branwell will share them. I shall write a story about the Duke of Wellington.' And she was gone to her room, burrowing in the box where they kept their paper. When he emerged dressed and shaved, pistol and watch safely stowed, she was still lying on her stomach on her bed in her shift, scratching in pencil in her tiny, short-sighted writing. She didn't hear him when he spoke to her. *That*, he thought, *is how it should be. Completely absorbed. Nothing else exists for her at this moment.*

⚬⚬⚬

Pat's cough tore at his chest, and he spat phlegm into the heather, abandoning manners in solitude. There were bright spots on his cheeks, and his head seemed to open and shut with every step. Descending into Keighley he slowed his pace after consulting his watch: he had scarcely the stamina to hurry, and he was well ahead of his appointed time by keeping to his habitual canter. *I'm too old for this*, he thought. *Most men of my age either ride or take a gig, or have their own carriage.* But he had decided long ago that a carriage was out of the question; even a horse would require food and a groom's wages. The money was better spent on tutors and books and saving for the future. He hired a horse occasionally and used the local carter if really necesssary. He enjoyed his walking and covered miles with the greatest ease; but today, with his cough, his headache and a fever, he felt old. Paddy was ahead of him, flying over the heather, chasing rabbits and disappearing into holes. When they arrived at the meeting-place he tucked him, as he did all his accompanying dogs, beneath his chair.

He sat for a moment to regain his breath, amazed at the sound of his own breathing. William came and stood by him.

'How are you, old man?' enquired Pat gently. He had not seem him since Jane's funeral at her father's church in Cross-stone. He had lost his colour and a lot of weight. He sat down heavily in the chair beside Pat.

'So, so,' he replied listlessly. 'You told me it would take a long time before I felt any better. I believe you. Jane and I' – he paused, wringing his hands – 'we were not as you and Maria were. Having no children was difficult for us. She so longed for them.' Tears came into his eyes; reaching into his pocket he drew out a handkerchief and blew his nose. 'But I miss her so dreadfully.' Pat felt his own tears rising. 'I wish so much we had had children, so that I could see her in them. You are so lucky, Patrick.'

'I know. Every day I see something of Maria in all of them. Her eyes, her hands, a look, her voice, a movement – I see it all the time; it reminds me of my loss but it strengthens my resolve to do everything we had planned for them.'

William rose so that he could reach deep into the pocket of his coat. 'I've brought you her Greek Prayer Book as a memorial,' he said. 'Look, I've inscribed it inside. You always appreciated her scholarship, and she admired you greatly; I think she sometimes wished she had married you, not me,' he smiled ruefully.

Pat took the book and gazed at the inscription. 'This is a great honour. You could not have done anything kinder.' He took William's hand in both of his and clasped it for a moment. 'Oh my dear friend,' he whispered softly, 'what a lot we are asked to bear!'

'You may be asked to bear a little more,' said William, glancing over Patrick's shoulder. 'Carus Wilson has just arrived.'

'Then I cannot remain.' His head was thumping, and he felt hot. He stood up and faced the back of the hall. There he was, as black and smooth as Charlotte frequently recalled, portly, well-

194

tailored, superior. He said goodbye to William and walked to the door where Theodore Dury was greeting new arrivals.

'I'm sorry, Dury,' he said quite loudly, 'Please give my apologies to Mr Wilberforce when he arrives. I would not have missed him if I could possibly help it, as I have very good reason to be grateful to him, as well as admiring his cause. But I cannot remain in the presence of one to whom I have vowed never to speak again. You know enough of my circumstances to understand.' He bowed slightly, clicked his fingers at his dog and left without looking at Carus Wilson.

Out on the moor the wind had whipped up, and he pushed himself into it, battered by the rain which followed in a summer storm of such ferocity that he felt his body would break with the effort of keeping upright. He kept Paddy close to him, lacking the strength to deal with any emergencies in rabbit holes; sometimes he had to sit on the wet ground and cough until the blood flecked his lips. It was dark now, and he missed the most direct way because the pain in his head blurred his vision. Once, when he had fallen and was struggling to get up with Paddy tugging at his coat, he wondered if his time had come; in his feverish state he saw visions of the children pursued by Carus Wilson as they fled down the lane by the parsonage, which had collapsed into a ruin. He pulled himself up, fastened the dog to his arm with the thin cord he kept in his pocket for the purpose, and made a determined effort to keep steady in the wind. The dog understood the need for restraint and kept close to him every time his coughing forced him to stop. They made a sad sight, sick man and anxious dog, struggling up to the parsonage door. There was a single candle burning at the bottom of the stairs; too tired to light his own he took it from the stand, plunging the hall into darkness, his shaking hand a wobbling shadow on the wall. Twice he leaned on the banisters to steady his breathing. *Oh God,* he groaned inwardly, *I am really ill.* His lungs, full of phlegm and water, did not respond to his efforts. *I cannot die. What will happen if I die?*

❦

The early sun falling on his face woke him; unable to close the shutters he had fallen on his bed in his shirt and drawers. The sheets were wet with his sweat. The rasping in his chest reminded

195

him of Elizabeth's desperate gasping. *Please not me. Not yet. Not until they are older. However faithless I have been, however doubting, I will trust and love You more.* He pulled himself up; the floor hit the ceiling, and he fell with a crash.

He opened his eyes to Bess and the doctor. The hammer and pleximeter were still in Dr Andrew's hands; he could see the pewter box for the leeches. *Just leave me alone.* Bess took up a spout cup and offered it to him. *No!*

'Keep him in bed, Miss Branwell. Tie him down until he learns to take a gig. He thinks he's immortal.' *I do not.* 'You'd better get someone to take the services. He won't be able to get out of bed for some time.' Pat heaved himself on to his elbows at this challenge, then fell back just as quickly. 'Use the blisters; they can't do any harm. For goodness sake, Mr Brontë,' he said good-humouredly, 'try a little weakness like the rest of us.' He snapped the instruments back into their case. He turned to Bess. 'I'll be back every day until he's out of danger.'

She paused before she opened the front door. 'I think he's exhausted,' she whispered. 'He has had to bear more in the last few years than many men bear in a lifetime. But his health is essential.'

'He must pull through,' replied the doctor. He corrected himself. 'He will pull through. For the sake of the children.'

'For the sake of the children,' repeated Bess fearfully. Tears came into her eyes. 'They have no one else but me!'

'Then they are lucky', he said, putting his arm round her shoulder. 'They are very lucky, but he will pull through. He's a strong man. He *is* exhausted. This will make him rest.' He squeezed her shoulder, almost wishing to comfort this good woman with a kiss. What a burden she bore, with what uncomplaining dignity. Instead he settled his hat, bowed to her and walked away.

๏

Pat was feeling better. Sitting up in bed he welcomed the sounds of the house around him and listened with special pleasure to the children's conversations in the room next door. They amazed him with their incessant writing activity, their dialogues and planning. *If only I had their imagination: they see no limitations, they soar into their imaginary worlds, whereas I am grounded too solidly on this earth.* He thought about his novel, untouched for weeks through disappoint-

196

ment and the frantic activity of the parish which drained creation from him.

Anne's head appeared round the door. 'Mr Plummer is here, Papa,' she said softly, 'May he come in?'

'Of course.' Plummer's kindly face appeared above Anne's. 'Come in, dear sir, if you can bear the company of a boring invalid. How can I ever thank you for all you are doing for me!'

The Reverend Thomas Plummer sat on the chair at the side of Pat's bed. He thought he was looking better. The cough, still constant, was drier, and although he was still flushed, the bright red spots had disappeared from his razor-sharp cheekbones.

'You are a good man, Plummer,' Pat continued, 'to keep the trustees happy and the parish nurtured, with all your other commitments.'

'I've enjoyed it. The school practically looks after itself now. I've enjoyed the change of parish work.' His eyes twinkled. 'You practically run a school yourself here! As well as the parish.'

'Indeed,' murmured Pat. 'They've missed a lot of teaching while I've been ill, but they are always busy, always busy.'

'Have you never thought of sending Branwell to me at the Free Grammar School?' asked Plummer.

Pat fixed his short-sighted blue eyes on the church tower, now pitted with his pistol shots. He often missed these days. 'I have, I have but – Anne, it is time for your tea now, I am sure,' he said gently to the little girl who had stayed curled up on his bed. She quickly left. 'I have, but he is a difficult boy to teach.' He stopped, his long fingers plucking at the sheets. 'You remember your *Hamlet*, Plummer? That's Branwell, even though he's still a child. So much talent, such ease of learning, he absorbs Greek like a sponge, and yet he has a . . . a fragility, almost a flaw which . . . which . . .'

'Which?' encouraged Plummer.

'Which makes him unsuitable for school,' sighed Pat. 'He sometimes becomes . . . overwrought. He can be so desperately unhappy if things are not right for him. He becomes enraged, and then it is all over, and he is a loving son, and brother, a brilliant talker, author, musician, painter – there seems to be nothing he cannot do.'

'Do you not think the company of other boys would help?' queried Plummer gently.

Pat sighed again. 'No, I fear not. When he has these . . . fits . . .

197

he needs comfort, and we give it to him here. Age will strengthen him, and then he can go to the university. I' – he added, in a sudden rush of confidence – 'did not have much formal schooling myself. But by the efforts of educated men I reached Cambridge. Branwell will be the same. He has more opportunities than I did.' Embarrassed by his unfamiliar confession, he leaned forward and patted Plummer's hand. 'But thank you for your concern. I greatly appreciate it.'

When he heard the front door close behind the headmaster, Pat lay back, eyes closed and thought about what he had said. *Fragile*, he had said. That was it. Like a brilliant glass, catching the light. Let go of the support and he would shatter. He needed his father to guide him to maturity, stability. Then he would shine with his full brilliance.

He opened his eyes when someone banged on the front door. Footsteps in the hall. Tabby's Yorkshire voice enquiring the business. An elderly man's voice, high and wavering.

'Does the parson live here?'

'Yes.'

'I wish to see him.'

'He is poorly in bed.'

'Indeed. I have a message for him.'

'Who from?'

'From the Lord.'

'Who?'

'The Lord; he desires me to say that the Bridegroom is coming and he must prepare to meet him . . .'

The door slams. Tabby tuts. Charlotte – is it Charlotte? – sobs.

'Just a mad old man,' mutters Tabby. Steps towards the kitchen. The door bangs shut. Patrick knows he is going to die.

22

Taby said just now come Anne pillopatate i e pill a potato
Aunt has come into the Kitchen just now and said where are
your feet Anne Anne answered on the floor Aunt papa opened
the parlour Door and gave Branwell a Letter saying here
Branwell read this and show it to your Aunt and Charlotte –
The Gondals are discovering the interior of Gaaldine Sally
Mosley is washing in the back Kitchin

> Emily and Anne Brontë, 24 November 1834, *Diary Paper.*

'Branwell!' Charlotte shot across the Roe Head drawing room and
hugged her brother. His normally pale face was red from the
exertion of the twenty miles he had walked across the moor from
Haworth, and his red hair unattractively plastered against his head
with sweat. What would Miss Wooler think? Charlotte enveloped
him until he pleaded to be released from the heat of her embrace.
He collapsed into a chair by the bow window and looked out at
the garden.

'It's a lovely place, Charlotte,' he said, admiring the sweep of the
lawns and the trees in full leaf. 'You must be really happy here,' he
added, somewhat wistfully. 'How I would love to go away from
home to learn!'

'You will, Bany, you will!' Charlotte's reassurance was swift.
'You'll go to Cambridge like Papa and do all things we girls never
can. It will come soon.'

Branwell hesitated. 'I'm not so sure that I want to.' Charlotte's
eyes grew huge in disbelief. 'Not Cambridge, anyway. I'm bored
with Classics, although I love the literature. They don't really teach
much else at the university. They certainly don't teach painting, or
writing, or music.'

'How could they teach writing?' Charlotte laughed and sat down on the floor by his chair. 'No one could teach that. We just do it. We just know how to. But tell me how everyone is.'

Before he could answer a young maid entered with a tray of cold drinks and food. 'Mistress says, Miss Brontë, that Mr Brontë is to refresh 'imself and then she'll be in to see you both.' She smiled shyly at Branwell, whose ready response made her blush. She bobbed a curtsey and quickly made her exit. Charlotte took note.

'You're a terrible flirt,' she said, severely. 'One day it will get you into such trouble. There's not a girl who smiles at you whom you don't raise hopes in. Anyway, tell me about home.' As she said the word her eyes became moist; however happy she was anywhere, she keenly missed Haworth parsonage and its inhabitants.

'Well,' began Branwell, tucking into his bread and meat, 'your sisters are as difficult as ever, worrying the life out of me that their writing is going to be better than ours, although their dreary stories are rooted in Haworth moor and quite deadly compared with ours. Charlotte' – he said biting a chicken leg ravenously – 'it's damn' ('Don't,' said Charlotte, 'you know you shouldn't swear, particularly not here') 'difficult with you being here. Our stories are just not getting done. I write all day, I've done hundreds and hundreds of pages. Papa even mildly reproved me for not getting down to my Greek.'

'It would be mild,' murmured Charlotte.

'But I'm painting too – I'm probably to have lessons from Mr Robinson, you know the painter we saw at the Arts Society exhibition in Leeds.'

'Goodness me,' said Charlotte, 'is Papa really thinking of paying two guineas an hour just to have you taught? I doubt that's much of an investment.'

Branwell put down his tray and tweaked a strategic pin in her carefully coiled hair, which began to slip its anchor. She jumped up with a squeal and was halfway across the room when Miss Wooler entered.

Charlotte stopped stock-still. The headmistress smiled at them both. Branwell stood to attention.

'Charlotte, what a pleasure to meet your brother.' She held out her hand – small, white and prettily plump – then motioned both of them to sit. 'What a journey you have had – we are at least twenty miles from Haworth. But then your father is famous as one of the greatest walkers in the county. Are you going back today, or would you like to stay with us?'

It occurred to Branwell that it might be pleasant to stay in this charming place among a dozen girls and Miss Wooler's sisters, but Charlotte's eyebrows shot up, her mouth pursed and her head shook. Clearly he was not expected to accept.

'You are very kind, Miss Wooler. Unfortunately I have to return, as tomorrow I have a painting lesson booked with Mr Bradley of Keighley. Otherwise it would have been delightful.'

Miss Wooler nodded. That was the response she expected and preferred. She didn't really want a lively young man staying overnight and stirring up her girls' imaginations. Charlotte did enough of that with her ghost stories in the dormitory. 'Your father is tireless in his efforts for the education of you and your sisters, is he not?' She paused, smiling. She was small, dressed completely in white. *Quite pretty in a way*, Branwell thought. *I wonder what the old man made of her when he came to visit? She's known to be quite clever, and he'd like that.*

'Charlotte, stay with your brother as long as you like; I'm so pleased you've had this unexpected visit.' She rose to go, offering Branwell her hand again. 'Do come again, Mr Brontë, whenever you've gathered sufficient strength again for the journey.' She swished out in a flurry of white lace.

'Quite a lady,' murmured Branwell after the door was shut.

'Yes, she is.' Charlotte was firm in this opinion. 'She really cares for us. I dreaded coming here after Cowan Bridge.' Her voice shook. 'I really dreaded it, even though I knew Papa had been to inspect it and meet Miss Wooler, and had chosen it because it was near so many of his friends.'

'So that they can check up on you?'

'In a way. I hate them asking me out to tea, and having to chat about nothing at all, but at least there's someone I can talk to if there were anything wrong. Not that there is.' She turned round from the window and took his hand. 'But seriously now – how is everything at home?'

'Oh much as usual: Emily and Anne writing all the time, interspersed with bursts of piano practice. Emily's getting really good.' His forehead puckered. 'She's better than I am. It's somehow her instrument. All those deep feelings she has' – and he

201

swept his arm across his brow – 'whereas the organ suits me better, as I can be brilliant and technical. Papa is raising money for one in the church. He's really deeply, deeply musical for a man who can't play a note. We went to the Keighley Philharmonic last week, and he hum-ti-tummed all the way home, and for at least two days after. I, of course, wanted to be a conductor . . .'

'The very great Wiggins, proficient in all areas of music and the arts,' murmured Charlotte sarcastically. 'You have to choose, you can't do everything.'

'Why not? Some days I feel I can do anything; but some days are darker,' he added quietly.

'But what of Papa? How is he?'

'He's well, but somehow . . .' – he paused, taking Charlotte's hand. 'He changed, didn't he, after his illness? Well he's never quite got back to his normal self. He seems worried, distracted . . .'

'You know why he's worried,' cut in Charlotte sharply. 'But you forget, Bany, too often. I remember particularly because of that old man at the door. It's not just that we might lose Papa, as we lost Mama, Maria and Elizabeth. That's too dreadful, but if we lost Papa we'd lose our home and each other.'

Branwell appeared chastened, then surprised. 'Aunt would take care of us. She'd never let us be without a home.'

'Aunt has fifty pounds a year, which she hardly spends because she saves it for us. She lost her home in Penzance by staying to look after us. She has no house. Fifty pounds would do nothing for four of us. And Aunt is older than Papa, and a Branwell. They don't live as long.'

'I didn't walk twenty miles to be reminded of my grim prospects, Char. Take me to meet your delectable friends and raise a fellow's spirits a little.' He took her arm and went out onto the sunny lawn where the girls were gathered reading.

༻࿓༺

Patrick and William Morgan were standing on the site of the old barn in Church Lane. The carter had just finished lugging away the materials which couldn't be used again, leaving piles of stone, wood and mortar for the builders who would come after him.

'It's good, Pat, good,' William said, looking at the site and leaning on his stick. He had aged since Jane's death, becoming thinner and more stooped. 'When do they start to build the school?'

'You know what it's like trying to tie a builder down as well as I do,' smiled Patrick. 'They'll probably start and then disappear to finish a barn which is needed more urgently for the harvest. Education would not be a priority over the protection of hay and straw.'

They walked back towards the parsonage, stopping to look at the church tower where the clock was being mended. 'Still aiming straight, Pat?'

Pat laughed. 'No,' he said. 'I can hardly see the marks I make. It's just a blast every morning to get rid of the powder. I don't expect I could hit a Luddite if one jumped through the window. Although it's the Reform Bill which is leading to rioting now, is it not?' His voice was anxious. William would not think with him on this, as on so much else.

'You and politics, Pat – whenever will you leave your rebellious Irish ways behind? Even the children are immersed in the life of the Commons and the Lords!'

'And so they should be.' Pat was firm on this. 'Every man and woman – and, yes, I mean woman,' he added mischievously, 'should be aware of how the country is governed. My girls are every bit as intelligent as Branwell, and they often take opposing views from mine. The debate gets warm, if not hot.' He smiled at his recollections. They had reached the steps of the parsonage and were about to enter.

'You are so lucky,' sighed William, turning his back to the church and looking at the house. 'Every time you come home to this house you come into a house full of talk and laughter, to kisses and hugs. I go into emptiness and quiet. I find I talk to the housekeeper because I have no one else to speak to. I talk to my parishioners too much because I have no one at home; I see them exchanging glances when I've stayed too long.'

'Then you should think about marrying again,' said Pat gently. 'It was not for me, but it could be the right way for you. When Jane's mother died, John Fennell was soon remarried at sixty-nine, and now has a little boy and another on the way. That *was* a surprise.'

They stood still, marvelling at the miracle of the old man's fecundity with his new young wife. William had often felt it betrayed his mother-in-law's memory, was not quite seemly, but he could understand the loneliness.

Sitting in the parlour after they had joined the family for dinner, they discussed the school building and the organisation after it was built. It would provide education on Sundays for the children who worked in the mills, and during the day for some, now that there was to be a forced reduction in working hours for all children in factories. Bess joined them with her sewing.

'You've heard how well Charlotte is getting on at Roe Head,' she said proudly to William. 'She is at the top of the class. Patrick could hardly bear to let her go to school again, but he saw reason in the end.' Pat pulled a long face over her head at William. 'After he was so ill it made sense that one of the girls should be educated again and teach the others, then if the worst were to happen' – and she looked severely at them both over her spectacles – 'they could all get posts in good families as governesses.' She snipped her thread and rummaged for more. Turning to William, she continued, 'When Pat was so very ill, I had to take stock. Much as we would both like the girls to marry and be safe for the rest of their lives, reality is not often so kind. Many of us have to do without the protection of a man, and the world can seem a dangerous place. With Charlotte's education the whole family is safer. Pat sees that now.'

'I'm sure you're right, Miss Branwell,' said William. 'Death alters our lives overnight; when I think of my own dear Jane and her mother . . .'

Patrick jumped up. 'Let's not be lugubrious,' he said sharply. 'I think I know as much about death as the next man. We've done the sensible thing with Charlotte, and she has achieved brilliantly. Branwell will be outstanding at something and will be able to look after his sisters when we're gone.'

Bess folded her work. 'Yes. Branwell is the great hope of this family. The bond between him and the girls will never be broken, and he will always care for them. Now, Patrick, are you going to do your accounts or your sermon now, or do you want me to read to you?'

'Reading would be nice. My eyes are tired after the work on the school plans.' Picking up William's hat and stick, he accompanied him to the door.

'You're as good as married,' said William, laughing softly.

'She's a good and loving woman,' said Pat joining in his laughter. 'But not a wife.'

⟡

'Tell that one again, Tabby,' said Emily, settling her feet on the chair on the opposite side of the table, and folding her arms in anticipation of a good, long session. 'Not the fairies, but the one about the family up on the moor by Withens. I want to check the details against Papa's version.'

'You'll do no sich thing,' grumbled Tabby, taking up her knitting and making for the chair by the fire, deftly removing the cat with the end of her knitting pins. 'Ah know what Ah know, and if the Reverend knows different, that's his business.'

'But did he really bring a child back that nobody had seen before?' persisted Emily.

'Ah niver said no sich thing!' Tabby was adamant. 'You're muddling it oop with some tale of your faither's.' She snapped her needles sharply so that the firelight flashed reflected round the kitchen.

'She's right, Em,' said Anne from the other side of the table. She pushed her feet against Emily's and braced herself. They often did foot wrestling beneath the table, occasionally falling off the chairs if the contest were particularly long. 'It was Papa who told us about the foundling. It was our grandfather, when he was brought by Welsh Brunty from the south of Ireland to County Down.'

'Yes.' Emily's voice was slow. She unfolded her arms to encompass Paddy, who was standing on his hindlegs and digging his nose against her elbows and settling his front paws on her lap. She lifted one brown floppy ear and whispered into it, 'And when the child grew up he pushed all the others out of the nest like a cuckoo . . .'

'What did tha say?' asked Tabby deafly. 'That dog's got muck on its feet, and it'll be all over thy clean apron. The fairish will get him if ever Ah have my way.'

'You and Aunt Branwell, you're a reet pair,' muttered Emily from beneath the table, settling the little spaniel comfortably on the floor, near to the blanket she had always provided for Grasper since he was a puppy. 'No dogs upstairs, no cats, no birds – whatever happened to all God's creatures?'

'In their place, which is outside,' rejoined Bess, entering the

205

kitchen with a pile of lace to be washed. 'Their place is outside. I have never understood your father's liking for animals in the house.'

'Must be because he's Irish,' responded Emily swiftly. 'They say the Irish keep their pigs in their houses . . .'

'That's very rude Emily, very rude . . .'

'It's not meant to be, Aunt. It seems sensible to me that we should all live together. We eat the poor things. To give them a comfortable life before seems to me a good way of saying thank you.'

'Where are your feet, Anne?' asked Bess, wishing to change the subject and discourage foot wrestling at the same time.

'On the floor, Aunt,' replied Anne, sliding them off Emily's chair rung.

'Good girl,' said Bess with relief. One could always rely on Anne to be doing the right thing. She went into the back kitchen to give Sally Mosley her lace collars.

'Quick, Anne,' whispered Emily, 'the piano.' Tabitha was left in the empty kitchen.

∽

Patrick had budgeted for two volumes which were not strictly to do with his offsprings' education: George Moore's *Life of Lord Byron* and Thomas Graham's *Modern Domestic Medicine*. The first he had handed straight over to the 'children', fervently believing that, despite the efforts of the more lurid pamphleteers and periodical writers, the man who had treated him so graciously at Cambridge, who loved animals with a passion similar to his own, and, most importantly, whose verses had a fluency and wit his observation told him the whole family would do well to emulate, could do little to corrupt the young. The latter volume he kept for himself.

His greatest problem was that he lacked a confidant. He had seen the anxiety his illness had produced in Bess, and he had readily agreed to her plans to reduce the children's vulnerability. He was now unable to admit to anyone the countless small ailments his flesh was heir to, and not only his flesh but his spirit and mind also. He had furtively looked up 'Hypochondria' in *Graham* following a bout of depression so severe he had feared his ability to continue as a priest. He thrust the book out of sight when Emily had come in to play the piano; *that* soothed him more than anything he now knew, but when she had gone he had continued with his reading, turning the pages almost fearfully lest he should discover some incurable or chronic condition. And if he did? Would he be able to summon medical help without alarming the family? The sound of Charlotte's sobs when the poor old man had come to the door at the worst possible time was still in his head.

Daily he faced the groaning of his interior organs – nothing new, but now instead of only responding to unhappiness or anxiety, his stomach and bowels were in a constant painful tangle. He had tried eating more, and less, and purging himself, then stopping up his bowels with arrowroot. His nights were seldom unbroken, sometimes he heard the church clock strike every hour, and often he rose and walked about the house, looking in on their crowded rooms. Anne was still with Bess, Emily and Charlotte in the children's study, Branwell with his father now that the other room had been made into a painting studio. He had wanted to sleep there as well, wishing to emulate artists who threw themselves down on a mattress in the corner at the end of a long day's painting, but Patrick secretly wished to know that he was in at night. Occasionally he would go into the parlour and walk around the table as the girls did in the evening, discussing their writing; he would open the shutters on clear moonlit nights and take the sheets of paper they had left on their writing desks, reading them with pleasure, pride and a little apprehension. Were they not too old still to be writing in these fantastic terms? But what pace it all had, what fluency. What a contrast to his own works.

His nocturnal perambulations made him tired by day, and he would doze in the afternoons before Bess came to help by reading to him correspondence, which would otherwise have strained his eyes. The truth was that he was exhausted – by the parish, the anxiety of the children's future, the ceaseless political problems which he could not leave alone. Education, reform, the plight of the poor – whatever the burden of the parish and family, his inner compulsion was to fight the issues of the day. He organised meetings, chaired them, checked their minutes, talked endlessly to people in Haworth about the poor, the bad water, the abuse of children in the mills, the high death rate among his flock which distressed him daily and provided him with painful reminders as he conducted funerals standing by the vault which contained his wife and daughters. Once when a man had blown his brains out and his family had pleaded with Pat for Christian burial, he had a fleeting feeling that it would be good to do the same. But fleeting only: his life was his family's security.

So he read and reread Dr Graham; Anne's asthma, Branwell's excitability, Charlotte's teeth, Bess's increasingly troublesome bowels; he made notes in the margins and tried to remember the successes and failures. Medicine seemed an inexact science, and although he willingly spent money on doctors, the disappointments he had endured in the past had taught him that self-help produced a cure just as often. Only Emily was immune to physical illness. She wound his silk stock for him, skilfully twisting it into an elegant shape, letting it grow larger every winter to protect his chest from the cold, and allowing him to drop his mouth into it when he visited the more noisome, fever-filled cottages where his dedication frequently took him.

Despite his anxiety and his ailments, he still struck out across the moor for many miles and walked with his family at a pace which sometimes left them breathless. He was getting old, that was true, but his stamina had not diminished; his hair was plentiful, though pure white; however did Bess maintain her fringe of auburn curls? His broad mouth stretched in a smile as he thought of the possible answers.

⤳

'That one's a survivor,' said Emily, tickling the tadpole as it scurried under a stone away from the myriad she had stirred up with her swishing hand. 'Now that one really knows how to get away.'

They had all walked to the place they had named The Meeting of the Waters – Emily, Charlotte, Anne, Branwell, assorted dogs and Ellen Nussey, Charlotte's friend from Roe Head. Pat had urged the visit after Charlotte had spent some time at Ellen's home, The Rydings, at Birstall, and although Branwell, who had accompanied her there on the journey had referred to it as 'paradise', Pat was confident that their own well-scrubbed home had intellectual spark and humour enough to make an attractive sojourn for Charlotte's young friend. He had pressed for the visit warmly, to such an extent that Branwell had suggested to Charlotte that perhaps Ellen's brother, Henry, was the real attraction.

'He may see you as a clergyman's bride, Char,' he speculated, knowing exactly the reaction it would produce.

'If ever I marry,' came the vehement reply, 'it will not be to some nimini-pimini curate!'

Emily murmured, 'You mean like Papa when he left Cambridge?'

This, as were so many of Emily's statements, unanswerable, and Charlotte swept from the room to concentrate on the domestic rearrangements needed for Ellen's visit. To be truthful, it had occurred to Patrick that if he had failed to make a fortune from his novels and stories (he had quite a store of beginnings now, but no endings), widening his daughters' social scene was another road to security. It saddened him to think that they might spend their lives with men whose minds were not half as good as their own, or even dull or cruel men, but all his reforming and campaigning would not change the world enough in his lifetime to make them anything but governesses.

And Ellen's visit had cheered the whole household. Pat felt remorse when he saw how Bess sparkled in the company of a young and sophisticated girl, recalling (at length) her own youth, and naughtily offering the amazed Ellen a pinch of snuff from her ancient box. *Would Maria too have dried up in Haworth?* he thought, but dismissed the idea because he knew that Bess's trouble was being the aunt rather than the wife and mother.

'And the spirit of the man was always felt hovering in the house and on the moor for the rest of time,' he concluded decisively, running his napkin over his wide mouth and brushing the crumbs from his waistcoat. Ellen's eyes were bright with fear. The father was as bad as his daughter for creating terror with his stories. Some were from his old parishioners; others seemed from further away, both in time and place. Breakfasts had become prolonged as Pat and Bess vied with each other for their audience. A new one was a challenge not to be missed.

The visit ended with a trip to meet Ellen's relatives at Bolton Abbey on her way back to Birstall. Pat had hired the best gig he could raise, imported from Keighley, and certainly an improvement on the covered cart the family usually travelled in. The carriage which Ellen's relatives swept up in was certainly smarter, but the Brontës' delight was hardly blunted by the comparison. Branwell was exceptionally brilliant that day, so much so that Emily had suspicions he might be fortified with nips of rum. But could it matter: they were out for the day with other young people, who were probably surprised by Ellen's shabby friends but impressed by

209

their wit. Bran was in his element, Charlotte pleased, Anne happy and Emily observant.

෧෨

'Money, Patrick,' said Bess that afternoon, when the house no longer vibrated with the sound of voices and the banging of feet on the bare stairs. Tabby was asleep in the kitchen, tired out by the visit but smug at her success with the charming Miss Nussey. 'Miss Nussey's visit has put me in mind of several things I had previously been considering.'

'And what, pray, are those?' replied Pat warily.

'Do you realise I have been living in this house for nearly fourteen years?'

'I never forget the debt I owe you for your support and the love you give to all of us . . .'

'That's not what I meant at all.' Bess's tone was unsentimental, practical. 'You know that I have, as Maria had, fifty pounds a year. I have contributed to my keep since I came . . .'

'I wish you hadn't,' said Pat. It was always a bone between them.

'Neither is that the point.' Bess was undeviatingly on track. 'My point is that over the years I have accumulated money which lies in the bank gathering interest and doing little else. Money should be a metaphor for what you want to do.' Patrick's eyes flashed bright blue, amazed, from beneath his raised, tufty brows. 'I have thought hard, and there are two things we – this family – needs.'

'And they are, my dear?'

'Education and a curate.' She raised her hand to stop his interruption. 'Education for the protection of our children in the future, and a curate for you to stop this endless overwork and strain. I can't stop you working beyond your capacity, Pat, because to do everything right is in your nature' – there was a catch in her voice – 'but I could make life easier for you. Employ a curate. I will help to pay him.'

Pat was silent, overwhelmed by the offer and suddenly battling with tears. He quickly turned to the window and fixed, as much as he could, his eyes on the graveyard. She had touched him on the raw with her empathy, and his frailty was evident in his response. He took a deep breath. Turning back, he began:

'My dear, I can't possibly let you do that. But you are right that I need help. Perhaps God has prompted you to speak to me' (he knew she always preferred this line when decisions were made) 'when I couldn't admit my weakness myself. I will write to the Church Pastoral Aid Society and see if they will finance a curate. Goodness knows there is enough work as the parish grows bigger.' He sat down next to her. 'And what of your other plans?'

'Branwell – as he is unable to enter the church because of his lack of belief,' she sighed deeply, genuinely distressed for Branwell as much as for his prospects, 'if he therefore cannot go to the university, he should have some other training. He says that he needs to go to the Royal Academy if he is to be a portrait-painter. I could pay for that.'

'Do you think that is right, my dear?' said Pat slowly. 'I find this difficult to say to anyone. I trust I have your complete confidence?' She nodded. 'Branwell and Charlotte both paint and draw. So does Emily, but we are talking about human likeness here. They have both had lessons. I find Charlotte's work . . .' – his pause signified his difficulty – 'I find Charlotte's work – *better*. I know little of the visual arts, but her portraits of Anne are so like. You and I know the resemblance Anne has to Maria; my heart turned over when I saw the drawings. When she coloured them in I cut a lock of Anne's hair because not only is it beautiful on Anne but it was just the colour of Maria's.' He crossed the room to his desk and opened a drawer, taking out a lock of hair tied with a ribbon. Stroking it gently, he continued, 'The point is – is Branwell good enough for the academy? I know he has been taught by Robinson, but his painting of the girls seemed to me to lack . . . life.'

'But that is why he needs to go!' Bess was triumphant in her logic, her support for Branwell, as ever, total. 'He will be taught by the best teachers and make a name for himself in London. The boy needs direction, Pat. He is too much with John Brown. He's a good man, but Branwell is spending too much time in the village. The girls do not do that.'

'If Charlotte accepts Miss Wooler's offer of a post as a teacher, and Emily goes with her free, the house will feel like Cowan Bridge all over again.'

'Stop it, Pat,' said Bess firmly, 'you know it is not like that, and they have to go.'

23

Though he is far advanced in years, and has suffered much from ill health [Mr Brontë] ... displayed his pristine energies and faithfulness. That his life and services in this place may be long continued, is the fervent prayer of every churchman, to which every dissenter, who has the cause of religion at heart, will not fail to add his hearty Amen.

Leeds Intelligencer, 1st April 1837

The pain behind her eyes fractured the page as she struggled with the small, inky script. Charlotte had been up since six that morning and, apart from an hour after dinner, she had never been out of the company of her pupils. Could the quality of the girls Miss Wooler recruited have changed so drastically since she and Ellen and Mary Taylor had been pupils there? She had accepted Miss Wooler's offer of the teaching post because her pleasant memories of the school promised both pleasure and duty fulfilled. Papa had never said that any of them should find work, but his determination to leave them able to earn their livings in the thrall of good families when he died had made them all conscious of his financial burdens. They knew his stipend; his frankness about life in general meant that there were few secrets at the parsonage. But these girls, this life – it was intolerable.

She pushed the sheets of paper away and sank her head in her hands, massaging the pain away. Outside in the twilight the wind stirred the willows, wreathing their fronds for the Duke of Zamorna to lurk in. She rubbed her eyes, knowing she must banish the fantasies which were fast becoming a means of survival for her. The door clicked softly, and in the gloom she could see Emily's shadow steal across the room to the window seat.

'Emily?'

'Yes, Charlotte.' No more.

She left the unmarked essays and joined her sister on the seat. Emily was so thin that she seemed to fold to nothing as she hugged her knees, chin down, dead eyes searching among the trees. Her cheekbones were like razors, skin pallid; her eyes would not meet Charlotte's.

'Em, it can't go on – you'll be ill. When you're unhappy you're just like Papa – can't eat and thin as a rake in a week. Why won't you tell me what's wrong?' She felt guilty that she had failed to notice Emily's decline, absorbed totally in her own misery. She had hardly seen her some days, as Em slept with the boarders and Charlotte had her own room. She should have been finding out what was wrong weeks before.

'It's all wrong, Char. I'm wrong, because I should be seizing this opportunity. I hate it, hate it here. Miss Wooler is kind, I know, but I can't bear being crammed in with people I don't know and would never have chosen to know. I even share a bed with a stranger.' She shuddered. 'I can't bear strange feet near to mine, bodies which smell different from ours. And we never go out – just a short walk in the gardens or on the road if we're accompanied. It's torture for me. I know I should try to bear it like you do, but I can't.' Tears were falling on her cheeks, and she brushed them angrily away. 'I just can't.'

Charlotte's heart contracted. Whatever disagreements she had had with Emily in the past, she loved her deeply and knew that Emily's admission of defeat signalled desperation. Her physical frailty, coupled with tears she had hardly ever seen before, stirred Charlotte into action.

'I'll send to Papa,' she whispered, cradling the skinny frame in her arms. 'He wants us to be happy. If he could see you now he would have you home straight away.' She wanted to tell her father that she too was unhappy enough to return to Haworth; but her pride overruled her heart. She settled Emily on some cushions where she could see the trees and the moon rising above them; she pushed aside the despised essays and started a long letter to her father.

◈

When the rancid fish hit Patrick on the side of his face he thought immediately of Cambridge and his gathering of the herrings placed on the staircase by Henry Purefoy Browne. Removing the dead fish deftly from his collar, he kept his eyes unflinchingly on the crowd as he dropped it at his feet and said:

'It is my intention to finish my speech in support of Mr Wortley. In this election you have to choose between the candidates, and nothing you throw or say will stop me putting my point of view forward in the tradition of a democracy. These things should be decided by debate, as they are in the Houses of Parliament, and this country believes in a man's freedom of . . .' Another fish whistled through the crowd; this time it hit Patrick squarely on the mouth and stopped his flow.

Branwell sprang onto the platform, his red hair burnished by the light of the surrounding flares which lightened the darkness of the winter evening. His face was contorted with rage, his small frame rigid as he faced the jeering crowd.

'If you will not let my father speak, you shall not speak your-selves!' he shouted above the din of the jeering crowd. They whooped and hollered even louder, cries of 'Come on, Irish! Let's see what you can do!' growing in volume. Branwell's voice rose to a scream, and Pat, who had wiped his face and was ready to rejoin the debate, was aware that his son was reaching his boiling point. He moved towards him, to cheers from the electors, and laid a hand on his shoulder.

'Come away, Bran,' he said softly. 'We cannot continue this debate in these circumstances. One cannot win them all. Come away now.' Branwell wrenched his arm away and shouted, 'You are not fit to vote! You are Philistines and scum!' Pat overpowered him, determined to remove him from the platform and the increas-ing number of missiles. 'See you in the Black Bull, Irish!' came a voice from the back. Branwell's mouth was foaming, and he was fighting Pat quite hard. Eventually they reached the ground; a shaft of light broke the darkness where the door of the Black Bull had opened. Pat dragged his struggling son inside, and Sugden slammed the door behind them. Sitting in the parlour, Pat thanked the landlord for his sanctuary.

'This hostelry has a good record with the clergy, Mr Sugden,' said Pat, unperturbed and gratefully accepting a glass of whiskey. 'Do you recall helping Mr Redhead to safety when I was first appointed to Haworth? Sip it, Branwell, for goodness sake – it's not a mug of ale. You've helped us tonight.'

214

'Stay as long as you like, Mr Brontë,' replied Sugden, putting more logs on the fire. He liked the parson and knew that he enjoyed a glass or two; he minded his own business and left folk to mind theirs. He saw more of Branwell, as the lad clearly had a taste for drink, and he helped Sugden from time to time by amusing the travellers who found Haworth a dull resting place. Branwell talked well and even better when the grateful visitors rewarded him with a kindly glass.

Pat stretched out his long legs in front of the fire and listened to the crowd heckling the next speaker outside. Despite the stinking collar he was still encased in, he was glad that the people would bother to come out and test the parliamentary candidates. It amused him to recall his anxious flight from Ireland and its politics: there was no flight possible from Yorkshire, where during the last twenty years he had tilted and wrangled with his parishioners, trustees, fellow clergy and Bess. Suddenly a great roar filled the air; Branwell rushed to the window. His wail brought Pat to his side. In the street a small group held aloft a human effigy sprouting carrots for red hair and clutching a potato and herring, and then tossed it into the air as they set it alight. Branwell screwed up his eyes in the light of the flames and beat his forehead with his fist.

'Come away, Bran,' said Pat. 'It's nothing, just fools playing.' He made a mental note to tell Branwell about the herrings on the staircase of St John's. He pushed the boy back into his chair and motioned to Sugden to put up the shutters. As the bar clanged into place, the landlord said, 'That's the end of it, I reckon. Let me fill your glass, and then ye can walk back t' parsonage. Shall I fetch John Brown to go with you?'

'Thank you, but no.' Pat held out his glass, still enjoying the fire and, he had to admit, the company. 'Not for Branwell, Mr Sugden, he is, after all, the secretary of the Haworth Temperance Society, so perhaps a small glass of ale for him.' Pat smiled at Branwell, who sat hunched in his chair, not weeping but near to it, disappointed at his father's decision. Pat cuffed him affectionately on the knee. 'He defended me tonight most bravely, Mr Sugden, and no, we will manage without John Brown. I do not need protection from my own parishioners. I'm sure the trouble was, as usual, from outside the village.'

Later, Patrick strode out into the street, arm in arm with his son, and walked unmolested up the lane to the parsonage. A few late drinkers came out of the White Lion and tipped their caps to him. As ever, they were reduced to silence by their courageous parson.

⌒⌒

As if trouble with Dissenters was not hard enough, Patrick had problems with dissent within his own family. Was Charlotte really a dissenter? Or possibly merely a 'protestant', a protester? He stopped playing with words and thought about his conversation with her.

'Papa, I cannot believe that you actually enjoyed teaching!' Her hands were torturing the edge of her shawl; her wet handkerchief lay in a ball on the floor of his study. He had closed the shutters early so that no callers at the front door should see her distress. 'They are oafs – stupid, stupid oafs and blockheads, and I hate being with them! How could you have liked it?' The storm of tears began again. He patted her knee and let her cry.

'My dear,' he said, 'I loved teaching because I knew I was giving to the children something they could not have possibly had other-wise. If you can bear me to say it, I used to reach the end of a day and feel fortunate to have work which I enjoyed so much and was paid to do.' She sniffed and looked at him from out of her second handkerchief. 'I don't think any of you, not even your dear mother, can understand what it was to have education when I had expected none. It was a privilege I wanted to pass on to others who, like me, did not have it as their birthright. But I can see it is different for all of you.' He got up and put more coal on the fire, waiting for a flame to burst and then adding more. 'You haven't really had the company of duller-brained people. Not everyone is clever, Charlotte. Not even all those who appear to be are.' He smiled at her.

'You mean Uncle William?'

'I didn't, actually,' replied Pat mildly, 'but since you mention your particular – *bête noir* – is that what the French would say? – I will admit that, yes, he is my greatest friend but he is a long way behind me. I accept he is therefore a few miles behind you and your brother and sisters. But Charlotte – it is very easy to teach clever children. The skill is in teaching the less clever.'

'I know, Papa. I really do know, but I find it so hard.' Another storm of weeping.

216

'I wasn't always so tolerant, Char. I have to admit to you that in Drumballyroney I had a scheme whereby I encouraged the parents, who had to pay a penny a week, to send their clever children in the day and the less bright at night. Which was, naturally, only an hour or two. I told myself I was encouraging the best use of their resources. I was really making an easier situation for myself.' He looked sheepish. 'But I did enjoy the rest: the day-children were not clever like you and your friends; they were just average, but desperate to learn. I gather yours are not.'

'Some are.' Charlotte sounded slightly penitent. 'The others are silly and empty-headed and drive me to think about the writing that Branwell and I do, all the time. I immerse myself in our stories when I should be analysing clauses with them. I rely on my life within far too much.' She looked worried. 'I would like to write, Papa, like you did.'

Pat felt troubled. He was deeply impressed by the writing he had seen by his children, but two things bothered him. One was their continuation with the themes they pursued as children; the other their ability to cope with the disappointment of failure. *He* had coped, but he had had some modest success, and the fulfilment of a wife and family, and his vocation, however uncertain. These children were sensitive beyond normality, and this was showing in their inability to live away from home. He shifted in his chair, and said:

'When Mr Southey wrote in reply to your letter – can you remember what he said?'

'"Literature cannot be the business of a woman's life, and it ought not to be. The more she is engaged in her proper duties, the less leisure she will have for it."' Charlotte's eyes were closed and the words came unhesitatingly. She remembered only too well.

'I think that was a little . . . harsh,' said Pat. 'Carry on with your writing, but it will have to be for pleasure. And try to write about things which will give you less . . . anxiety. And be pleased that you wrote a letter which merited a reply from none other than the Poet Laureate. Branwell has not that comfort.'

'He wrote the most awful letters!' Despite herself, Charlotte laughed. 'He said to Wordsworth that there was not a writing poet worth sixpence!' Patrick looked grave. 'Is he really going to the Royal Academy? He seems to change daily between that and a tour of the Continent.'

217

Patrick was wise enough not to give the reason he thought that the academy was not the place for Branwell. 'Your aunt and I have discussed it, and she is willing to pay for some form of education for Branwell, as she was for you at Roe Head. We think the idea of a tour of the Continent is better. But not just at the moment.' He closed his eyes, and there swam before them a vision of Branwell, alone, overexcited, friendless, imbibing too deeply to cover his shyness. He opened his eyes again. 'We are indebted to your aunt for her generosity. She loves you all as her own.'

Charlotte blushed. 'And I am her least-loving niece. Oh Papa, what a failure I am! Hopeless at my work and unkind to my kind aunt!'

'Remember that you chose to go to Roe Head as a teacher. You can choose to come home at any time.'

She smiled at him through watery eyes. 'That freedom makes it even harder to give up! I wish you were whipping me back to work.' She blew her nose hard and getting up, kissed the top of his head. 'Goodnight.'

'Don't sit up late,' he had replied, walking towards the stairs to wind the clock.

⚯

William Hodgson gripped the edge of the pulpit, white-knuckled and puce-faced. Above him in the next tier Patrick ground his teeth and prayed for him to finish. This was not the way. Hodgson, the answer to Bess's prayers and an efficient curate to Patrick, had a naturally inflammatory preaching style and enjoyed a row. His antipathy to Dissenters had at first amused Pat and Branwell, for they had all attended a meeting where the Dissenters had proposed to abolish their contribution to the church rates. The parsonage party had naturally been the only people to vote against the motion, and they had laughed as they did it. Pat understood the intellectual argument the Dissenters had for non-contribution, but in practical terms he felt the church played a valuable secular role in the village as well as a spiritual one. His leadership of the campaign against the Poor Law Amendment Act had been an essential part of his ministry: he was outraged that decent people who had fallen out of work through no fault of their own should be herded into the newly built workhouses and husbands and wives

218

and children split up. Hodgson's voice rasped on, a gravelly shout: Pat banged his feet on the floor of his own part of the pulpit and hoped the young man would hear and come to a swift conclusion. Beneath them sat Emily, Anne and Charlotte, impassive, embarrassed; the congregation muttered and fluttered.

Pat was weary, weary of the row with the Dissenters. It was wrong, all wrong for Christians to behave towards each other like this. The following Sunday he avoided a public row over the rates by removing the vestry meeting which would decide the church rate to the school. For four hours he battled to maintain dignity and reason and achieved it. When he collapsed by the fire in his study, the pains in his stomach vying with the pains in his chest, Bess tutting and clucking round with warm whiskey and slippers, he was not surprised to be told that Hodgson was leaving to take up his own ministry at Colne. Deprived of his recent gift, Pat concluded that it might be easier in some ways without him.

∽

The last notes of the Beethoven sonata hung in the still air, their rich texture replaced by the thin mean wail of the wind tugging at the shutters. Emily turned from the piano and sat with her palms together between her knees, head down, waiting for Pat to speak. At last he could.

'You're rich, Emily, rich.' He paused and shifted in his chair. 'When you can play like that you will never be lonely.' Emily looked up, surprised. Loneliness was not a concept she understood. 'You have an instant channel for your emotion, a true expression of your feelings through the music. No one can ever take that away from you.' Emily waited; she understood now what he was saying. How greatly it would have helped him to have her skill as he faced life without their mother. 'And your playing – it has a brilliance I never expected.'

'Do you understand now why I hated Law Hill so much?' Emily's question was anxious. 'I had to teach those girls the very basics of the instrument, endure their thumping. You can't make people musical, Papa. That and the writing and reading . . .' – her hands came up in a gesture of hopelessness. 'I thought because I could see the moors I would survive it. I didn't realise the depths of my intolerance, my inability to endure that which I don't like.'

219

Pat smiled, looking in to the fire. 'I suppose telling the girls you preferred the company of the house dog to theirs *was* a little intolerant. Neither you nor Charlotte are built for teaching.'

'But it's all we can do!' Emily's tone was exasperated. 'There's nothing else we can do to earn money!'

'You don't have to.' Pat's tone was gentle. 'We're all right.'

'But you've got four adults to support as well as yourself and Aunt, and only your stipend!'

'Aunt pays her way,' said Pat. 'She also saves and helps with your lessons and fees. I save. Charlotte has supported herself at Roe Head, although I doubt that she should continue. We do not have expensive tastes. We shall manage. The last thing I want is for my children to be unhappy. It would make little sense of my life if you were.' He poked a snoring puppy with his foot. 'Are you pleased with the dog?'

Emily's face softened as she gazed at the puppy. 'What a welcome when I crept defeated back from Law Hill! He's so beautiful.' She crouched by the box and fondled the silky ears, the little animal not even stirring in its secure sleep. She got up and went to some papers she had left on Pat's desk. 'Look – I drew him yesterday. Do you like it?'

Her father looked intently, far too closely, at the drawing. 'It's remarkable,' he said. 'Em, is there anything you can't do?'

'I can't put up with stupid people, I can't live away from you and the moors and the family. You're right, I can draw and write poetry and play the piano; I can bake the bread and help in the house. But there's a lot I can't do. Am I like Branwell?'

'No,' he replied firmly, 'You are not.' He tried not to discuss the children with each other, but now they were older, it seemed a reasonable thing to do at times. 'I have a theory about intelligence, and talent, you know. There is little point in having the greatest gifts if you don't have other things to go with them.'

Emily frowned. 'Like?'

'Like application and stamina, organisation and dedication. Branwell has great brilliance. He will need a lot of application to use it.'

'And you see me as the same?'

'Certainly not. You don't like being away from here, but that will not stop you developing your talents. You've achieved already in your music; you have an inner steel which Bran does not have. He will always need support. He's going to have a studio in Bradford in Field Place.'

'Near Uncle William? Is that the support?'

Pat blushed slightly and got out of his chair. 'My dear, I can never forget Cowan Bridge. I was away from all of you, and things happened which should not have. I have to feel there are people about who will help if need be.' His voice trailed away, memory wrecking his composure. Emily looked up sharply. He would never lose the pain of those early days; their father with his sorrow and courage had often been the inspiration of their romantic writing, a fact of which he was wholly unaware. She patted him vigorously on his shoulders.

'What about the ducks?'

He recovered. You could always trust Emily's sense of mood. 'If you could just keep them in the yard most of the day . . .'

'Or Aunt will have them caught and cooked – I understand. I suppose they do make a noise and a very slight smell. As long as they sleep in the house I don't really mind – it's the fox I worry about. I don't think Aunt feels the same about animals at all. Is it a Branwell trait?' She waited to be amused; Pat loved to speculate about inheritance.

'Your mother and her aunt both liked animals out of the house. I always had them in. There were a few discussions about the dogs.' He smiled, remembering. 'We usually reached a compromise. It's just that you and Anne have extended the species to be admitted.'

'Aunt didn't like being met by Adelaide and Victoria on the landing,' said Emily. 'They had strayed up the stairs. I had no idea they would climb steps, quite clever really, isn't it? I do try to keep the dogs off the beds, particularly since Paddy rolled in that dead sheep on the moor and tried to rub it off when Martha had just put all the clean sheets on . . . I'll try to keep them all a bit more confined. Aunt really hates Hera inside. You'd think she'd realise a hawk has to flap his wings a bit; he doesn't mean to frighten her. And Tabby's a bit silly about him, too.'

'It's just a matter of us all having to live together.' He raised his hand to stop Emily's interruption. 'I know you feel that some of the humans aren't being sufficiently tolerant, but we have to offset a human being's contribution against an animal's. Your aunt has

221

been with us for nearly twenty years.' He tried to sound stern. Emily put her arm round his shoulders, ruffling the fine white hair.

'I don't know how you do it, Papa. Weighing Aunt against me, and Tabby against Aunt, and me against Charlotte, and the trustees against the ratepayers – I'd tell the lot to take a jump at themselves sometimes.'

'It's a small house, Emily, and I love you all – even the trustees from long familiarity. Don't sit up late, my dear.' He turned to look up into the startling dark eyes. 'Shut the ducks securely in the peat store before you go up.' Her face creased with mirth as she picked up the puppy Keeper from the box and shut the door softly behind her.

⊙↺

The rain had soaked her clothes, plastered her pretty hair against her face; still she hugged the tree, her hands bloody on the gnarled trunk. She would not turn to look at the great house; she could feel the rough wood scoring her face, her tears salt on her lips where they mingled with the blander rain. At her feet she saw the remains of the birds she had just killed, banging their heads with the stone until their beaks froze open as if begging for water.

In the distance Anne could hear the children, running around the shrubbery in the rain, out of her control. She had seized the birds from Cunliffe as he pulled their wings and feathers off, their tiny screams hardly heard; at first he had resisted, shoving her away, swearing at her, using words she had never heard before, words he had learned from his sottish uncle in their drinking sessions. But when he saw the sheer fury in her face, the rage that made her body strong, he gave way and with a final oath threw them at her. Left with a pile of mutilated half-alive fledglings, she had seized the stone, shut her eyes and banged at them until the little beaks parted in a final gasp.

Mrs Ingham had dismissed her after she tied the children to the table in order to gain a moment's peace for her writing. She took the reprimand from the pleasant wife of a tyrannical husband as no more than her due. She returned home to Haworth very little older but much wiser.

Patrick, faced with his third returning daughter, tried the same arguments but with no avail.

'I do have to go again, Papa. There is no question of staying at home and doing nothing.' He often wondered why his friends thought Anne, his youngest child, was the mildest. No such thing. Her position as the baby of the family had produced in adolescence a fierce independence. She had endured her setback at Roe Head, when illness had forced her to return; now she had this. He had to admit that he had never had to teach the idle, bad-mannered children of the aristocracy or the new manufacturing classes. He could scarcely believe what his daughters told him at times.

'Papa,' she continued sternly, 'I must have another job. I do not intend to stay at home and be the little sister. If I stay here, Charlotte and Branwell will just condescend to me. You've no idea how angry it makes me! They don't think I have a thought worth thinking, and Emily is so good with the household affairs that I'm no use there. I will make a life for myself. It will help me, and it may help you a little.' She looked directly at Pat, who averted his eyes. 'You cannot find it easy with four of us at home.' Imitating his mannerism she raised her hand firmly to prevent his conciliatory interruption. 'I have learned a lot from the Inghams. I will never put myself in positions where children can behave as theirs did. So I will go elsewhere.'

'Please stay a little, Annie. Give yourself a holiday and me the pleasure of your company. All of you are now at home. Just enjoy yourself. You haven't met Willy yet.'

'Willy?'

'Weightman, the curate. He is a tower of strength; he's becoming my right hand. He's very amusing and your sisters and Branwell love him. He's a great benefit to us all.'

'Ah – Miss Celia Amelia as Charlotte calls him.' Anne giggled. 'He's caused quite a stir.'

'Charlotte can be very unkind,' said Pat crossly. Weightman was the greatest help he had had since he came to Haworth. He loved the young man like a son; sometimes he felt guilty comparing him with Branwell, whose career was beginning again, tutoring boys in Lancashire. 'He is diligent, intelligent and cares deeply for our parishioners. Charlotte is very critical of young men, your brother included. Her two proposals were smartly refused because she was contemptuous of Mr Nussey and Mr Bryce, and their calling as curates.' He paused. 'I don't think it ever occurs to her that her contempt for them might be seen to include me.'

'She certainly doesn't,' protested Anne quickly. She recalled a conversation she had had with Emily when Charlotte had received her two proposals within two months, and had raucously destroyed their characters on the basis of their vocations. They had wondered to each other if she realised that her criticisms were tactless in the light of Pat's profession. Emily had decided to mention it. Charlotte had rounded on her:

'Of course, Papa doesn't think that!' she had almost shouted. 'How dare you suggest it!' The shouting had brought Bess out of her room. They had never discussed it further, fearful of Charlotte's capacity for a row. Anne got up from her chair and hugged Pat. 'I'll stay a bit while I seek another post,' she said softly. 'It's not that I don't want to be with you, dearest Papa; I'm just not going to be the baby for the rest of my life. I'll give myself two months – you'll be tired of us all being here by then.' She put her fingers on his lips. 'Yes you will, you find the noise and rows quite distressing at times, I know you do!'

Pat took her hand and sighed. 'I'm getting old,' he said rather mournfully. 'Don't let me get crabby, Anne. I want to keep enjoying you as I have done all your lives.'

There was a tap at the door; it opened without the caller being bidden to enter.

'Weightman! At last you can meet Anne. My dear, this is William Weightman of whom we have been speaking – this is my daughter Anne,' and he pressed their hands together.

Weightman's brown curls shimmered as he bowed low over Anne's hand. 'I trust you are no longer on strike, Miss Anne,' he said silkily. His brown eyes were laughing as he fixed them keenly on her.

'Oh Papa!' gasped Anne. 'You didn't tell him – oh really – that was three years ago and I . . .'

'I was trying to give Weightman a flavour of your character, my dear,' interrupted Pat matter-of-factly. 'In your absence. You know how one tries to pick out salient features in a personality if one is writing a novel – I decided that your leadership of the hunger strike against your favourite aunt was a good indication . . .'

'Mr Weightman,' said Anne firmly. 'You will ignore the ramblings of this old cleric. It is true that I suggested to my sisters that we didn't eat until our dear aunt agreed to let Tabby stay here after she had injured herself in a fall on the ice in Kirkgate. Aunt soon agreed – she was only concerned about the household arrangements and was soon persuaded that we could manage. Neither Tabby nor Aunt is getting any younger. It was soon resolved.' She shot Pat a dark look. 'I can't think why Papa told you *that*.'

'Because he thought it would help me to get an idea of his youngest daughter.' Weightman was looking at Anne as if he understood her perfectly. 'Care for the elderly is an attractive trait.'

'My father may get little if he carries on like this,' replied Anne tartly. Pat was finding the exchange hugely amusing.

'Are you busy, Miss Anne?' enquired Weightman. 'It's a beautiful afternoon and I'm sure the dogs would love a walk. May I ask your father's permission to accompany you if you felt like going for the stream?'

'Well . . . yes,' said Anne, surprised but pleased. 'The dogs would love a walk. May I go, Papa?'

'Of course, my dear. It will do you both good.' He opened the door for them, watched while Anne fetched her shawl and bonnet, then climbed the stairs to the landing where he waited until they came into sight. Anne's small frame leaning towards the tall Weightman, framed by the beauty of the summer moor, suddenly moved him deeply. Just like Maria and him. If Charlotte couldn't bear curates, perhaps his little Anne could.

24

His character wore well; the surest proof of real worth. He had, it is true, some peculiar advantages. Agreeable in person and manners, and constitutionally cheerful, his first introduction was prepossessing. But what he gained at first, he did not lose afterwards.

Reverend Patrick Brontë, *A funeral sermon for the late Rev. William Weightman, M.A.*

Weightman sprang up from the purple heather in which he had been lying for the past half an hour. 'I must go, sir,' he said to Pat, who was seated more sedately on the flat crag above Hill Top. 'The cholera has reached the bottom of Kirkgate now and the Feathers are very, very sick. The baby went down with it this morning, and I said I'd look in this afternoon.' He smiled at Branwell who had been lying next to him. 'Enjoy your shooting: do you want a short trip tomorrow? I think I could manage an hour after matins is said.'

'Yes yes!' Branwell stood up, and Grasper was on his feet immediately, expecting to be off to find more birds. 'Come in as soon as you can, old man. It'll make my day.'

They watched the lithe figure bounding away back to the road. Pat turned to Branwell and motioned for him to sit again.

'We really must talk, Bran,' he said quietly. 'I've left it until we are alone and out of the house. I want you to tell me why the Postlethwaites sacked you.'

'Probably for the same reasons that the Inghams sacked Anne and the Sidgwicks didn't plead with Charlotte to stay.' Branwell's tone was flippant, and his father did not like it.

'We've always been friends, Branwell, and I expect you to tell me the truth.' He sounded severe; he meant to. 'I agree your sisters are in the same position; but they have been perfectly frank with me, and I'd be obliged if you would be, too.'

Oh God, thought Branwell, *he's going to get it out of me. Why do I want his approval so much when I can't do anything which deserves it?* He walked towards the crag and sat next to Pat. Before them the moor stretched out, rolling, beautiful, green fields dotted with sheep and great swathes of purple where the heather survived triumphant against the efforts of man. The air was filled with bleating as the flocks shuffled gently across the landscape. Pat listened, remembering how distressing he found it after Maria's death, watching the lambs with their mothers and knowing his own were without one. His journeys then would bring him near to tears. Time was, after all, a healer.

'I drank too much and wrote too much.' Branwell was looking across the valley and throwing small sticks for Grasper to fetch. 'When I met Hartley Coleridge his encouragement went to my head; I concentrated on the *Odes* of Horace and forgot the two boys . . .'

'Your translation is excellent.' Pat had seen the rendering into verse and was impressed, proud too that Branwell's love and ability in the Classics could only have come through him. No one else had ever taught Branwell anything, except painting and music. 'But the letters you wrote home to John Brown were not in the same vein, hardly . . . discreet . . .' His voice trailed away.

Branwell's fine ruddy complexion took on a deeper hue. 'I don't know why I did it,' he said hoarsely. 'I told John to destroy the letters because I knew they were not fit to be seen by anyone else. Why do I do such stupid things? It was not a proper way for the incumbent's son to be writing to the sexton, even if I expected them to be destroyed!' He beat his fist against his forehead and groaned.

'That is true.' Patrick was always relieved when Branwell came to the right conclusions by himself. 'Dear boy, I don't mind having to come and fetch you from the Black Bull now and then; we've given good service to Haworth and the people are tolerant of weaknesses they can understand – but a man of your age writing like a schoolboy!' Pat leaned down from his rocky seat and snapped a sprig of heather to put between his teeth. 'Grow up a bit, Branwell. Was there a reason for the smut?'

Branwell turned his face away. Did his father know, or was he

227

going, as ever, to find out? Either way, out with it. 'I knew, in your biblical sense, the girl who helped in the Postlethwaites' house. I know you would never have done such a thing, but men do, and I am pretty weak, Papa. I was trying hard to succeed at the job, but when things got too much for me I drank, and then she seemed so willing, she really seemed to like me.' She would, thought Pat; he's handsome and witty and stands on no ceremony, and he's had precious little opportunity here to cut his teeth without the presence of his family.

'Is there to be a child?'

'I think there may be. I feel so badly about it, as I can't go back and find out without the Postlethwaites seeing me.'

'We will have to find a way,' said Pat. 'Leave it to me for the moment, and for goodness sake learn from it. I can't live for ever, and you need to be employed.'

'I think I shall be. On the railway!' Branwell turned and faced his father with real excitement in his face. 'It's a new age, Papa! Steam defying time! The world shrinking. I want to be part of it.'

'Tell me more,' said Pat, 'but first give me a pull-up for my knees aren't what they used to be.' The young man extended a hand, picked up his gun and whistled for Grasper, who had taken advantage of the absorbed humans and run off after anything which took his fancy. Branwell's free hand rested on Pat's shoulder as they strolled down the hill into the village.

☙

'Can you manage all that?' enquired Pat anxiously of Weightman. They were in the study with the table covered in paper, listings of the money raised, and the shirting, coal and food to be distributed to the suffering people of Haworth.

'Of course I can!' Weightman's tone was reassuring, warm. 'If you can manage the organisation at this end and do most of the services and the baptisms and funerals, I'll be able to get into the village and see the distribution is done fairly. It may seem like a soft option but, sadly, there is a need for scrupulous supervision.' He leaned back in his chair and put his pen down, rubbing his inky fingers together to clean them. 'They simply must stop this nonsense with the corn – if the price doesn't come down, however much we try to raise in relief the families of the men without jobs will starve. I've never seen such distress.'

Anne put her head round the door. 'There's a suitable post, Papa, in the newspaper. I shall apply.' She looked at Weightman. 'One less mouth to feed – although I'm not joking about your problem,' she added quickly.

'I should hope not. But I'll misuse the funds if it will persuade you to stay!'

Pat saw Anne's blush. 'Apply if you want to, my dear, but only if you want to. I lived on nothing at all when I was young, and it's very easy. And we have a lot more than nothing.'

When they were alone again, he said, 'You get on well with Anne.'

'I do indeed,' replied Weightman enthusiastically, 'and with all your family! But Anne – she is special – such spirit hidden beneath still waters . . .' His gaze shifted from the rolls of paper, and he looked directly into Pat's eyes. 'But I am too young at the moment – there is little I can give her . . .'

'I understand,' said Patrick. 'I didn't marry until I was thirty-five, and you're a long way off that. There's plenty of time. But you have my blessing – you know you have that.'

They put the lists in order; Weightman placed them in a leather pouch and took them with him to his lodgings. Pat sat by the fire musing on the possibility of Willy marrying Anne. He could take on the parish, they would have children, the trustees would build an extension to the parsonage where there was plenty of ground to the north of the house. There would be room for them all, and he, Patrick, could die rather than strive to stay alive. He put his feet contentedly beneath Keeper for warmth and fell into an untroubled sleep.

თ

'Should we really have let them go, Pat?' Bess's tone was querulous as she interrupted her reading from *Blackwood's Magazine*. She was reading to him in his study to keep them both awake while they waited for the return of the girls, Ellen Nussey and Weightman from the Keighley Mechanics' Institute.

'Just keep reading, my dear. There's not the slightest reason to fear for them. They are with Weighman, a respectable man of the cloth; he will not harm them, nor will anyone else if he is with them.'

'But it's so late, nearly midnight, and the wind has got up!'

Taking her side, the wind gave a particularly vicious tug at the shutters.

'Just read, my dear. I always find that in moments of agitation it is better to fix one's mind on something else.'

As she obediently raised the periodical in line with her spectacles, Charlotte's voice was heard and the tramping of feet in at the gate. Bess dropped *Blackwood's* and stood up. 'The coffee! I sent Martha to bed as she has to be up early. I must get the coffee!'

Pat followed her out of the room and met the giggling party in the hall.

'Such fun, Papa!' Charlotte's cheeks were pink, and her eyes shone. 'Willy gave the most *erudite* lecture, and the whole of Keighley was there – the cream of Yorkshire society! How grand they think they are, and I don't expect they really understood a word of it, but they clapped and clapped!' The coats and bonnets were piling up on the banisters at the foot of the stairs; Emily kicked off her wet boots and made for the dining room and the dogs.

'Well done,' said Pat, affectionately chafing Weightman's shoulder. 'Now, get in by the fire and get warm – Miss Nussey – get right close to the fire and warm your hands and feet.'

Ellen laughed. 'I'm not the least bit cold, Mr Brontë. Willy had us doing alternate running and walking to keep warm, and Emily beat him on the last stretch of the road.'

Pat beamed. Their high spirits pleased him. 'Your aunt is coming with the coffee,' he said just before Bess entered with a tray. Weightman took it from her and bade her sit down. Charlotte seized the coffee pot and poured into the fine blue and white cups. She handed to Ellen and her aunt first, then her sisters, then Willy. She poured him a particularly brimming cup and gave him a dazzling smile. Pat caught her glance and noted her ringleted hair, different from Emily's and Anne's simple styles. *She pours scorn on my curate*, he thought, *but there's something there – the hair, the glow. You could do anything with her now.*

Bess gave a small shriek. 'What have I been thinking of?' she wailed. 'I forgot to include your father and myself and Miss Nussey in my calculations! There won't be enough coffee! Oh how foolish I am!' She sounded near to tears.

Anne crouched down by her chair. 'It's all right, Aunt,' she soothed, 'there's enough, and Emily will make more if we need it. We've kept you up so late, it's not surprising you forgot how many

230

there would be.' Pat saw Willy watching Anne, his eyes soft with love. Charlotte said:

'Yes, Aunt, you must be tired. Would you prefer to go to bed now? We can manage, and Papa is here.'

Bess looked at Charlotte, and then at Anne. Anne nodded. 'Come on, let me help you up the stairs. I'll fetch your candle.' She quietly guided Bess from the room.

'That's better.' Charlotte sat in the chair next to Weightman. 'She does get so fussed. And I want to talk to you, Mr Weightman, about some valentines which were received in this house. Aunt doesn't know, but Papa does, because he always sees the post first.'

'Yes,' smiled Pat. 'Three valentines with a Bradford postmark; a good thing the penny post has come in, or we would have been bankrupted receiving them. And no doubt the reason I could not find you on an afternoon near to the date was because you were walking to Bradford and back to preserve your anonymity.'

'Not much chance of that with Charlotte around.' Emily was sitting on the floor by the fire, her arms round Keeper.

'And before I forget,' said Pat, 'how was your tea with the Collins before the lecture? It was very kind of them to invite you.'

'They were delighted to have such good company in these young ladies,' said Weightman. 'The moment I suggested it there was instant agreement.'

'I don't think Mrs Collins enjoyed it very much,' said Emily, spreading the dog's ear across her palm and stroking it with a finger. 'She seemed as if she hardly dared to speak. Anne noticed it, too.'

'Is that so?' Pat frowned. He had heard some disturbing rumours. But this was not the time. 'I'm too old to be up at this time. Don't . . .'

'Sit up late, girls!' Everyone, including Weightman, finished his sentence. Pat smiled sheepishly. Anne came back into the room. Charlotte shot Weightman a bright look.

Oh dear, thought Pat as he wound the clock on the stairs. *Anne loves him. Charlotte doesn't. So why does she want him?* He slid the key back into his pocket and creaked his way up the final stairs.

∞

'A school!' Anne's voice was incredulous. 'Why on earth does she want us to start a school here?'

231

'Because she hates working away from here, and I suspect she resents me doing nothing at home.' Emily, on the floor with Keeper, dragged him gently by his back legs nearer to the fire, where he lay, belly upwards, in pure contentment. The firelight flickered on him, and he turned his face to the warmth, whiskery mouth slightly open.

'But you don't do nothing! With Tabby retired and only Martha here, Aunt couldn't possibly manage. You're our housekeeper, Emily.' Anne was indignant.

'It's a bit more complicated than that.' Emily's face was stretched in a grin. 'It's all to do with how we see ourselves. I know I can't manage to live away from home and Papa; you know you can't live here if you're babied by Charlotte; but Charlotte is torn: she sees herself as dutiful and responsible for the rest of us and she always wants to know what's going on, but she wants to be independent too. So every time she gets a governess post to prove her independence, she quarrels with the family so that she's back here in a flash.'

'But I left the Inghams quickly, too,' said Anne guardedly.

'But you've been at Thorp Green some time now, and I think you'll do any thing to stay there and see it through. Papa doesn't want you to if you don't like it, you know'

'It's getting better now. I'm very careful to anticipate situations. And I get lots of time for writing.'

'Gondal?'

'No, not Gondal, Em. Reality.'

Emily ignored this. 'So she's asked Aunt to help us finance a school, to be run here, so that we can all be at home together. Papa agrees, and Aunt, as ever, will provide the money. I want us all to be together but not with a house full of silly girls.'

Anne shrugged, unable to make up her mind.

'And there's more, Annie. She thinks that we would get better pupils if we had had some Continental education like the Taylors. She wants Aunt to pay for us all to go to Belgium so that we have good French to add to our skills.' She rolled over on the rug with Keeper, laughing. 'To add to my skills of baking and cleaning! I wish she'd just leave us be!'

Martha knocked and entered. 'May I put out the tea, Miss Emily?' she asked. Emily and Anne jumped up.

'Leave the tray, Martha,' said Emily, 'we'll lay, and you can fetch the tea. Sometimes I think we work that girl too hard,' she continued when Martha had gone. 'She does everything except for what I do, and the washing.'

'She seems to like being here,' said Anne. It's as if the Browns have become part of the family. Branwell and John, and now Martha, who is almost like a younger sister.'

'I'm glad you said that. That's how I see her.'

Patrick and Bess came in, and Bess sat down to pour the tea. 'I'm glad you're home for this,' she said to Anne. 'You know that Charlotte has written to me and asked if I would assist with you all going abroad to study. She says she's ambitious as your father was when he came to England.'

'It's a fair point,' said Pat. He ate little but enjoyed his cup of tea. 'Charlotte can usually think of a way to get her point across.'

'True,' said Emily, handing Keeper a whole buttered scone. Bess took a breath but let it go. 'But I wish she wouldn't try to organise our lives. I can't go because I can't leave Keeper, and the ducks and Hera. There's no one else to look after them.' Realising the weakness of her argument, she gave the dog an extravagant fondle. 'Poor little thing,' she crooned, holding his massive head. 'You need me, don't you?'

'And I can't go either,' said Anne firmly. 'I have given Mrs Robinson my word that I will stay for a good period of time because the girls need consistency. They had too many changes before me, and it was disastrous for their education and their manners.'

Pat looked at them both over his glasses. 'This is not wise,' he said. 'This is an opportunity. It's not the same as going to a governess post. You have had no chance to go to the university, and you took me to task as children about that. This is the nearest you will ever get to formal instruction of a kind similar to the university. Your education has been almost entirely provided by me and your aunt. It would do you good to have a wider outlook, and in a different country it would be exciting.' He paused. 'I would have jumped at it.'

'Well,' said Emily, 'let Charlotte go if she wants to. I'll stay and help Aunt, and Anne wants to continue at the Robinsons'. Let Charlotte go.'

Bess and Pat exchanged looks. 'It's not as simple as that,' said Bess. 'Your father vowed after Cowan Bridge that he would never send you anywhere he had not seen or was not near enough for visits from him or our friends. We have agreed that at least two of you should go.'

'And I'll accompany you on the journey so that I can see the place you are going to.' Pat's statement rocked Emily.

'But Papa, you hate being away from home as much as I do! And you haven't been abroad since you came to England in 18 . . .'

'1802,' said Pat precisely. 'Then take it as a measure of my concern for you that I'll come. These old bones have but rarely slept out of this house since we came.'

'Your father has never had a holiday,' said Bess. 'He didn't even take up Mr White's kind invitation for a week with Charlotte at Upperwood. The change would do him good. But those' – the teapot was placed firmly on the cloth – 'are my conditions.'

They're just like a married couple when it comes to dealing with us, thought Anne. Aloud she said, 'Will you let Emily and me discuss it, Papa? It's a lot to take in.'

'By all means,' said Pat and Bess at the same time. They returned to his study and another section of *Blackwood's.*

'Are you sure you'll be all right alone, my dear?' asked Pat. 'Why don't you come with us?'

'No,' said Bess. 'My little ailment makes it easier for me not to stray too far from home. Of course I shall be all right.' She settled herself by the fire and took up her glasses. 'Willy will take care of everything, so don't fuss. You're longing to go.'

'My own little ailment is slightly easier to live with, as long as I have a guide.' Pat was sympathetic. 'You would be on your own with Martha. The Browns would be nearby. Branwell would not be too far away at Luddenden Foot if you were to need him.'

'I know he would return at once in an emergency,' said Bess. 'He's a good-hearted boy. There is really nothing to worry about. Isn't exciting to see his poem published in the *Halifax Guardian*?' She gathered up *Blackwood's* as if to emphasise the family's literary success.

'It is, indeed,' replied Pat, smiling at the *Guardian* which still lay open on the table. 'It will transform him to have such recognition.'

25

In judging the father of a family by his children . . . [what] we have found in your daughters can only give us a very high idea of your worth and your character. With pupils like this we had very little to do; their progress is more your work than ours . . . we only had the slight merit of providing suitable material for the praiseworthy activity which your daughters have drawn from your example and your lessons.

Constantin Heger, letter to Patrick Brontë,
5th November 1842.

Emily slammed the lid of the trunk down hard and sat on it. 'This is it, Charlotte,' she said. 'Not another chemise or handkerchief; *not a thing*. We're going to a school; no one will care what we wear; we're there for six months *to learn*.'

Charlotte leaned forward and slid the curling tongs through a gap which had opened as Emily relaxed her assault on the trunk.

'It's better to take too much than too little,' she replied as mildly as she could. 'We may stay a little longer and it's better to have everything than to spend money there which could buy us . . .' – she thought desperately for something her sister would like to buy – 'piano lessons!' she finished triumphantly.

'We're staying for six months and not a day longer! I agreed to six months. I did not agree to any extensions. Be fair, Charlotte. I'm coming only because you have to have someone with you to stop Papa worrying. I am not doing any more time.'

They were in the room over the porch, which had become the packing room. 'You make it sound like a prison sentence,' replied Charlotte. She stood by the window and looked out. Willy was coming up the lane, his arms full of papers. 'Willy's coming for his

235

last briefing from Papa. And do try to enjoy it, Emily; we'll have a wonderful time.' Her eyes gleamed with excitement.

'I'm coming, and I'll do my duty. I don't think it's possible that I shall enjoy being in a town among a lot of strangers.' She shuddered. 'I shall set my mind to it and just work and work so that I shut out everything else.'

Charlotte sighed. 'Come downstairs. Willy will stay for tea, and Branwell's coming over – did you remember?' Emily's face changed, and she ran down the stairs, jumping the last three and nearly felling her father as he came out of his study. He was followed by Branwell.

'We didn't hear you come, Bran!' Emily hugged him. He looked well, and Pat was flushed with the pleasure of having spent an hour talking to him. 'And you've got another poem published!' She squeezed his shoulders. 'Better than any of us! Just like your father.' And she gave Pat a broad wink.

She began to pour the tea. Bess was finding it harder to rouse herself from her afternoon nap these days and was often late coming down for tea. Charlotte took two cups from her and went to Branwell and Weightman, who were deep in conversation.

'We are well prepared for our journey,' she said. 'Everything is packed, tickets booked and received, and we have rooms waiting for us in London.'

'I wish I was coming,' said Branwell. 'Six months in a girls' school would suit me well. Would you come, Willy?'

Weightman laughed. 'I fear the incumbent of my parish would disapprove. Sir, may I go to the Pensionnat Heger?'

'You may not because it would prevent me doing so,' said Pat with a chuckle. 'You will stay here and look after the parish and my sister-in-law while I travel abroad and take my ease.'

'Papa is vastly well prepared,' put in Emily, pouring more hot water onto the leaves. 'He's been working on his French phrase book for at least three weeks. I saw it last night. It's got all the really useful words that a traveller needs, like *l'âme* – the soul – and *le génie* – genius – and *la raison* – reason . . .'

'Don't mock,' said Patrick severely. 'You never know when you will fall into conversation with a Frenchman and need to discuss *la philosophie*. I have all the words for food and money and rooms as well,' he said apologetically to Weightman and Branwell.

'You can have no idea,' explained Branwell to Weightman, 'the life Papa and I have led being outnumbered in this house four to two. Even our aunt sides with them most of the time!'

'I do what?' asked Bess entering. 'I am always scrupulously fair. The imbalance has always been age and experience pitched against youthful impetuosity. Tea, please, Emily.'

'I'm going to miss both of you so much,' said Weightman, rising from the sofa and taking a hand from both Emily and Charlotte. 'The house will be so quiet with Anne at the Robinsons' and Branwell at Luddenden Foot. No one to walk with, no one to . . .'

'You will walk the dogs, won't you?' interrupted Emily anxiously. She fixed her searching eyes on him. 'You promised, and I couldn't bear to think of them without . . .'

'Of course I will.' He dropped Charlotte's hand and took both of Emily's, aware of her real distress. He knew she didn't want to go and the animals were a concern to her. 'I shall take the dogs everywhere I go when I cross the moor, and I shall go out early in the morning with them every day. And sir, when you're back you'll take them, too – you always do. Don't worry.' He pressed her hands again, impulsively touching her shoulder. *What is he up to? There are tears in his eyes,* mused Charlotte. *He really can't help himself.*

'Thank you,' said Emily quietly. 'If I know that I can get through it.'

❦

'A traveller may and must', said Pat as the diligence clattered up to the Chapter Coffee House, 'always have a good bedroom to himself alone.'

Emily was coughing into her handkerchief. 'Is that so?' she spluttered.

'You can have no idea of the places I had to sleep when I first came to England. But when I had my degree and was in sight of an income, I came here and vowed never to do anything else. We have good rooms booked, and I know you'll be comfortable.'

'How can anyone live in this air?' said Emily putting her handkerchief back up her sleeve. 'It's like burnt soup.'

The horses' hooves slowed, and Charlotte quickly had her hand on the silk pull and slid the carriage window down into the door. The dome of St Paul's glimmered above them. 'I can't believe it! We're here, the city of Shakespeare and Milton – Byron has lived here – where is the National Gallery?'

237

'London is very big, Charlotte,' said Pat, who had descended and was waiting to hand the girls down. He paid the driver, who, observing the size of the tip, raised his hat and lifted their bags onto the step. The diligence rumbled away.

Inside a bent old man shuffled to greet them. 'My name is Brontë,' said Pat. 'We have rooms booked for two nights. The bags are . . .'

'We're expecting you, sir. I don't remember you, but I was here last time you stayed – I must have been. I had just started as the boot boy. Mr Thompson remembered your name when you wrote, as he said it is unusual. He said it was soon after Trafalgar you came and yours was one of Lord Nelson's names. He looked back at his books.'

'Well, well.' Pat beamed. How different this was from his first trip! 'These are my daughters. Time has passed, has it not? No children when I stayed here last – what a lot has happened since then.'

They sat to eat their dinner in the softly lit parlour, surrounded by clergymen and others. Emily, trembling slightly, was glad that Pat was with them. She felt ill at ease in the company of all these people she didn't know. With him there it was all right.

'I came here,' he reminisced, 'because I knew it was the place that writers and publishers came. It seems a little different now. I sat on that window seat' – he nodded in the direction – 'and listened to them talking, and thought the world was opening up to me as a writer.'

'But you did write, Papa,' said Charlotte, looking at him earnestly. 'We've always loved to look at your books on the shelves at home. I would love to add to those volumes.'

Pat smiled at her. 'I wish you could,' he said. 'It's difficult for anyone who is not known, and very difficult for a woman.'

'Every writer is not known to start with.' Emily wrinkled her brow. 'I just can't see how you can bear to let anyone read what you've written. I never could.'

'Oh Emily!' Charlotte faced her with pink cheeks. 'I would love to be famous and have people read what I have written! What is the point of writing if it's not read?'

Pat wiped his mouth, stood up and went to talk to Thompson over by the door.

'His blue coat really looks very fine,' said Charlotte, gazing at

Pat's back. 'Do you know, he took his old coat which had been made by a tailor in Cambridge for our tailor to copy and the measurements were almost exactly the same!'

'Mmm.' Emily, too, was staring at Pat's broad back. 'He must have been quite a sight when he first came to England. Didn't he have red hair, redder than Branwell's? With those blue eyes he must have stopped a few hearts.'

'Come, girls,' said Patrick, 'I have a short journey to make. You may accompany me.'

They went out into the quiet street and heard the raucous calls of vendors above the clatter of carriages, drays and water carts in the distance at St Paul's. In the late afternoon the puddles on the cobbles were almost frozen; the flares in front of the shops blazed and waned in the stiff breeze. Charlotte was excited; Emily looked frightened. Pat took her arm and drew her to him.

'I just want to see if there is a bookshop still here which I once knew,' he said to her. 'Just walk a little way with me. We'll be all right.' He took Charlotte on his other arm. 'The man was called George Moffett. He was kind to me at a time when I felt like getting back on the boat and returning to Ireland. He was the first person not to mock my Irish voice and to speak to me about literature.' They reached the end of Paternoster Row. The shop was there, it still sold books, but there was a different name above the shutters.

'No, we won't go in. I want to remember it as it was.' They walked around St Paul's, two tall thin figures and a little one, swaying against the wind, their faces turned up to the great dome as the bells boomed out the hour.

෨෧

'Oh, this is wonderful!' cried Emily as the waves crashed over the side of the packet. A mountain of dark blue sea rose up on her left-hand side, then disappeared as rapidly as it had appeared. She threw back the hood of her cloak so that the spray stung her face; licking her salty lips she laughed out loud.

'Emily, come back from the rail,' called Pat from where he was firmly tethered to a pile of coiled ropes. 'People have been swept away by slipping on the wet deck. Take care!'

She joined him on the ropes. 'Is Charlotte still below? This is the most wonderful thing after stifling, dirty London. I loved the paintings and the architecture, Papa, but how could people live there?'

'As you've said many times, Em,' replied Patrick dryly. 'Charlotte is quite sick, but the stewardess is looking after her.'

Emily suddenly felt selfish. 'Do you want to go below?' she enquired anxiously. Away from Haworth and the familiarity of house and village he sometimes seemed frail when he hesitated, unsure of what he saw.

'No, my dear. I like the bluster as much as you, and I've once felt queasy but have never been sick. What a sight it is!' He clamped his hands rounds his stick and smiled broadly at the heaving, voluminous seas. The spray soaked both of them.

Charlotte recovered her colour and her enthusiasm as the diligence rumbled and creaked towards Brussels. She sat, mostly in silence, gazing at the countryside and small towns they passed through, occasionally murmuring, 'I'm really here!' or, 'This is Belgium!' When they arrived in Brussels, Patrick, who had spent the final half-hour joltingly studying his handwritten manual, had prepared a perfect sentence and soon had a carriage with all their bags stowed in it, without any problem. Emily watched him carefully, interested in his ability to manage immediately the foreign environment with dignity and intelligence. The servants on the boat, the cab drivers now, all accepted his natural authority. His courtesy and cheerfulness no doubt helped. At last the hooves clattered along the rue d'Isabelle. Emily clutched Pat's hand as they drew up outside the Pensionnat Heger. He let her cling to him under the guise of politely helping her down, then kept her hand tucked into his arm. Charlotte was first out and had pulled the bell. The door opened, and they were soon in the presence of Madame Heger.

The drawing room was glittering, chilly and Continental, with a porcelain stove giving out a faint heat. Emily felt a sudden lurch of homesickness for Haworth. It was filled with light filtering through pale muslin curtains which shut out the walls of neighbouring buildings. Madame Heger rose from her silk-upholstered chair and extended both hands to the two girls, then a single one to Pat. He bowed, lightly brushing her hand with his lips. She was quite young and handsome, with magnificent thick hair, extravagantly piled. Her dress was sober yet elegant. She was unlike any woman Pat had ever met.

240

By the time she had served them coffee and cakes and talked in her charming but hesitant English about the school and their duties, Pat was totally convinced that he and Bess had done the right thing. This woman, who had her own young children, would look after his daughters. She understood their needs, had already allocated them a private area in the dormitory and exempted them from the daily mass; she 'added, in French, that she and her husband had received a very favourable impression from the letters Charlotte had written.

'Your girls, Mr Brontë, will be useful to us, and we hope to be very useful to them. My husband feels he will enjoy teaching such willing minds. He is not here because he is teaching at the *athénée*. But he will teach your girls their literature and French.'

Pat was pleased because, after all, the girls had been used to a male tutor all their lives, as well as male masters for painting and music. He left the pensionnat pleased at the girls' opportunities and convinced that Emily would quickly settle once she could fill her time with learning. The few days he spent at the British chaplaincy with the Jenkins were a combination of new sights and old stories, drawn out through their mutual link with Mr Jenkins' brother, who had been Pat's friend and colleague since his earliest days in Yorkshire. He could not remember when he had enjoyed such leisure in the company of sympathetic people. His health, too, despite the strange environment and food, was perfect. Each day he returned to the pensionnat to see Charlotte and Emily. They had settled quickly, and Emily had immersed herself immediately in the French language and piano lessons at the conservatoire. Her motivation was sufficiently strong for her to brave the walk alone across the unfamiliar town, arms folded, music clasped within them, her hair streaming free in the wind to the amazement of the elaborately coiffured *Bruxelloises*.

When he arrived alone at the village of Ligny, the torrential rain did not deter him from struggling uphill through the mud until he was above the field of Quatre Bras where he could look down on the site of the Battle of Waterloo. It had rained like this for the battle; narrowing his eyes he peered through the sheet of vertical water and saw the Great Duke riding the field on Copenhagen, in touch with his men, encouraging, guiding, commanding. A mist descended; the screams of the wounded rose up to him, the smell of smoke and blood. When it cleared, his vision remained misty with the tears he found pouring down his cheeks for the Duke of Wellington and his soldiers.

Several days later, having journeyed through northern France, over the Channel and back to London, he stayed a night again at the Chapter Coffee House. Eating his dinner, he reflected that not only was the room peopled by the presence of those he had observed so admiringly forty years ago, but now also by his daughters. He caught his intended train to Leeds, but was nevertheless surprised and pleased to find Willy and Branwell waiting at Keighley with the Haworth horse and cart, which Bess had hired to bring him easily home. *I am a lucky man*, he thought. *My daughters safe and my sons here to greet me.*

෦෨

'I have been ashamed of myself many times, but never have I been so ashamed of Haworth!' Branwell circled his father's chair, creating a little draught which Pat felt keenly.

'Sit down, Branwell, you're making me dizzy,' he said feebly. Since his return from Belgium, where he had felt so well, he had found the following months debilitating. The death of his old friend Dr Andrew soon after his return had shocked him deeply: not only had the man been a fearless fighter of disease in the village, but he had seen Patrick through the deaths of Maria, then his two daughters, as well as his own illnesses and consequent anxieties. He felt bereft and lonely, anxious and out of sorts, for the doctor had been cultured, interested in politics and had a deep concern for the poor and their inevitable sicknesses. The proposed memorial for this deeply loved physician had involved Patrick and Branwell; Branwell had asked his friend Leyland to appear before the memorial committee.

'He went straight from his convivial dinner with us into the lion's den,' continued Branwell, now perched on the piano stool. 'I don't think they would have been so rude if you had been there, Papa.' Pat sighed. His attempt to make Branwell feel independent and valued had misfired. He realised that his presence at public meetings tended to moderate the behaviour of the more bellicose villagers. It had not occurred to him that a simple decision about the doctor's memorial could have produced the 'gothic ignorance and ill-breeding' that Branwell described. They

242

just couldn't tolerate a man who earned his living through his art.

'But it's agreed?'

'Yes. Leyland will bring the tablet here, and John Brown will letter it under his supervision. They seemed happier when a local man was involved. For the life of me I can't see why, as John is every bit as much an artist with his lettering.' Branwell paused, glancing at his father; were there tears standing in his eyes? 'You do miss him, don't you, Papa?' His voice had softened at the sight of Pat's sadness.

'Yes, I miss him. He guided Willy and me when typhoid and influenza hit the village. I have few real friends, Bran, and he was in the village rather than miles away like your Uncle William. And with Emily and Charlotte and Anne away . . .'

'And only your unsatisfactory, unemployable son for company . . .'

'That's not the case,' replied Pat firmly. 'I regret your dismissal from the railway as much as you do; but I accept that the nature of the work and your desire to write made you careless of the detail a company like the Leeds and Manchester Railway requires of its employees. Without your mother in my early years I could have fallen into the same kind of muddle.'

Dear old man, thought Branwell. *Has he ever been against me?* 'Did you like the poem I finished at Luddenden Foot?' he enquired.

'Immensely. And your aunt has been reading to me all the others published in the *Intelligencer*, the *Herald* and the *Guardian*. You have been extraordinarily successful!' He felt for his spectacles, but dropped them back onto the pile of papers. They were little use now.

Later Bess came to read the day's newspaper to Pat, and Branwell remained, enjoying the sound of his aunt's voice, its warm Cornish note unaltered by her years in Yorkshire. Looking at the two old people he was thankful for her love and strong sense of duty.

Despite his frail state, Pat turned out to the Black Bull that night to bring Branwell home, knowing his son's tolerance of alcohol was nothing like his own. Two hours entertaining the assembled company rendered him first highly excitable and then nearly paralytic. John Brown would bring him to the side door and Pat guided him home, hooked over his shoulder. Branwell had not infrequently pointed out that it was a case of the blind leading the blind drunk.

꩜

The hot summer had brought in its wake a raging cholera epidemic. Pat had often debated with Dr Andrew the cause of the deadly disease, and despite lack of proof they had both striven to obtain a clean water supply for the village, studying the relative merits of elm and metal pipes, and ignoring the protests of the parishioners who had their own wells and resented the increased rates which would benefit those dependent on the common pumps. Weightman had urged Pat to do the burials, which were legion, and the daily services, while he visited in the village and performed the last rites in the stricken cottages. His argument was that Pat's age made him more vulnerable to infection, and Branwell and Bess agreed. In the midst of such sickness, death and exhaustion, Bess stoically supported her two clergymen, helped the lone Martha in managing the parsonage, and bravely endured her own symptoms which were worsening every day. She was more used to worrying about Pat's health than her own; she prayed hard that her discomfort would diminish as she trailed between the privy and her room, attempting to disguise the frequency of her trips by examining carefully the washing in the yard or checking, in Emily's absence, that Grasper had returned from the moor, or that the geese were safely penned away from the fox.

She had finished reading to Patrick, for the fourth time, the letters which had arrived from Brussels earlier that week (he had just said, 'They could be living in two different places, don't you think?') when she dashed from the room muttering about the need to get the dogs in now that it was getting dark. When she returned, Pat asked mildly if she had found them, then pointed to the corner by the window. She blushed. Both dogs lay in a senseless doggy sleep.

'My dear, what is the matter?' he began, laying down the letters he had been trying to read again for himself. 'I've noticed that you have become exceedingly but unnaturally zealous in your care of the animals. What is the matter?'

Bess felt tearful. She was filled with a great longing to tell Pat, but had become used, over the years, to bearing her problems alone; not that he was an uncaring man, but her womanly instinct respected the magnitude of his suffering, and she had found little to complain of herself. But now a sharp pain drove her to confess; after all, the girls were doing well, Pat's initial depression over Branwell's dismissal from the railway had disappeared in his delight at the publication of his poetry and the pleasure of his company at home. She leaned forward, shifting a stay, trying to ease the spasm.

'If only Dr Andrew were alive,' she breathed. 'I would have consulted him. The truth is, I have such difficulty with my food. I have tried all your remedies, but nothing seems to work. You are right; my concern for the animals is a disguise for my incontinence in various forms.'

'We must get the doctor straight away. We'll get a man over from Leeds at once.' His heart was thumping, stomach clenching. He stood up and held her by the shoulders affectionately. 'How could I have failed to notice! My greatest friend and I . . .'

Branwell burst into the room. 'Papa, you must come – Willy is ill – it's cholera I'm certain – I don't know what to do . . . ' – he flung himself onto the window seat, weeping uncontrollably. Bess went to him and held his head and hugged him.

Patrick picked up his stick. 'You stay with him,' he said to Bess. 'I'll go to Willy.' He swept out of the front door hatless; his speed through the cobbled lanes left him breathless. Passing the piles of refuse and the overflowing privies at the top of Kirkgate, he held his handkerchief to his mouth. He thought fleetingly that little had improved since he came to Haworth, and cholera, which had not existed in England when he came to the village, had taken a strong hold easily in the overcrowded, insanitary housing which the mill workers were forced to occupy. Arriving in West Lane, he entered the curate's lodging, brushing past the terrified landlady, rushing without ceremony into Weightman's bedroom.

The stench of vomit hung in the air, despite the good house-wife's constant effort to remove the bowls and buckets which this terrible disease rapidly filled with the victim's fluids until the body was finally drained and dehydrated. Exhausted with the effort of retching, Weightman lay on his pillows, eyes closed. He did not move. Pat stroked his brow. He was horribly cold; it could not be long. Familiar with the rapid onset and progress of cholera, he knew this was the end. Clasping the young man's hands, he wept unrestrainedly. *My son, oh Absolom, my son*, beat in his head. Half an hour later, he drew the sheet over the handsome pallid face and said out loud, 'Dear God, I cannot suffer this again. Deliver me.'

He made a monumental effort with Weightman's funeral. He wanted everyone to know of his goodness, his courage, his kindness and his humour. There was no other person who had helped him so greatly in his professional life; in fact, he had relied on him too much and would now reap the crop of that over-reliance. He preached his funeral sermon to a packed church, for the villagers of Haworth, strangers to sophisticated manners, were friends to a decent, devoted parson and picked him out as sharply as a fox on the sheep-rich moors. Thus they had judged Weightman for his fearless attendance in their cottages in the terror of this cholera epidemic, which he had paid for with his life. Contrary to his custom, Pat wrote the sermon, not trusting himself to speak extempore without tears; and he intended to publish it so that the young man's goodness was preserved. The effort drained him. That night, as he struggled to write to Emily and Charlotte and then to Anne, he was overwhelmed with grief. Bess took the pen from him.

'I'll do it,' she said. 'Tell me what you want to write.' Between them they chose the words, as gently as they could for Anne because Pat knew she loved Willy and would weep for him as he had, but many times more. When they had finished and sent Martha to the post office, Pat said:

'The doctor is coming from Leeds tomorrow. I'm sorry you have to face it so soon.'

'Thank you,' Bess replied. 'I can face it. We are in the hands of God, remember?'

❦

They took turns by Bess's bed at night; Branwell, glad to ignore the Black Bull since Weightman's death, helped his father so that Patrick could sleep a little and cope with the demands of the parish which he now faced on his own. The young man sat all through the small hours. Pat often stood silently listening to them talking when he came to relieve Branwell. *There is so much goodness in the boy; such talent too, such gifts, such humour.* Bess slept little and talked about Penzance; Branwell reminded her that it was her tales of the sea which had first inspired him and his sisters to write their island stories. She talked about his mother and held his hand and

246

said how proud she would have been of his success as a poet. She talked to Pat about Maria and the days at Hartshead and Thornton; he hated the painful sharpness of his memories and was glad when she dropped off to sleep. When she woke, contorted with pain, he held her hand tight – her Branwell hand, small and fine, the nails as beautiful as Maria's, whose hand he had clutched in this same room, with this same brutal pain. The cancer obstructed her bowels and would not release her easily. He told her over and over again how he loved her and had been saved by her devotion to the family. 'How would we have managed without you?' he said, his short-sighted eyes fixed on hers. She smiled, understanding through the laundanum that he was saying he loved her.

When she died, after a particularly bad bout of pain, Patrick and Branwell were with her. Her last sharp scream reminded Pat of Maria. He shut his eyes. *What have I done? It's all happening again.*

Without Willy to take the funeral, he had to ask James Bradley of Oakworth. Anne had returned home, very thin, her face pale and shadowed, grief for Weightman etched round her eyes, fresh tears for the aunt who had nursed her as a baby. She supported Branwell at the service. Pat observed her closely, impressed by her care for her distraught brother. Pat stood with William Morgan, bound to him by their long memories of Bess. It was two days before Emily and Charlotte arrived, after a cold and difficult journey from Brussels. Emily's grief for her old sparring partner was tempered by her delight at being at home.

26

I am quite contented for myself, not as idle as formerly, altogether as hearty, and having learnt to make most of the present and long for the future with the fidgetiness that I cannot do all I wish; seldom or never troubled with nothing to do, and merely desiring that everybody could be as comfortable as myself and as undesponding and then we should have a very tolerable world of it . . . I have plenty of work on hands, and writing, and am altogether full of business.

Emily Brontë, *Diary Paper*, 30th July 1845.

'There is no question of it!' Emily's voice was low but determined. 'I agreed to six months, and I did more than that. If Aunt had not died I don't think I could have dragged you away. There are things for me to do here.' She was standing by the parlour window, arms folded tightly, shoulders hunched, her furious eyes fixed on the grey church tower.

'What, for instance?' Charlotte's colour was high, but she was fighting to stay calm. She had to get back to Brussels, and Emily had to come with her.

'Look after Papa, for one. Branwell is going with Anne to the Robinsons at Thorp Green; if we go to Brussels he will be entirely alone. He relied on Aunt for her company, for reading to him, for her housekeeping. His sight is worse than ever. She did the accounts, and he doesn't even have a curate.'

'Martha will look after Papa,' said Charlotte silkily. 'You know she loves him, and John will help her. Branwell and Anne could come in an emergency. There's a curate coming soon. You can't want to give up Monsieur's teaching just to keep Papa company.'

'Ah, there we have it!' cried Emily, rounding on her sister. 'That is what all this is about. I wouldn't have said it, Char, if you weren't so utterly bereft of feeling for anyone else, but that is what all this is about. You're mesmerised by Constantin Heger! It was embarrassing to see your devotion. I'm sure I wasn't the only one who saw it. Those stupid girls were laughing at you behind your back. He's a good teacher, but there would be good teachers here. Papa will always pay for teaching if that's what you want.'

Charlotte abandoned the peacemaker mode. 'How dare you! Of course I value Monsieur as teacher, he's outstanding, inspiring. If you're implying . . .'

'Not implying – stating. I think you're besotted with him. If you want to go back you go alone, and you can slave away at his clever structured style exercises as long as you like; they're deadly and devoid of imagination. I won't say a word to anyone about your motives, but I won't come with you.'

'Anne would stay here if you really wanted to come with me.' Charlotte's voice was quiet, but had a hard edge. 'She said to Papa she would. He prefers her to go back to the Robinsons, as Branwell is tutoring the boy. He wants her there to keep an eye on him, but it's really not necessary.'

'Not necessary! Have you looked at Branwell lately? He hasn't recovered from Willy or Aunt: they were both important to him, as they were to Anne.' She paused, and came to sit on a chair by the paper-strewn table. 'Anne loved Willy, Charlotte. She can't get over him. It's better that both of them are away from the reminders, and Papa is worried that Branwell will drink if there's no one he can talk to.'

The room had grown dark, and Charlotte sought a candle to gain time. 'Anne knows nothing of love – it was all in her head, part of her novel-writing. *Passages in the Life of an Individual!*' she said scornfully. 'How can she know about real passion?' Emily looked at her sister's hot cheeks and was confirmed in her earlier view. 'Aunt has made us independent,' Charlotte continued carefully. 'We each have five hundred pounds, except for Branwell, whom she expected, all those years ago, to make his fortune.' She laughed shortly. 'Monsieur has written to Papa and requested our return. I shall tell Papa that I will go alone and pay my own way. You may tell him what you like.' She moved the candle to the table, opened her writing box and began a letter to Brussels.

☙

The books Emily propped up on the kitchen table while she was kneading the bread were a source of irritation to Tabby. After Bess's death she had returned to live at the parsonage to help Martha, but mainly, Emily suspected, because Pat had thought both she and Charlotte would return to Brussels; Pat had suffered enough from gossip throughout his years in Haworth, for however much respect he had in the village, there was always some vindictive soul who would start a rumour, like the one that he was drinking excessively when Dr Andrew had recommended a mild alcohol solution for his eyes. Living alone with a fifteen year old girl would not have been a good idea.

'You'll have to shift them books, Emily, if I'm to get this potato pie done,' Tabby grumbled, limping towards the table from the back kitchen. 'Books was never meant for the kitchen. Nasty dusty things near the food.'

'Just going, Mrs Aykroyd.' Emily dexterously replaced the German book with a heavy pie dish she knew Tabby wouldn't be able to lift from the dresser. 'I'm going to read the newspaper to Papa now, but I'll be back soon to plague you. Shout when the bread's risen.'

She went along the hall to his study; her soft steps did not warn him, and she found him inert, turned towards the windows, his pale blue eyes seeing little. He jumped when she entered, feeling guilty at his inactivity. There was little he could do with his paperwork without help. Worst of all, reading had become almost impossible.

'Don't move,' said Emily. 'I've come to read to you, and I'll do anything else you need help with.' She sat directly opposite him, so that he could see her face quite clearly in the sunlight. 'Do you want the news first, or shall we catch up with the registers for the burials and baptisms?'

'Let's have a treat first and then do the dull stuff,' said Pat. 'Why don't you read me that poem again?'

Emily took a breath. 'You know that I don't like to, Papa. I can just read them once, and only to you, and then they go away.'

'Please,' he said.

She knew the one he meant. Closing her yes, she began:

250

'Cold in the earth – and the deep snow piled above thee,
Far, far removed, cold in the dreary grave!
Have I forgot, my only love, to love thee,
Severed at last by Time's all severing wave?

No later light has lightened up my heaven
No second morn has ever shone for me . . .'

'That's it,' he murmured. 'How could you know?'

'You don't have to be told a thing to know it,' she replied, throwing a log on the fire and disturbing the sleeping Grasper. 'Your love for our mother has been there all our lives.'

Pat stumbled as he failed to see that Grasper had moved. He sat near to the piano. 'Now, some music,' he said cheerfully. 'What's it to be?'

The pile of music on the floor by the piano had grown with the years and was precarious, often falling to Martha's enthusiastic dusting. Emily removed from the top the Haydn sonatas she was working through and started to sort the lower volumes. She paused at the 'Favourite Waltz' of von Weber, lying next to two sets of quadrilles by Henry Smith; the last time she had played those was when Ellen Nussey stayed and they were all at home: they had danced up and down the hall and in and out of the parlour, Ellen and Willy instructing them in the steps, even whirling in and out of Pat's study in his absence. Branwell had collapsed with laughter, exhausted by his attempts to provide a male partner with Willy for the three girls. She put them aside. Things were different then.

'What about a swift rattle through your old favourite, "The March of the Imperial Regiment"?' she asked. 'And you've really enjoyed *The Battle of Prague* – the one by Kotwara – since you returned from Waterloo.'

'Yes, play that. I particularly like the way he has the Word of Command, the Bugle Call for the Cavalry, and the Answer to the First Cannon. That I will enjoy.'

Emily mounted the stool and gamely played her way through the entire *Battle of Prague* – Prussians and Imperialists, Running Fire, Cries of the Wounded, ending with God Save the King. Her father sat close to the piano, his foot silently keeping time, listening intently. She followed it with large sections of Haydn's *Creation* and finished with Handel. Pat was flushed with pleasure.

251

'That was wonderful. You play brilliantly – no, don't deny it; Miss Nussey says the same. You are the most musical of my children. That is why you write good poetry. Rhythm and music are essential to a poet. Why don't you play the flute with Branwell any more?'

'Just time and opportunity, Papa. Next time he's home we'll start again, for he's very good. We always have tremendous rows, but once we get going even I admit we do well.'

Tabby had shuffled along the hall, unable to make Emily hear from the kitchen above the sound of the piano. 'If ye can stir yerself from yer piano playing,' she said with a sniff, 'Bread's risen and needs t' oven.'

'I'll come back and read the paper later,' said Emily.

'Good,' said Pat. 'And I need to write a letter to the *Guardian* about the Irish rebellion.'

∂∂

'That's the postman,' said Emily as she dropped the glistening golden eggs into the bowl. 'No, Tabby, don't go.' Tabby's ears, formerly sharp and alert for the post which she regarded as an important duty to take into 't' Maister', were growing deafer by the year, and she had not heard the knock on the parsonage door. 'Let Charlotte go,' she mouthed at the bewildered old woman as Charlotte's form passed the kitchen door in a blur.

'Ah can't think why she's always mitherin' at the postman,' muttered Tabby, easing herself gingerly into the chair by the fire. 'Time was when she was content to let others run around for her and never stir a bone.'

Emily crouched on the floor near her and in a piercing whisper close to her ear said, 'She's waiting for a letter from Brussels. It's important to her. Don't tell anyone.' Tabby's discretion was steadfast; nothing ever went from the parsonage into the village, and she had trained Martha the same. The lack of solid gossip forced the villagers to invent their own.

'Ah see,' she said, piercing her knitting and starting to clack her needles. 'Ah'll say nowt.'

Emily wiped her hands quickly and went out into the hall. She could hear that her sister was above her on the landing by the muffled sobs. She stood at the bottom of the stairs, gazing up towards the window and wondering whether to go to Charlotte. She waited a minute, listened to the clock in the silence, then took the stairs two at a time. Charlotte was in the study over the front door, sitting on the truckle-bed, knees up to her chin, head on her folded arms.

'Nothing, Char?' she asked quietly, kneeling beside her.

Charlotte raised her head and shook it slowly. Her eyes were red from weeping, her small face drawn and blotchy. As she looked at Emily, her eyes filled with tears and her face crumpled.

'I – can't – bear it!' The words came jerkily, she breathed in hiccups. 'I just can't bear it!'

'Don't you think,' said Emily in a whisper, for the door was wide open, 'don't you think it would very difficult for him to write? Madame was quite . . . possessive . . . wasn't she? They are still a young couple, still having their family.'

Charlotte heaved with sobs. 'Don't, don't don't! I can't bear to think of that!' She stopped: she had said too much. 'I only want a letter from a friend, Emily. We were friends when I was in Brussels; he was my friend, my teacher . . .'

Emily felt it was time for reality. 'It's nearly a year now. If he were going to write he would have done so. You're torturing yourself. You can't sleep, you can't work at your writing. You're ill. Why don't you write one last letter, and then try to put him from your mind? Or write about him? Papa always says it helps to write one's miseries away. And Anne says so too.'

Charlotte gave her a long, hostile look. 'How can either of them know what I am suffering?' Her voice was cold. 'I will write to him again. I have to. But it can't be the last time.'

Emily shrugged, sensing there was nothing else she could do. She made a final attempt.

'Do you remember when Mrs Collins came and told Papa about her brutal husband? The beatings and the loathsome diseases he had given her?' Charlotte nodded silently. 'Papa said to her that despite his being a clergyman she should leave him, however much she loved him. She had to give him up. There was no compromise, and Papa knew that. That is what you have to do.' She shut the door behind her and started down the stairs. As she turned the corner she saw Patrick standing anxiously by his study door.

'Charlotte?' he said worriedly.

'Yes,' whispered Emily. 'But don't say anything, she still thinks you don't know.'

'How could I not know when she grows pale and ill and rushes past my door every time the bell rings? She loves that man. It is a tragedy that she loves a married man. It is a blessing he lives so far away.' He turned to go back to his work. 'It will take time. Lost love brings great grief. It will take a long time.'

You know all about that, thought Emily sadly, returning to her baking.

⌗

Occasionally Pat wished it was his ears and not his eyes which had deteriorated. He opened his door a slit, not daring to make the gap larger.

'How could you, Charlotte? How could you?' Emily was shouting, and her feet were pounding the floor above him, from the children's study, into his bedroom, to and fro, to and fro in her anger. 'Damn you, Char, damn you' – Patrick winced – 'I shall never, never forgive you or trust you again. Can't you leave anything alone?' A rumble of feet on the stairs. He closed the door, easing the lock without a click. He heard Emily go into the dining room. Scampering steps pursued her.

'I didn't mean to upset you . . .'

'Upset me? Upset me? I'm not upset – I'm mortified, wounded, I hate what you've done, and I don't want to talk to you. Go away.'

'Emily . . .' Pat heard a low growl and presumed Emily was hugging Keeper, who resented Charlotte's intrusion. 'Emily, the only reason I told you that I'd looked at your poems was because I thought they had a wonderful music . . .'

'Don't,' said Emily fiercely. 'You won't make me feel better by flattering me. I know they're good. But they were not for you to read. I'd really enjoyed going through my work and selecting from Gondal and putting in other poems I have written ever since we were young. It was for me, my pleasure, not for anyone else to read and certainly not for you.'

Pat decided this was a moment for intrusion. He opened his door noisily. Grasper shot out, thinking it was time for tea.

'Is there something wrong?' he enquired mildly. 'I thought I heard you shouting upstairs and wondered . . .'

'Yes, there is something wrong.' Emily had two bright spots on her usually brown cheeks. 'Charlotte has been to my writing box and has the audacity now to offer me a criticism of my poetry, which she should never have read. There is something very wrong.' She retired to the couch with Keeper, her face to the wall.

Pat sat at the table, hoping that Martha had heard the row and would be too frightened to venture out of the kitchen with the tea. Charlotte was staring out of the window, her expression guilty.

'Emily,' said Pat, 'I'm sorry that you feel so outraged. It is a shock to find that one's work has been read, if one did not intend it.' Charlotte caught her breath. 'I am sure Charlotte will not mind me saying this now because we have buried it, but she also read my work.'

'But we've all read your books,' said Emily, turning round.

'This was not my ancient, published works,' said Pat with a chuckle, 'this was attempts I had made to write novels when I was desperate to make a little money to leave to you in the event of my early death.' He laughed. 'That we seem to have averted.'

Emily sat up and looked interested. 'What novels?'

'I can hardly remember,' said Pat vaguely. 'It's a long time ago. I started one about a young woman, a bit like your mother, and set it when the Luddites were about. Then after Cowan Bridge . . .' His voice faded.

'That is the best.' Charlotte, shameless and enthusiastic, came over from the window and started to talk to Emily. 'It's such a good story, if only he would finish it. It's about an orphan girl at a terrible school like Cowan Bridge – the suffering, the relationships between the pupils – he's just got to the bit when she has to leave to earn her living as a governess.'

Emily shuddered. 'With respect to you, Papa, I can't think how anyone would want to read about a governess.' She seemed calmer. 'You should write about real things like the loves and quarrels of the people you know well round here. That's really interesting.'

'Well,' said Pat, 'the point is that Charlotte read my papers when I was out and has apologised to me. We have put it behind us. If she had thought we both wrote badly, without any spark, she would have kept it to herself and we would be none the wiser. We must take her interest as encouragement. And put it behind us,' he said firmly.

'We often read each other our writing, Em,' said Charlotte. 'I didn't think you'd mind.'

Emily climbed off the couch and lowered Keeper to the floor. 'Well, I do. All right,' she added wearily, 'but if it ever happens again I shall leave this house.'

Pat and Charlotte looked startled at such a radical suggestion. 'Yes, I shall, with Aunt's money, I shall live on the moor' – she was trailing out of the room. 'With the dogs,' continued the disembodied voice from the hall, 'somewhere up by Top Withens . . .'

Pat said to Charlotte. 'You shouldn't have done it. I thought you had learned your lesson when I was cross with you. No more.'

'I'm sorry, Papa,' Charlotte replied meekly, but her eyes were far away. The poems. What if . . .? Fortunately Martha, finely judging the level of noise, entered at that moment with the tea.

෴

The house seemed crowded after the return of Anne and Branwell, and the comings and goings of the Reverend Mr Nicholls. Charlotte had abandoned the hope of ever receiving a letter from Monsieur Heger and no longer rushed for the post; Branwell, who had been sacked by the Robinsons ('Again?' groaned Charlotte), spent most of the day in bed and his nights at that Black Bull. Anne looked ill and worried, but had kept her counsel so far, and the Reverend Arthur Bell Nicholls, who appeared to be a satisfactory ('But oh so dull,' giggled Charlotte) curate for Patrick, entered and left the house politely, quietly, obligingly. He walked the dogs, fetched the newspapers, guided Patrick to the church, became his amanuensis and his companion. His Irish voice blended well with Pat's, and Anne remarked that their father's accent had relaxed into a broader brogue.

The girls had resumed the habit of dispersing around the house in the day for household tasks and writing, then spending the evening in the dining room reading to each other and talking. Pat seldom joined them. He was deeply depressed by his lack of sight, and although Nicholls made life much easier for him, he couldn't bear the idea of living with blindness. He could hardly bear Branwell's latest escapade either.

'What happened?' he asked, when Branwell had spent the day upstairs in tears after the note had come from Mr Robinson,

256

terminating his employment. 'When I visited you and Anne at Thorp Green you seemed so happy. You liked the place, the work was not too demanding, Mr Robinson didn't put restrictions on you. Personally I found Mrs Robinson a most charming, woman; her clerical background . . .'

'She is, she is,' sobbed Branwell. He was weeping unrestrainedly, which unnerved Pat. He was unused to such raw emotion in adults, even in Branwell. He took Branwell's hand.

'What is it, Branwell? I still don't know why he dismissed you.' The young man sobbed on. Lack of sight had rendered Pat sharper in other ways. 'It's not – surely it's not, that you are distraught at leaving Mrs Robinson?' He felt cold and couldn't continue.

'I loved her,' whispered Branwell. 'And she loved me!'

'This is not possible,' said Pat gravely. 'I know a little of the world. Ladies in her position do not fall in love with the tutor. You are mistaken.'

'No,' said Branwell hoarsely, 'she loves me. She said so. She said she was lonely because her husband ignored her and was always ill; she's a beautiful, beautiful creature, and he treated her so badly. I made her life worthwhile. She told me so, and she told me she loved me.'

Part sat up straight in the darkening room. 'No,' he said, feeling cruel. 'It cannot be. Women of her class do not compromise themselves with their servants. Yes – I said servants. That is what a tutor is. I have been one. If she has compromised herself with you she will deny it and forget you.'

'No, no!' shouted Branwell. 'She will not. She will write to me. We will meet. She said so, she said so.' He collapsed into another storm of weeping.

Patrick sat still and let the weeping spend itself. He was appalled. If this were true and not a figment of Branwell's imagination, fuelled by drink or unhinged by misery, it was truly appalling. 'Come Bran,' he said quietly, 'come with me to the parlour. If you sit with the girls you will feel better.' He propelled him through the door. Two things whirled in his mind. A guilty longing for Willy Weightman and the propensity of his children to fall in love with married people. He shook his head to clear it. Opening the parlour door he said to Emily, 'Branwell will be better if he is not on his own, I think. Anne, come with me for a minute.'

When they were settled comfortably in front of the fire in his study, with Flossy, the spaniel Anne had brought home with her from the Robinsons, on her knee, Pat said:

'I can't understand what's going on, Anne. You must help me. If Branwell has been . . . has had any sort of relationship with Mrs Robinson other than a professional one, it is very serious. There could be all sorts of trouble.' His heart clenched at Anne's face. Her misery was palpable.

'I can't be sure,' she said. 'Who knows what has gone on but the two people it concerns? But it is quite likely, Papa; for the past year she – Mrs Robinson – has wanted Branwell with her all the time, reading to her, advising her on various aspects of Edmund's education. She said she could not discuss it with Mr Robinson as he was too ill. They have spent hours together alone. Branwell has been elated, then miserable if she has gone to visit relations, or if Mr Robinson recovered and was around more.' Tears came into her eyes. 'It was such a delight for me to have Branwell with me; he took over Edmund's Latin from me, he was good company and amusing. They all loved him. And then, gradually, I realised what was happening.' She blew her nose hard, almost turfing Flossy onto the floor. 'It spoiled everything. I was trying to persuade Lydia to abandon her liaison with her actor from the Scarborough theatre, and she didn't take kindly to my remonstrations while her mother and Branwell were so obviously entranced with each other.' She paused. 'And he wouldn't listen to me.' She looked anxiously at her father.

'I didn't expect him to.' Pat's voice was warm. The last thing he wanted was for Anne to feel she should have prevented this debacle. He sighed. 'He makes up his own mind; but he knows right from wrong. His misery now is a result of his self-indulgence.'

Anne looked up from her handkerchief. 'That is hard,' she said.

'I know,' said Pat. 'It was meant to be. If I had been harder in the past, he might have done better by now. I am largely to blame for his weakness.'

Anne got up and deposited Flossy in his lap. She kissed the top of his pure-white head. 'Perhaps you're also responsible for your perfect daughters,' she said, smiling at last. 'You've got your deserts now, Papa. All of us at home!'

'That's the way I prefer it,' he said, 'if you're happy.'

☙

'Well?' said Charlotte defiantly. 'We've got thirty pounds, haven't we, between us? So why not do it?'

Silence hung over the still parlour. It was late: Patrick had gone to bed, the dogs had been out and were settled for the night, Branwell was at the Black Bull. The fire was nearly dead and gave only a small shower of sparks when Emily shuffled the remainder of the day's coal out of the scuttle. She returned to the couch and said nothing.

Anne, looking up from her neatly written sheets, tried to remember what Charlotte was talking about, and failed. She had been aiming to finish a chapter that evening and was barely aware of the conversation round her. She could sense there was conflict, though.

'Well?' Charlotte wanted a reply. Anne looked at Emily. She was not going to get one from there. To keep the peace, she said, 'Tell me again about your idea, Charlotte.'

'For goodness sake!' Charlotte slapped the papers she was holding impatiently on the table. 'The poems! We've all read each other's poems, and I think we should publish them. It would cost about thirty pounds. But we have to agree.'

'I don't agree,' said Emily flatly. 'It's a silly idea. Whoever would want to buy poems written by three sisters? And our poems are so different from each other's.'

'If you mean you think that mine are inferior, then say so.' Charlotte had been stung by Emily's criticism of her poetry, although she had to agree that her sister was right. Her own verses, set against Emily's, were conventional and mediocre. But she was desperate to get into print and thought the combination of their three styles might prove more successful than hers alone.

'I think that some of yours lack a vitality which I think essential in poetry.' Emily was not vindictive but honest. 'But I don't want to publish anything. I'm happy for you and Anne to do so. Why don't you ask Branwell to join you? He's written more than any of us and has been published in the newspapers. He hasn't any money, unlike us, but we could pay his share.' She waited to see Charlotte's reaction to this.

'I'd rather not publish at all than do it with Branwell.'

'Charlotte!' Anne was shocked. 'That is dreadful! You always wrote with Bran, and he's terribly hurt by the way you treat him now.'

259

'That is his own fault.' Charlotte was savage, her lips working. 'He's ruined our life here with his drinking and hysterics. We can't have people to stay because of his outrageous behaviour. Papa never sleeps because he lies awake waiting for him to return at night and then spends the rest of it listening to his ravings and emptying his slops.' She shuddered. 'If you want Branwell involved, then I have no more interest in it.'

Emily was torn between allowing this to happen and achieving her other goal. She joined them at the table, her hazel eyes luminous in the candlelight.

'It involves quite a lot of money,' she said slowly, drawing a pattern with her forefinger on the cloth. 'If Papa knew, he would be very anxious at us spending money he would prefer us to save for the future. He's particularly worried now because he fears the trustees will say he cannot function as the incumbent because he is nearly blind, and we'll all be out of here.' She looked directly at Charlotte. 'His life is intolerable at the moment. I'll agree to the publication and put in my ten pounds, if we do the same and try to get Papa's eyes operated on. It can be done now. And Papa won't spend the money on himself because he fears for our future.'

'What a good idea!' Anne was enthusiastic. 'I know you asked the Taylors about a surgeon, Charlotte, and they didn't know a local man, but surely there is someone in Leeds or Manchester? Even London would be worth it.'

While Charlotte sat silent, Emily continued, 'There are new hospitals in Manchester. I'll go with you to find out.' Both sisters looked at her in astonishment. Brussels and London, she had said, were her last big cities. 'This is important, and I'll do it. Let's go soon.'

There was a crash in the hall which shook the room. Emily ran out and found Branwell lying full-length on the flagstones. He must have come back on his own, without John Brown. She heaved him up until she had his arm round her shoulder.

'Come on, Bran,' she said softly, 'try to be quiet, old man, or you'll wake everyone.' She dragged him towards the stairs. Anne picked up his hat and followed behind. Together they struggled up the stairs until they got to the top, where Pat was waiting in his nightgown.

'Go back to bed,' whispered Emily, 'we can manage.' He turned obediently and let the girls deposit their brother on his bed. They pulled off his outer clothes.

'Could you see that . . .'

'Yes, Papa – Emily always does that,' Anne said, as Emily made Branwell use the chamber pot. Patrick felt utterly impotent and ashamed that they performed these tasks as a ritual, without flinching. He used to be able to manage the buckets and pots alone, but without his sight he was usually too late.

'I'm going to empty it, and I'll bring it back in case he vomits,' Emily whispered. 'You try to sleep. We'll hear if he wakes.'

Later they both returned to the parlour where Charlotte was sitting miserably. 'It's as well you can both do that,' she said, 'for I cannot.' Tears fell down her cheeks. 'I used to love him so much! Now I can't bear to be near him.' She wiped her eyes. 'But I agree about Papa; we'll publish the poems and have the operation. I agree he can't be left like this.'

∞

In the end Patrick agreed to the operation if he paid for it himself. Emily and Charlotte took the train to Manchester, Emily enduring Charlotte's railings against Branwell as they passed through the stations where he had worked. When they arrived in Manchester, Charlotte was amazed at the speed at which Emily had them whirled round the city until they had found an eye surgeon who seemed competent to do the operation. He was against couching Patrick's eyes, regarding it as dangerous, but would remove what he was sure, from their description, was a cataract once he had seen it and diagnosed it ripe for removal. He wanted them to bring Pat for an examination and then, if it was ready, stay for the operation and remain a month in Manchester.

On the way back to Haworth Emily said that she could not bear to live for a month in Manchester and that Charlotte would not survive a month with Branwell. They put it to Anne that it would be better for Charlotte to go to Manchester, and for Emily and Anne to remain at home to cope with Branwell.

'So it is all arranged,' said Patrick wryly. 'I am a lucky man to have such managing daughters. I mean it – it – it is a lot of trouble to you all. But I am worried about the parish and Branwell.'

'Mr Nicholls will manage the parish; I expect he will give us a hand with Branwell if we need it,' said Anne. 'He's not unaware of what goes on. Living so close to us he cannot fail to hear the comings and goings.'

'He's very discreet,' said Emily. 'If he hears Bran coming up the lane from his window he comes straight out and deposits him on the doorstep. Then he goes and hides behind the wall until he's sure we've taken him in. I've seen him.'

'Really?' Charlotte was amazed. Her opinion of curates had not changed. This was an act of imaginative kindness she would never have credited a curate with.

'Nicholls is kind,' affirmed Pat. 'He has put up with me without complaint for nearly a year. He didn't expect to have to shoulder the burden of the parish. He will look after you all if you need it.'

The rooms they hired in Manchester were spacious and pleasant but taxed Charlotte's sparse housekeeping skills. Eventually they were settled, and Dr Wilson pronounced Patrick's eye ready for the operation. It took place in the sitting room, without anaesthetic; Wilson warned Patrick that there was a risk from possible infection, but he only replied, 'Then I may never feel Keeper's head on my knees again!' The surgeons were astonished at his courage and patience; he was seventy years old and neither feared nor complained.

He had to rest in a darkened room for nearly two weeks before the bandages could be removed. The Manchester weather, wet and dreary, did not encourage exercise; neither was it desirable to leave Patrick alone in the house. Anticipating a month of inactivity, Charlotte had come equipped with paper and pens and had packed, without his knowledge, a couple of Pat's old unfinished manuscripts.

A week after the operation, she peeped into the bedroom where he lay, bandaged and bored, or possibly asleep – it was difficult to tell. The heavy curtains were drawn, and the only light came from a single candle burning in the corner of the room, its sconce shielding Pat's eyes. His white hair gleamed softly in the faint light; his breathing was light and easy. She left the door ajar and took out the manuscript about the orphan governess. Settling herself at a table in the window, she read it for an hour, then took up a pen, chewed it, doodled in the margin of her paper. The sky outside was grey steel; soon the rain was battering the window, running in sheets against the panes. She started. 'There was no possibility of taking a walk that day,' she wrote. She felt excited. 'We had been wandering in the leafless shrubbery.' Not the right rhythm, but she could go back – 'the cold winter wind had brought a rain so penetrating . . .' She was off; the changes would come later. No time to stop now.

27

Well, some may hate, and some may scorn,
And some may quite forget thy name;
But my sad heart must ever mourn
Thy ruined hopes, thy blighted fame!

Emily Brontë, *Stanzas*

'The money *is* important,' said Anne as she wrestled with the parcel's knot. Carefully she extracted the manuscripts from the brown paper without tearing it.

'I know, I know,' replied Charlotte. 'Put them back in the paper, and I'll write a quick letter.' She did so, apparently without thinking. It was one she had written several times before. 'Whose turn is it this time? Newby's?' She spun the parcel Anne had retied towards her and scored out the last address. Finding a small clear space she wrote: *Thomas Cautley Newby, Publisher, 172 Mortimer Street, Cavendish Square, London W.*

Emily entered the parlour and laid her shotgun on the table. Keeper was scampering at her heels. They were both muddy. She craned her neck to read Charlotte's writing.

'Still on their rounds, are they?' she said. '"Despite the total failure of their *Poems*, which sold two copies,"' she intoned in a mock reviewer's voice, '"the celebrated authors Acton, Ellis and Currer Bell are importuning every publisher in the land."' She stood the gun in the corner of the room, a habit she knew irritated Charlotte, who thought it worthy of a farm kitchen. 'Papa's sight is now good enough for him to see if I hit the targets. Time for me to stop!' She flung herself on the sofa, and Keeper joined her.

'I thought you agreed with us that we had to make money.' Charlotte was frowning. 'If Branwell . . .'

264

'Yes, I do agree.' Emily cut her short. 'I wouldn't have agreed to attempting to publish *Wuthering Heights* if I didn't think our situation with Branwell was critical. Poor old lad, he . . .'

'Save your sympathy for Papa, Emily. Branwell is convinced that he is near the end of his life. If we lose the parsonage and have to keep Branwell for the rest of our lives, we *need* to publish. Branwell will never work again. Since Mr Robinson died, and that woman,' her mouth twisted – 'raised his hopes then dashed them again, he isn't capable of anything.'

'He may recover.' Anne was staring intently at the brown paper parcel. 'It would be good if we could make some money so that we can look after him should anything happen to Papa.' Her eyes suddenly filled with tears.

Emily got up and took her by the shoulders. 'Papa is so much better now that he can see. Don't worry,' she said affectionately. 'We'll make money, and Papa will live, then we can all say farewell to the trustees and go and live in splendid isolation on the moor.'

'Or in Scarborough,' said Anne.

'Or abroad,' said Charlotte. She picked up the parcel and opened the door. 'I'm going to the post office now,' she said. 'Ooh, sorry Mr Nicholls, I didn't see you there.' And she was gone, leaving the curate bemused in the hall. He went into Patrick's study.

Emily shut the door. She and Anne were shaking with laughter.

'She doesn't see it, does she?' chuckled Anne. 'He moons about and hangs on her every word. If only he knew her opinion of curates! Seriously, do you think we should go on and on sending the novels away? It's so disappointing when they come back time after time.'

'Yes. I hate it as much as you do – more, I suspect. And thank God I made Charlotte agree to noms de plume. Anyway,' she said, rubbing her palm and hunching her shoulders, 'we need the money . . .'

⌒〇⌒

'God's teeth!' cried Emily. The smell of burning wafted into the hall. She flew up the stairs and into the bedroom where Branwell lay. It was midday; the sun was shining, but the room was shuttered and dark. The only light came from the blazing bed curtains. She seized Branwell and flung him into the corner of the room. 'Wake

265

up, wake up, you idiot!' she shouted, running out of the door and hurtling down the stairs.

'Give me that!' she shouted at the astonished Martha, who had just come into the kitchen with a bucket of water from the well. Back up the stairs she tore and threw the water at the hangings. Branwell was stirring in the corner of the room. She could hear Anne coming up with another bucket. She pulled Branwell to his feet and grabbed him by the neck.

'Wake up, wake up,' she shouted, shaking and banging at him. She had once beaten Keeper for sleeping on the clean beds, and this action was similar. The fire died. Branwell dragged himself out of his cloud of alcohol and laudanum.

'If you smoke in bed at least stay awake, Bran!' Emily was still shouting. She took a deep breath and lowered her voice now that the emergency was over. 'You'll burn the house down, you silly old thing,' she said, quite gently. 'Now get up and wash and stay out of here so that we can tidy up. Don't tell Papa,' she said to him firmly. 'No, don't tell Papa, it's a good thing he's out. He's terrified of fire.'

'But he'll notice the bed curtains have gone,' said Anne.

'No, he won't,' said Emily. 'Men never notice if you move the furniture or change things. They never know where anything goes. So he won't.' They worked quickly, systematically, opening windows, washing the floor, folding clothes, stacking papers in heaps, removing the tobacco, candles and dirty linen. Anne gave the furniture a violent polish with the hardest beeswax and turpentine they had to sweeten the air.

'Let's go outside,' she said, after they had settled Branwell back in bed and returned their equipment to the kitchen. 'A bit of gardening would help. Let's pick those blackcurrants at the front.' They went out together into the sunshine and were immersed in a conversation about Anne's current novel when Charlotte appeared on the steps holding a piece of paper. She had remained in the parlour during the commotion. Her eyes were shadowy, hopeless.

'It's from Newby. He wants to publish *Wuthering Heights* and *Agnes Grey*. But not *The Professor*.' Her voice broke.

Oh Lord, thought Emily. *Now what.*

☙

266

Emily was tapping on the side window of the Black Bull for some time before Sugden opened the door. When he did, he had Branwell ready.

'He's not too bad, Miss Emily.' The landlord panted as he handed Branwell over. 'He's been talking to t' travellers and forgot his drink.' Emily took Branwell by the arm and forced him upright.

'Thank you,' she said quietly. She never lingered, just started off across the graveyard with her unsteady burden.

'Sorry,' mumbled Branwell. 'I'm sorry, Em; didn't mean to stay a lon' time.' His head fell forward, he became heavier. She lurched to one side, tripping against a gravestone, almost dropping him. A bulky figure loomed out of the shadows.

'Is that you, Mr Nicholls?' she called softly.

'Yes.' He stepped forward and heaved Branwell onto his broad shoulders. Emily liked the man: unobtrusive, dark and brooding, a real friend who saw a need and supplied it. Charlotte's prejudice against curates often missed buried treasure. Relieved of her burden, she led the way back to the parsonage, opening the door noiselessly. Nicholls approached the stairs with practised ease, swinging his body away from the banisters to allow Branwell free passage. He entered the bedroom Branwell shared with Pat and gently lowered the body.

'Are you all right now?' he asked.

'Yes,' she replied; she didn't want to involve Nicholls in putting Branwell down for the night. She quickly covered the now sleeping form; she would return later with Anne. 'Thank you,' she said as they made their way down the stairs as quietly as possible. Not quiet enough. Patrick was standing at his study door.

'Thank you, Nicholls.' He looked very old; the nightly ritual of Branwell's rescue was wearing him down. Depriving him of money had little effect: he always seemed to get it somehow, whether from Mrs Robinson who attempted to buy his silence as she husband-hunted, or from friends who responded to the remnants of his charm. The day that Pat had found the letter to John Brown asking him to meet him in the lane with fivepennyworth of gin was a black one for Pat. The sexton had dropped it where anyone could have found it. It symbolised the depth of Branwell's degradation.

Arthur Nicholls's face, behind his strong black beard, was full of concern. He liked Branwell when he was sober, but he ached for the family who daily and nightly endured his excesses. His interventions were intended to protect Charlotte, whom he thought the most sensitive and delicate of creatures. He had also conceived a great affection and respect for Patrick. He had never met a woman like Emily; daily he thanked God that Charlotte was shielded by her sister's devotion to Branwell.

'Come in,' the old man said. 'Have a dram for your trouble.' He ignored Nicholls' dismissive hand and poured him a glass. 'Emily, you need one too, come and sit with us a while.' Emily glanced towards the ceiling. Pat said, 'He'll sleep for bit. Leave it.'

Outside Emily could hear the wind rising, and she knew it would be a full moon. She was wondering if she could use Nicholls as a chaperone to get out of the house. Her father was always nervous when she went out alone at night. She took the glass gratefully from Pat and swallowed deeply.

'He's been so much worse since Mr Robinson died. He had unrealistic hopes.' Pat nodded. 'But I wish you could have known him before, Mr Nicholls.' (Somehow they had never got round to calling him Arthur.) 'He was such good company, such fun, a brilliant talker, a good musician. He . . .' – she paused, her amber glass suspended, remembering. 'We used to play flute and piano together. He was so impatient if my accompaniment wasn't perfect. I once said, "Look, Branwell, just this one chord needs eight fingers – and you've only got one line of music to read." "You've got ten," he said. "What's the problem?" ' She laughed, but there were tears in her dark eyes. She lowered her head so that her hair shielded her face.

'Life is like this,' said Pat, refilling the glasses. 'I remember having to explain it to my dear wife. Ups and downs, ups and downs. My sight is better, and I can walk and visit and read and preach when I thought that was all gone forever, but poor Branwell is in the slough of despond. But he will get better. He has talent. And sometimes,' he added, 'I feel it is my fault that he drinks too much. I have enjoyed a dram all my life. Perhaps if there had been no drink in the house . . .'

'No, Papa,' said Emily firmly, 'he has had an example of moderation from you. It's something within him – his unhappiness – I don't know . . .' Her voice faded. 'But whatever happens we shall look after him. He'll stay with us.'

Nicholls looked at her when he thought the tears had gone. 'Do you want to take your usual walk before bed, Miss Emily?'

'Yes,' she replied. 'I shan't be long, Papa. Don't wait up. I'll lock up.' She kissed him and fetched her cloak. Pat was pleased at this friendship. Nicholls was totally reliable and would never take advantage of his daughters.

She was right: the moon was full and the night air sharp and damp. When they reached the lane she said, 'Thanks – I won't be long.' Throwing her shawl over her head she set out for the moor at a fast pace, striking out on the old packhorse trail, watching the late rabbits scuttle as she came. She climbed onto the rocks and stood looking across the valley, then stretched out her arms as if she were enfolding the world. Her tiny silhouette against the moonlit sky was seen by Nicholls as he waited outside his lodgings. Half an hour later she returned, her cheeks whipped by the wind, her eyes bright.

'Thank you,' she said. 'I just don't want any more worry for him.' She turned to the parsonage door, and he heard the key rotate in the lock. Sure of her safety, he returned to his little room at the Browns'.

ல

'Have you got any money?' whispered Anne, shutting the parlour door behind her so that their conversation could not be heard by the bailiff standing on the doorstep. It was a bitterly cold day, and the wind blew beneath the door. Charlotte pulled her shawl closer.

'Do you mean cash or capital?' she replied. She knew what Anne meant but was not going to make it easy. 'I shouldn't think that you and Emily have any – the amount you have to pay Newby towards publication will leave you practically bankrupt!'

Anne sighed; Newby's refusal of Charlotte's novel had made for some awkward evenings. 'I mean cash,' she hissed. 'The bailiff wants six pounds for Branwell's debt at the pub he goes to in Halifax, and he'll arrest him if it's not paid.' She threw two sovereigns on the table. 'That's all I have here; Emily has two also – what have you got?'

Charlotte wearily felt in her writing desk and produced a sover-iegn. 'I can get more, but not today.' They kept little cash in the house as Patrick paid all the expenses. 'You'll have to ask Papa.'

'We were trying not to,' muttered Anne, seizing the sovereign and going back to the hall. She went into Pat's study. He was with Nicholls. She hesitated, then closed the door firmly, standing with her back against it 'It's urgent,' she said. Nicholls knew enough anyway. 'The bailiff is here, and we're short of a sovereign.'

Pat drew his keys out of his waistcoat pocket and opened the drawer of his table. 'How much is it?' he asked. He took out the full amount, his hand trembling, and gave it to Anne. 'You are not to pay Branwell's debts,' he said severely. 'He is my responsibility. Give the money back to your sisters.' He pushed the papers away from him. 'I can't do any more now, Nicholls. Come back this afternoon if you would.' Nicholls left, almost pushing the bailiff off the step. Anne handed him the money. He had had an interesting morning. He didn't often collect from parsonages, or from sweet girls. Anne slammed the door and then closed the parlour door quietly on her father, who was sitting with his white head in his shaking hands.

Returning to the parlour, she rolled Charlotte's sovereign across the table. 'Papa paid it all; he looks like death.' She sat down and leaned back on the chair's back legs. 'Just keep sending *The Professor*,' she said. 'Someone will take it. You know that publishing isn't about merit. It's what fits at the time. Just keep on.'

Charlotte looked at her sister wryly. She had more tenacity than any of them. The baby had turned into a woman with a will of iron. She would take her advice.

Emily put her head round the door. 'Branwell needs help – will you come, Anne?'

Pleased that Charlotte had reached for her pen, Anne fetched a clean shirt from the kitchen and went upstairs.

◌◌

'So I am not to know – and Ellen is not to know – and Branwell is not to know?' Patrick was balancing the slim volume in his open palms; he couldn't get further than that.

'Yes,' said Charlotte. 'You are not to know because you are a respectable clergyman, and the reviews of *Jane Eyre* indicate that it is a dangerous and immoral book which your family should have no part in; Ellen is not to know because I have chosen not to tell her and it would be embarrassing; and Branwell is not to know because Emily thinks it will make him miserable.'

'Well,' said Pat,'I will go along with it all as long as we are consistent. I will pretend that I am such an old fool that I never knew what went on under my nose, or with my own unfinished manuscript' – Charlotte caught his amused glance over his spectacles – 'as long as we stick to it. We cannot change our minds later. But none of you has ever told me why you took the name Bell?'

'Oh, no very good reason. We just played with names, and Emily, because she disagrees with my view of curates, thought she would torment me by using Mr Nicholls's middle name.' It had been such a hurdle of compromise and negotiation, this publishing. And Emily and Anne were still adamant that they would stick with Newby, despite the very much better terms offered by Smith Elder. Charlotte had practically promised the handsome Mr Smith that Acton and Ellis Bell would transfer to him.

Pat put the book on the highest of his book shelves, next to *Wuthering Heights, Agnes Grey, Cottage Poems, The Maid of Killarney* and the rest of his own works. There was a folder where he kept Branwell's published poems and his letters to literary magazines.

'Branwell will not see them there,' he said, as Charlotte looked anxious. 'He rarely comes in here these days, and if he does his chair is by the fire and his head is down. But I am proud, Charlotte, very proud. Your work and your sisters' is better than anything I have ever written and, sad to say, than Branwell has. He has never reached his peak.' His face was stricken as he talked of his son.

'But there is a problem, Papa. Since the success of *Jane Eyre*, Newby is claiming that all the novels are the work of Currer Bell. We cannot allow such deceit. It's not fair on Mr Smith.'

'Then you must tell him. He will be a man of honour and will protect your secret.'

'He'll have to, Papa. Emily will be so angry if her identity is revealed.' They looked at each other in mutual horror at the consequences of this. 'Anne will come with me to London; we need to go tonight. I shall pack a box to send to Keighley, and then we'll catch the night train.'

'You must travel first-class at night.' He reached for key and opened his money drawer. What a world it was with these railways, up to London in a night!

'There's no need for that,' said Charlotte. 'Remember that I have all the money from *Jane Eyre*. And we'll stay at the Chapter so that you'll know we'll be safe.'

'Do you want me to come with you? You should have a chaperone . . .'

'No,' said Charlotte. 'You shouldn't be racing about at your age. We will be together.' She was looking forward to travelling alone with Anne. 'We'll whirl up and back in a couple of days and then everything will be safe again.'

Later, as Patrick laboured over the accounts with Nicholls, the younger man stood up to stretch before the onslaught of the next mountain of work. His height brought him close to the top of the shelves, the new titles sharp in the candlelight.

'A new book?' he enquired mischievously. He knew what went on.

'Yes,' said Pat, 'but it's all a secret. You may have read the reviews of this one.'

'Do you have a favourite?' asked Nicholls, hoping that Pat would choose Currer Bell's *Jane Eyre*. He had been excited by their choice of name, hoping that maybe Charlotte was sending a message that she would like to change her name to his.

'I do, indeed. But you would never tell a soul. It's *Wuthering Heights*. It must be the Irish in me, but all the loving and the passion and the drinking – the undying love – it thrills me.' Nicholls raised his dark, bushy eyebrows. That was not his experience of being Irish. 'But *Jane Eyre* strikes a blow for unprotected children, and *Agnes Grey* for every good girl who has had to endure abuse in the governess class. My girls are crusaders, Nicholls. I tried to be, but failed.'

'But they wrote under your roof,' said Nicholls with rare insight.

'That is true,' said Pat, brightening. 'And their mother could write, too.'

∽

Pat's steady stride took him through the graveyard and to the Black Bull. Entering by the back door, he made his way to the private sitting room where he knew that Francis Grundy, Branwell's friend from his railway days, was waiting.

'Mr Grundy!' He extended his hand and had it grasped warmly. 'I know you are expecting Branwell, and he will come, but I wanted to see you to warn you . . .'

'Sit down, Mr Brontë, please,' said the young man. He had

become anxious at the sight of the old clergyman, hatless and disturbed. He remembered Branwell's letters, written from the depths of his misery, telling of the awful nights he inflicted on his father. The results were plain to see.

'I won't stay, if you will excuse me,' said Pat. 'I came to warn you that Branwell is much changed; he is very ill and sleeps little. He has a terrible cough which keeps us – him – awake. He has a shaking which comes over him at times.' Patrick paused. It was difficult to know how to describe delirium tremens without making Branwell out to be a hopeless drunk. He was, but he was also ill with consumption. 'Don't be shocked,' he finished rather lamely. 'He so wants to see you.' He raised his hand in farewell and departed.

Near the house he met Emily supporting Branwell. She had made an attempt to tidy him, but his hair was matted and his coat hung off his emaciated form. His eyes were feverishly bright in his gaunt face, his breathing fast and light.

'Can you manage?' he asked.

'Of course,' she replied, 'leave it to me.'

He watched from the window as they made slow progress across the graveyard; when she came back she went to the corner near the moor where the Browns had their family graves. ('Always choose a superior spot for your own, John,' Pat had teased the sexton in days gone by. 'Custom and practice, Mr Brontë, we've been here longer than most.') He saw her sink to the ground; propping her elbows on her knees she put her head into her hands, her fingers dividing her dark hair. It was difficult to believe, but she was weeping. She wouldn't want him to see, so he turned away. Her outrage at Branwell's decline had changed her nature. Her humour was gone; all that remained was an occasional burst of sarcasm or wit. She slaved to look after him; Anne helped her, dutifully, Charlotte ignored him. Emily acted as if it were her own life, as well as his, that was at stake.

He waited ten minutes, then went out. He saw Nicholls's bulk against the wall of the Browns' house. Seeing Patrick, he turned back into the house. Pat strolled casually towards Emily, as noisily as he could; he remarked to her that it was a fine evening. He pulled her to her feet as she wiped her face on her sleeve. Taking his arm, she came inside.

෴

During the night Branwell had become calmer. Pat and Emily had sat with him, releasing him to John Brown in the early morning. They were both in the kitchen with Martha and Tabby when John ran downstairs. Martha was the first to look at her father.

'He's bad, Mr Brontë, real bad. Coom up, he needs thee.' Pat and Emily abruptly left the table where they had half-heartedly been toying with bread and coffee; Tabby tutted and shuffled.

'I'm going to die,' said Branwell faintly. 'I know. I've wanted it ever since . . .' He stopped. In his present mood he wished to spare his father. 'I know I shall be happy.'

Patrick sank to his knees at the bedside. More than anything he wanted to make this easy for his unbelieving son.

'You will be, Bran, you will.' He took him in his arms and held him. The wasted frame shot through him a memory of all the others he had held, all his flesh and blood. He had little to thank God for there. But he wanted Branwell to be happy, Branwell who had never been successful, who had craved admiration and attention. 'God loves you, Branwell, and is waiting for you. He forgives you and loves you. You will be in His arms. He loves you.' He looked across the bed and saw Emily's face, set like a stone. She caught his look and briefly nodded. She, too, thought it was the right thing to do.

'Fetch Charlotte and Anne,' she whispered to John Brown. 'Martha, bathe his head.'

Pat marvelled at the tenderness the young girl showed as she stroked the wet cloth across Branwell's head. She had forgotten Branwell the drunken opium-eater, creating washing and mess, cluttering up the rooms she was supposed to be cleaning when he turned day into night; all she remembered now was the amusing young man she had known all her life, teasing her, telling her stories. Charlotte and Anne came in. Anne knelt by her father; Charlotte stood in the doorway, her face controlled, her eyes ravaged.

She will never forgive him, thought Emily. *But he won't know.*

But he did. A spasm of coughing wracked his thin body – so fierce that Pat could barely keep hold of him – and as he coughed he stretched out a hand to Charlotte. She buried her face in her hands. He lay back, panting, the bright-red arterial blood spattering his nightshirt. Patrick prayed; words would comfort him as they did all of them. Branwell's last word was 'Amen!'

They stood like a marble frieze around his bed, unable to move. The first to do so was Patrick. In the hushed silence of the room he struggled to his feet, the crack of his knees breaking the silence. He went to his study, locking the door behind him, and there he remained for the rest of the day, in utter desolation. Maria would have forgiven him two children killed by disease; would she forgive him one killed by unhappiness?

28

I sought, and soon discovered, the three headstones on the
slope next the moor . . . I lingered round them, under that
benign sky; watched the moths fluttering among the heath,
and hare-bells; listened to the soft wind breathing through the
grass; and wondered how anyone could ever imagine unquiet
slumbers, for the sleepers in that quiet earth.

Emily Brontë, *Wuthering Heights*, Chapter 34.

Charlotte stood in the kitchen doorway, arms folded, listening to
the sounds of the house. The whites of her eyes, stained yellow by
jaundice for two weeks, were clearer now. From upstairs she heard
Anne's persistent, dry cough; from the dining room Emily's
occasional deep bark. There was no sound from her father's study.
The hall was icy cold and the wind blew through every crevice it
could find, wailing and whispering. She shivered and turned back
into the kitchen where Tabby sat with her fidgeting rough hands
rasping on her smooth starched apron.

'It's yer faither I mun worrit about,' she said, 'These young
things will reet thenselves soon enough when t' spring cooms
round. But t' Maister,' – she lifted her hands in a hopeless gesture
''e cannot get over Branwell, even though 't were a merciful
release. 'E's like an old dog pining.'

Charlotte stared into the fire. Branwell's death had touched her
only on the day it happened. She had been too preoccupied with
the success of *Jane Eyre* to notice the progress of his sickness, and
her sisters' acceptance that she didn't help with his care insulated
her further. She was distressed the day he died, but she had never
forgiven him the waste of his talents and his inability to rise above
his anguish – *she* had loved a married man for years, but Branwell

276

had to die of it. Anne's clear head could despise the degradation but care for the brother; Emily loved unconditionally and was now paying the price.

William Morgan had conducted Branwell's funeral; visibly moved, his plump face glistening with tears, he could not believe that his dearest friend was bearing the terrible weight of bereavement yet again. He had come because Pat had asked him; but he felt almost unequal to the task. He remembered Branwell's birth vividly; his promise, his talent, Pat's hopes, Maria's pride in her only boy. His small, round form was a sharp contrast to Patrick's skeletal height and drawn face. His courage almost failed him. After the service, Emily had gone straight to the dining room and lain on the couch, clutching Keeper for warmth, her face to the wall. She would not speak.

The weather had been bitter, and Charlotte felt she would never be warm again. She pulled her shawl tightly round her and left Tabby staring at her hands; she knocked on the parlour door and went in. Pat was immobile in front of a dead fire. A single candle guttered at his elbow; the flame lurched in the draught she created. The room was very cold. Flossy lay on his feet.

'Papa, let me light the fire.' He didn't move, just looked up without speaking. She took sticks from the scuttle and laid them carefully in the way Tabby had taught her as a child. Cooking she could never bear, but she always felt she made a tolerable parlourmaid. She filled in her wooden tower with tiny pieces of coal, then took the candle and gently worked on the sticks. Soon she had a little blaze. She could now see her father's tragic face. *More grief for his only son than for his daughters,* she found herself thinking, quite bitterly. She stopped. *No point. Other things to live for.*

She was still crouched on the floor in front of the grate. She put a hand on his bony knee. 'Papa, I think we must get Dr Wheelhouse again. Anne is no better.' Pat jerked up. That roused him. Never neglect the children. Get help. Get the doctor.

'Send John Brown for Dr Wheelhouse,' he said. 'And we will have Mr Teale from Leeds after he has been. I will speak to Emily.' He walked out of the room as if in a dream, shuffling his slippers on the stone flags. In the dining room Emily and Keeper lay on the couch. Flossy had followed Pat and sniffed the other dog, nudged him nosily, then pushed at Emily's elbow. Unusually for these days, she smiled.

277

'My dear, I have asked Dr Wheelhouse to call again as Anne seems worse, or at least no better. And I am fetching Mr Teale from Leeds. I would like you to see them both.'

The smile vanished; she turned towards the wall. 'No, Papa.'

'Emily, you are sick. You can't go on without some treatment. Please let the doctors see you.'

'Poisoning doctors!' she said vehemently. 'What's the point? Did they ever cure Mama or Maria or Elizabeth? Or Willy or Aunt?' Her voice cracked. 'Or Branwell?' she whispered. 'Years and years Bran was ill; all the doctors you called, and not one could save him.' She clutched Keeper tightly, his tan coat curled in her fist. 'We all have the same disease, Papa. There is no cure for consumption. Haven't we lived in this village long enough to know that? Bran drank and took opium, but in the end his lungs gave up. That's what's wrong with me. Anne has the cough, hasn't she? Don't talk to me about doctors!' She turned back to the wall, her breathing fast with effort, her head resting on her arm. Pat put out a hand to her; Keeper growled.

'Don't,' he said. 'Don't do that to me.' Emily did not reply. She wasn't sure if he addressed her or the dog. He went out into the hall and met Nicholls coming in to fetch the dogs for their walk.

'You won't get Keeper to come,' he said, 'so don't try. Just take Flossy.' He returned to the parlour and Charlotte. 'She won't see anyone.' His voice shook. 'She understood grief in her head when she wrote her book. But the reality has broken her heart.' Suddenly he felt furiously angry. He slammed his fist on the table; the books and papers jumped and fell. 'Surely I have given enough! My wife, three children, my dearest companion – and now the genius of this family!' Charlotte bit her lip. 'There is no God!' he shouted. 'There is no God! Get out, Charlotte, get out and leave me alone.'

She stumbled out into the hall where Nicholls stood in horror with Flossy. 'Ignore it,' she said. 'Papa is not himself. Please get Mr Wheelhouse to call. Anne will see him. Please be quick.' He looked at the grief in the face he loved so much and yearned to comfort her.

∽

Martha had cried when Emily would not allow her to help her dress; even the dogs would have preferred her not to make the effort to feed them. As she did so a sudden draught, cutting

278

through the parsonage hall, flung her against the wall, almost breaking her visible bones. But she battled on to the kitchen, and with slow persistence cut up the food, almost dropping the bowls to the floor because she dared not bend. A sharp pain shot through her with every breath as she hauled herself, step by step, up the stairs. Collapsing onto the bed in the children's study, she said to Charlotte, with an irony which her sister mistook for sense, 'I will see a doctor now.' Keeper settled down beside her.

Charlotte ran to Pat. He jumped up with joy and took the stairs like a young man. When he got there, Emily was dead.

◌◌

'No, not William.' Pat shook his head. 'He could barely manage Branwell's service. He's old, he's known us through happy times, and it's all too much for him.' Nicholls, sitting opposite him at the dining table, thought, *That all applies to you.*

'I want you to do it, Arthur.' Charlotte looked up in surprise. Perhaps she had been too preoccupied with publishers to notice the strong bond between the two men.

'Of course,' said Nicholls. His handsome face was eager. He would have gone to the ends of the earth for this family. When things were settled he would speak to Charlotte. Surely the trust her father placed in him would recommend him to her.

The day of the funeral was cold and bright. They stood in the hall, muffled up against the wind. Anne had refused her father's pleas to remain in the house.

'What – not say farewell to Emily?' she whispered hoarsely. 'Papa – you would go if you were dying – so shall I.' A nerve in his temple twitched. She could not have meant to say that. Nicholls appeared in his surplice.

'Are you ready?' he said anxiously, looking at the mourners. Anne was clearly very ill; Charlotte looked stunned. He could hardly bear to look at Pat. The dull eyes which were sunk in his gaunt old face told of sleepless nights and grief-stricken days. *How much more can this man take?*

The procession through the gate into the churchyard was led by Pat, with Keeper at his side; Charlotte and Anne followed, then Tabby and Martha. Keeper had never behaved so well. He stood by the family vault for the interment, then lay quietly in the pew at Pat's feet for the service. When they returned to the house, he left

Pat and went upstairs, nails clicking on the stone, to Emily's room. He lay down by the door.

'Nicholls,' said Pat, 'will you get that piano out of there? Put it anywhere – as long as it's not under my nose. I don't want to see it. Get Brown to help you.'

He sat alone in the parlour, the others drank tea with Tabby in the kitchen. Anne drew close to the fire and tried to smother her cough. Suddenly, upstairs, the dog howled. Charlotte left the kitchen to fetch him.

'Don't,' said Pat from outside his door. 'Don't stop him. Let the poor beast howl. He can howl for all of us.' He shut his door. Keeper howled for two weeks.

๑๑

'He can't take any more, Char,' said Anne softly. She was sitting up in bed, her face turned towards the graveyard where the faint spring sunshine softened the grey tower. 'I don't want to die here. I don't want him to have to follow another coffin. I will be the fifth child he has buried at Haworth, as well as Mama and Aunt.'

Charlotte scarcely heard what she said for her tears. They had both spent a lot of time in solitary as well as shared grief. Emily had left a bigger hole than Branwell. 'This sibling thing,' she said, ignoring what Anne had said. 'It's the longest relationship anyone can have. But ours don't seem very long.'

'Exactly, Charlotte.' Anne's voice was gentle but determined. 'I am going to die like Emily and Branwell. But I don't want it to happen here. I want you and Ellen to take me away to Scarborough. I loved it there even though I was with the Robinsons. Papa will agree if he thinks it will make me well. Then we'll stay until it happens. That will be better for him.'

Charlotte looked at the thin face; her cheeks, like Emily's had bright red spots. The breath was rapid, stertorous unless she made an enormous effort. This baby sister was proposing to die away from the home she loved. 'I can't let you do that.' Her voice was steadier now. 'Papa would hate you to do it for him. He has tremendous courage. He would want you to stay here.'

'No.' Anne sat up straighter and pulled the blanket up to her chin. 'No. Perhaps I'm being selfish – perhaps I can't bear to see him go through it again. The grief of others is often harder to bear

280

than one's own. It would be easier for me to die if I didn't have to watch him being daily destroyed by grief. It would help both of us.'

Charlotte sobbed unrestrainedly. 'I can't bear to think of this house without you. There will be me and Papa, and no one else . . .'

Anne's sense of humour had not deserted her. 'And Mr Nicholls,' she said, mischievously.

'Anne!'

'Charlotte, he's besotted with you – his face is a picture whenever you come into the room. When I am gone you will marry Mr Nicholls, and all will be well.'

'Certainly not! He's, he's . . .'

'A curate? Well, then perhaps the handsome Mr Smith .'

Charlotte's face relaxed. That was not such a bad idea. 'But how would I ever see him again?'

'You will write more novels which will earn him hundreds of pounds, and in gratitude and love he will sweep you off to London to sit chained to a chair producing a novel a year for him – and a baby a year too.'

Despite herself, Charlotte laughed. 'Stop it, Annie,' she said, picking up the brush and starting to brush Anne's fine, gently curling hair. 'There will truly be no life for me if you leave me. So eat the strengthening meal Tabby is at this moment staggering up the stairs with, and get better.'

୧୬

When Charlotte's letter came from Scarborough, Patrick left the house and went onto the moor. He had not returned as darkness fell, and Tabby sent Martha to her father, knowing she would also find Mr Nicholls there. They were soon both standing in the kitchen.

'Maister said that my little bairn Annie was gone,' said the old woman, wiping her eyes. 'And then he was out of kitchen door and away to t' moor. Ah've had no sight of him since.' She covered her face with her apron and rocked to and fro. Nicholls looked at her in distress.

'I'll go on the route he takes to Stanbury,' he said. 'If John goes towards Keighley, we are sure to find him. Are you all right in the house on your own?' Martha moved protectively towards Tabby and said:

281

'Of course, we are. We'll bar doors and listen out for you and Mr Brontë.' She went into the back kitchen and came out with two lanterns. Nicholls and Brown lit them from the candle on the table. Nicholls said quietly to John:

'Will he have his pistol with him?'

'Always,' said Brown emphatically. He suddenly realised what Nicholls meant. Not for self-protection.

'I have my pistol with me.' Pat had entered the back kitchen and heard the conversation through the door left open by Martha. 'And I wouldn't shoot myself, Arthur. I'm not a coward. I'm sorry to have caused this alarm. It got late – I went further than I had intended – I was trying to . . .'. He sat down near Tabby's chair. 'It doesn't get easier. Every death is as bad as the first. Three children in eight months. Why does He not take me? I have little to live for and little to give. My children had everything to live for and everything to give.' He thumped the table. 'It's a punishment!' he shouted. 'Surely it's enough now? Now will you stop?' He shook his fist at the ceiling.

Nicholls took him by the elbow and raised him to his feet. He could see the fear and anxiety in the women's faces.

'Come, sir, come with me. A dram perhaps and a warm fire . . .' He put an arm round the old man's waist, another under his elbow. Slowly they made it to the parlour. Patrick's face was ashen, his hands icy cold. There was a faint blue on his lips. Nicholls looked at him in alarm. He must keep him safe for Charlotte. He poured the whiskey and obeyed Pat's mute instruction to have one himself. Anything to make the old man drink the warming fluid. Gradually the blue left his lips, and a faint colour returned to his face. He spread his long straight fingers out to the blaze that Martha had swiftly kindled. Nicholls heaved a sigh of relief.

'Charlotte says . . .' he waved the letter at Nicholls feebly. 'Read it for yourself. I cannot read it again.'

Nicholls took the letter to the window, bending his tall figure to the light. Charlotte said that she would bury her sister in Scarborough, with her father's agreement. She felt there was more anguish for both of them in bringing the body home and arranging a funeral in Haworth. Anne had said she would be happy to be buried in the parish church above the sea.

'Why not?' said Pat. 'Anne spent more time away from this village than any of my children. Let her have her wish.' He knew the reasoning behind Charlotte's decision, and it was not unwelcome. He doubted that he had the courage to face another journey into this church. Every time the family vault had been opened he had felt faint with nausea at the sharp rank smell which came from the piled coffins containing the bones and recent flesh of his dear ones. He would stand there remembering, how they felt in the hour of their death as he held the thin bodies. Let Anne stay in the fresh winds of Scarborough, beside the sea she had loved.

When Nicholls had gone and the shutters were up, the fire banked high by an anxious Martha, and Keeper and Flossy curled in tight balls as close to his chair as they could get, he turned in his chair and faced his bookshelves. The rounded edge of the second shelf still retained a tattered a scrap of glued paper bearing Maria's handwriting. 'Sermon Material', it said. They had never agreed about that. Her Methodism expected structure and discipline: he could preach for an hour without a note and never repeat himself, capturing the attention of simple people with his direct style. The third shelf was labelled 'Accounts' in darker ink on fresher paper – Bess, he thought, dear Bess who kept me sane in my grief and kept the trustees happy in money matters. And the top shelf, chosen to protect Branwell from the disciplined talent of his sisters, even the moderate success of his father: there sat the novels, stoutly bound with the names newly sharp on the spine: Acton Bell, Ellis Bell, Currer Bell. Then the slim volume of poetry; next to that the works of the Reverend Patrick Brontë, whose enthusiasm, he reflected dryly, outpaced his talent. Then the newspaper cuttings of Patrick Branwell Brontë. For a moment his face widened into a smile, until memory broke in and he shut his eyes in anguish and gripped the arms of his chair. All gone; all gone. Only Charlotte left. He must look after her.

29

To Miss Brontë, 112, Gloucester Terrace, London:

Many are the disagreeable discoveries which I make ... no
one takes me out to walk now, the weather is too cold, or too
wet, for my master to walk in and my former travelling
companion has lost all his apparent kindness, scolds me and
looks black upon me. Ah! My dear mistress, trust dogs rather
than men ... is the sincere wish of – Old Flossy.

Reverend Patrick Brontë, letter to Charlotte Brontë,
writing as Flossy, 19th January 1853.

He heard Charlotte's quick step up the path almost as soon as the
horse's hooves scuffed to a halt on the cobbles. The dogs were at
the door before him; Martha already in the hall, Tabby dragging
behind her. The moment he opened the door she was in his arms.
They hugged, clutching each other's thin bodies with an unusual,
desperate strength. Letting go at last, Charlotte stood back and
looked down at the dogs running around, pawing her skirts,
scurrying about the hall. She shook her head to flick the tears
away.

'They think that because I'm here Anne and Emily will soon
come,' she said. Patrick hugged her again.

'There, there,' he said. 'They will get used to it. We will all get
used to it.' His voice was shaking, and quickly he guided her in to
the parlour. She waited a minute to embrace Martha and Tabby,
then followed him and the busy dogs, trailing her bonnet strings
on the floor as she sank into a chair before the fire. Pat could
hardly take his eyes off her. The last three weeks had been unbear-
able. Now she was with him, the only remaining being of the last
thirty-seven years of his life. He knew he had to restrain himself.

'Are you well?' she enquired kindly, her eyes searching his face for signs.

'Yes, yes.' His reply was too quick. They gazed at each other, unable to speak what was in their hearts. *I have no brothers and sisters. All your children are dead except me. We have only each other.* Eventually she broke the silence.

'Papa, it was best to leave her there. She was so brave, so calm, so dignified . . .'

'As we would have expected,' he said gently.

Charlotte sighed. 'You always knew her gifts. I always underestimated her. If I could die as she did . . .'

'Don't,' he said.

'She loved you so much.' It was as if she had not heard him. 'She was determined to spare you more suffering.'

He leaned forward and poked the fire to hide his face. 'She knew I wasn't strong enough to bear it. I never thought I would sink so low in mind and body. I accepted her decision with love and gratitude. These last weeks . . .' – he paused, passing a thin hand over his face – 'these last weeks . . .' He stopped. 'We must put it behind us. Not our memories, but our grieving, or we may be overcome. I promised myself that when you came I would put it all behind me. You must bear up, Charlotte, or I shall fail.'

She looked at him, then shut her eyes as if to blot out the ravages of his careworn face. 'You're right,' she whispered. 'We have both lost our dearest friends and have only each other now. I will bear up, Papa, and so must you.' She smiled at him and gathered Flossy's front paws in one hand, stroking the thick wavy hair on her neck with the other. 'Work will help us,' she said. 'I've been writing . . .' – he raised his head, a flicker of interest breaking into his still features – 'I had a go at that story about the Luddites, and it's coming. You do have very good ideas,' – she almost laughed – 'it's just that you use too many words – and you need strong verbs, and more incidents, quicker changes, Papa.' Pat looked astonished. 'And it helps sometimes to make your readers smile a little!'

'You girls have an instinct. Despite all I have read, in Latin, Greek and English, I would never have thought about strong verbs!'

Martha's sleek head appeared round the door. 'Tabby says you should both eat summat.'

285

'Tonight we will join you in the kitchen.' Martha breathed in sharply. For three weeks he had hardly eaten and then only minute amounts on his own. 'Tonight we will all eat together and remember our loved ones and – yes – we'll talk about them.' Taking Charlotte's arm he walked her towards the kitchen. She knew he was doing it to help her confront the room where Emily had baked and Anne had peeled potatoes and Branwell had teased Tabby until she hit him with her knitting. She knew, and she was very grateful.

∽

She stood with her hands on the back of a chair; outside the wind was up and the familiar shakings and rattlings of the house comforted her, but she had to shut her eyes to block out the images of Emily, Anne and Branwell. She had moved from her usual chair at the table to the other side; she had tried to put the couch by the fire but it wouldn't fit; the writing boxes had gone from the room before she returned home. She pulled out the chair and sat down, her head in her hands, listening.

Nothing. Just the sighing and shifting of the wind and the house; sometimes a faint clatter from the kitchen; occasionally Papa's door would open to let out a dog, sometimes the same door would let in Mr Nicholls. Pat now came early to say goodnight to her, wrestling with habit to change the words to fit the lone figure at the table. They would kiss; despite his age she still had to stand on tiptoe to reach his lowered face. Then the steps down the hall to the kitchen and out to the privy and back – 'Goodnight, Martha, goodnight Tabby!' – slippers whispering on the stone stairs, a pause to wind the clock, more steps and finally the click of his door and silence. The poor old thing finds oblivion in sleep, she thought. '*Sleep that knits up the ravelled sleeve of care.*'

She had precious little of it herself. She dreaded going to bed and went only because the servants would not go and leave her up on her own. Night after night she watched the moon chase across the sky, heard the rain beating on the windows, the wind whimpering in the chimneys; then sometimes there came a night of such eerie silence she would get out of bed and stand, a tiny figure stark in the window, looking across to the church from the big room she now had to herself, wondering if the world had stopped and she was alone for ever. Such silence there had never been before.

There had always been a sister turning, breathing, sighing in her sleep. If they couldn't sleep they would sit together in one bed under a blanket and talk until they were tired. Never this silence, this emptiness. There had never been enough room in the house for all the children and the servants. Space had been a luxury. Now she had it, she hated it.

One night when she had been standing at the window watching the bats swooping from the church to the house, she saw a movement against the Browns' house. Clutching her shawl around her chilled body, she quickly pushed the shutters and fastened the bar as softly as she could. Nicholls was there, in the shadows, watching her room. She shivered; curates were a bane. Cheering up a little, she lay in bed and worked through the next chapter of *Shirley* in her head.

෮෧

When James Taylor called to pick up the manuscript, Charlotte insisted that he came and went in a day. Patrick, she had told the publishers, was not ready to receive visitors. He, disappointed at the lost opportunity for rare foreign conversation, knew better than to challenge the decision. He sensed a softening in Charlotte since her sisters died, but he was nevertheless clear that his increasing infirmities gave him a subordinate role. *Can it matter?* he would ask himself, as Charlotte, Tabby and Martha arranged his life in ways they thought best for him. *I am an old man; soon I will go on the same journey as the rest of my family.*

But he did manage a light lunch with Taylor, after exciting Tabby with the news that he felt a little hungry and might be tempted to eat if he were in the company of others. It worked well: the meal was prepared and laid out in the dining room for three as if Charlotte had given the order herself. Taylor, on his way home from Scotland where he had been holidaying with his parents, entertained Pat with stories of life in London and a few anecdotes of the Scottish capital; he was amused by the old man's vivid recall of London and Parliament and the great figures of his Regency days as well as the later decades he had lived through from the newspapers. Taylor perceived with interest the influence which had fired the children to think well beyond the grey moorland village that appeared so banal on his arrival.

And Pat perceived with pleasure that this young man had

strongly requested his employer to let him fetch the manuscript of the third volume of *Shirley* rather than entrust it to the post. There could only be one answer: he was interested in Charlotte and had seized this opportunity of visiting her. Charlotte's earning power rendered her financially less vulnerable than before, but without his tenancy of the parsonage she was still not secure and he would be happier if she had a companion, a husband, a rock on which to lean. He knew too well the strictures of the single life; he also knew Charlotte's record with proposals.

'And will you be coming to London soon, Miss Brontë?' Taylor's bright face was eager, his big nose more pronounced with his red hair still sleeked close to his head from the rain which had soaked him in the cart as he came up from Keighley. Patrick studied his features intently; there was a remarkable likeness to Branwell, but that might not help him. Charlotte sat up straight and reached for the bell to summon Martha; normally they waited until she arrived in her own practised timing.

'I think not for a time, Mr Taylor. Papa has not been well, and I would not like to leave him just yet.' Suddenly she remembered he was present. 'Is that not so, Papa? You wouldn't wish to be alone just yet?' The question hung in the air; he knew he was supposed to discourage the visit. But he had his own agenda.

'I shall be quite all right in the care of Tabby and Martha, my dear,' he replied smoothly. 'And you know that Mr Nicholls will sit with me in the evenings. I would much rather you went to London and met your public.'

Taylor laughed. 'You're so right, Mr Brontë! The whole of London would wish to meet Currer Bell! And besides, Miss Brontë would enjoy the company of distinguished writers. I know Mr Thackeray . . .'

'Mr Thackeray!' interrupted Charlotte, nearly knocking the dish of baked apples out of Martha's hand. 'I doubt a writer of Mr Thackeray's eminence would wish to meet me. I can't . . .'

'Writers are always keen to meet their peers,' said Pat firmly. 'Yes, yes, I'm sure Charlotte will be coming to London very soon.' He wiped his mouth on his napkin and rose a little unsteadily. 'Time for my rest,' he said apologetically to Taylor. 'Stay as long as you like. Charlotte will be glad of your company.' It was too late for Charlotte to detain him. Surprisingly nimbly he slid from the room; his study door clicked as he closed it firmly behind him.

ᘒ

The roof distressed Patrick. Like a gypsy he trailed from room to room while the men stripped off tiles and exposed battens and daylight, dropping plaster and bird droppings, crumbs of mortar and rotten wood which tripped him as he stumbled about in the unfamiliar rooms. Martha tried to make him comfortable by painstakingly simulating the order of his study wherever he was temporarily resident and the pattern of his bedroom wherever he had to sleep. He had not slept in the bedroom near the top of the stairs since Maria had died in there and he had moved to the room opposite. He lay there in the moonlight remembering her voice, the feel of her, the life they had had before they came to Haworth – even their life before the children: how sharp the memories were, how different from the mistiness of the present day when he frequently forgot what he was intending to do and would find himself halfway up the stairs unable to remember his mission. When he was moved to the opposite side of the house he lay in the bed in which Branwell had slept before it became necessary to watch him: the toy soldiers were more real in memory than the paintings which had eventually been stacked in the room, now in the cellar, banished like the piano. From here he had looked out to the moor in terror when the children were out in the bog-burst. Worst of all were the days when his study was in the dining room. The gentle tramp of the girls' feet in the late evening, the couch where Emily had lain, in sickness and in health, the dark patch from the dogs' coats on the wainscoting where they had jostled to be close to her, made his heart contract. He had underestimated the potency of memory when he agreed to wander the house during the repairs.

And Charlotte stayed away. He waited for her letters as she had for the letters of Constantin Heger, alert to the bell and the knock, holding his breath until Tabby had sorted parish from personal. He had despatched her to London when her constant tearfulness, her silent weeping in the evenings seared his heart. He could do nothing for her. He had given her Maria's letters one evening in an attempt to cheer her, and they did, although it filled her with

289

another longing – to have known her mother. He could talk more easily to Nicholls than he could talk to her: their shared daily tasks oiled their conversations. With Charlotte, their mutual desolation was salt to their open wounds.

By the fifth week, when the roof was sealed, basic order restored and the household returned to their own rooms, he received from Ellen Nussey news that Charlotte was ill. She had returned to Brookroyd after her trip to Scotland with George Smith, her attentive publisher, and his sister. His hopes had risen for an impending marriage when the trip was planned, but knowing Charlotte well he divined that her indisposition might indicate heartbreak. Before he could send for more news, Charlotte returned.

∾

'It's quite ridiculous!' Her cheeks flamed and she buried her short-sighted eyes in the *Leeds Intelligencer*. 'Even Martha is being particularly silly because of the reviews of *Shirley*. She says they are buying it at the Mechanics' Institute and the whole village will soon be reading it. And I shall give up buying my paper from Mr Greenwood if he mentions it to me once more–!' She flung the paper down and leaned on the back legs of her chair. The look she threw at Pat was hostile.

'Fame should be quite a comfort to you, my dear,' he said mildly, scooping the last remnants of his porridge. 'You have met great men, seen the Duke of Wellington, visited the Scottish capital in the company of a man of letters,' (Charlotte glared at him) 'and now you are famous in your own land. I gather from Martha that when Mr Nicholls was reading *Shirley* in his room he laughed out loud and banged his feet on the floor, such was his mirth at the portrayal of the curates. Are you not pleased?'

'You know very well that I hate the fact that Currer Bell is now known to be a woman and a clergyman's daughter residing in a remote village in west Yorkshire. I don't want to be bothered by local people who cannot believe that any of us could ever do anything so unusual as write a book. It's . . .'

'Charlotte, you cannot choose the bits of fame that you like. You enjoy the money and the travel and the company of other writers. If you can't put up with the local people, then go on a visit to

London again, or to the Kay Shuttleworths who are always asking you.'

She shrugged and sighed and moved away from the breakfast table to the window. In the graveyard she could see the grey forms of the men employed by the health inspectors as they moved about opening the ends of the graves and peering inside. Patrick had thrown himself wholeheartedly into the water improvement scheme for Haworth; the activity assuaged his grief in the belief that he would be relieving other parents from the serial deaths of their children. But Charlotte was little concerned with practicalities.

'I won't visit for a bit, Papa. I'll ask Ellen again to come here, and I'd very much like Mrs Gaskell to visit me here. I thought I wouldn't like her because our themes in *Shirley* and *Mary Barton* are so similar, but when I met her at the Kay Shuttleworths' I loved her immediately. She's a cross between a sister and a mother to me,' she added wistfully.

Nicholls tapped on the dining-room door and had just started to open it when there was a banging on the front door. Martha came hurrying up the hall. The Haworth carrier was on the step with his son holding a huge parcel. He placed it reverently on the floor against the wall, then retreated, cap in hand, sighing at the trappings of fame.

'Whatever is it?' Charlotte was out in the hall in a flash. Nicholls picked the parcel up with the ease of a big man and put it down on the dining table. 'It's addressed to you,' he said to Pat.

Carefully untying the string – too carefully for Charlotte's curiosity – Pat eventually revealed the portrait she had sat for in London. 'How kind, how very kind,' he said, beaming at the flattering likeness of Charlotte's greatly softened features. 'What a good man your Mr Smith is! To send a father a portrait of his only daughter!' His eyes were moist.

'And there's one for me, too,' said Charlotte softly, extracting a smaller parcel from beneath. 'The Duke of Wellington! Oh Papa – it takes me back to Bran and Anne and Emily and our stories – how could he know so well . . .?' Surprised by fresh grief, tears poured down her cheeks.

'He thinks a great deal of you to be so kind to us both,' said Pat taking her by the shoulders to comfort her. 'Don't you think, Nicholls? A true expression of his esteem!'

Nicholls buried his face in the wrapping paper, assiduously rolling string and smoothing paper. 'Indeed, sir. Very great esteem, I'm sure.'

◌◌

Patrick's spirits rose as Charlotte's fell. The triumph of his long struggle to expose the hazardous water which had relentlessly decimated the village for years was not diminished by the Haworth ratepayers' outrage at the prospect of contributing to the common good. They had, as Patrick had, their own safe wells and could see little reason to help the poor. Charlotte, struggling with writer's block, read and reread her sisters' works and attempted to sanitise their lives. Patrick was shocked at what she wrote about Anne and Emily in the new editions but feared to contradict her. He felt keenly the misery within her, her loneliness,

'Do you remember what Anne used to say about writing to purge one's feelings?' he hazarded one evening after a particularly difficult day. The air of the parsonage was chill, and the damp rose from the stone floors despite two good fires. Charlotte had been coughing in the night. She stopped stroking Keeper's greying coat and looked at him.

'What do you mean?' Her eyes did not really invite further comment.

'I mean that it can help to write about things which oppress you.' He leant forward in his chair and daringly took her hand. 'I did it with your mother, with the little children we lost. Without success.' He smiled apologetically. 'Too many words; not enough strong verbs.' The ghost of a smile played around Charlotte's wide mouth. 'But you could use this slough of despond; you could make it work for you.' He sat back from the fire, breathed deeply, amazed at his own daring.

'Not about Emily and Anne, or Branwell.' She huddled closer over the fire. 'It's too close, it's my whole life. I have been thinking of writing about . . . Brussels.' The words were muffled as she bent over Keeper, her face obscured. Pat stayed silent. 'I think I could use the setting well, there are interesting characters.' She stopped; tears were falling down her cheeks and landing on the dog's tawny back. *After all this time*, thought Pat. *She still loves him. But that is the way of true love.*

Nicholls entered on a tap at the door. Cold clung about him.

292

'There's sickness at the bottom of Kirkgate. We'll have burials soon.'

'Thank God we have support for the new water mains,' replied Pat. He got up and shielded Charlotte for a moment. 'Will you have some tea?' he asked the frosted curate. 'Sit down, and I'll ask Martha to bring some.'

'There's sickness here, too,' murmured Charlotte softly. She was holding the dog's head in both her hands. 'Look, Mr Nicholls, look at his eyes, so dim, and his breathing is very poor. Oh Keeper!' She slid down beside him and buried her head in his neck. Nicholls got down on his knees.

'He hasn't been well for some time,' he said, very gently. 'He found it difficult on the moor with me, and he hasn't come out with Flossy for two weeks.' He stroked the dog's back. 'Let me look at his face, Miss Brontë.' He bent over the dog and carefully examined his eyes, opened his mouth. He pressed the gums hard and watched the slow return of the blood. 'I think his heart is weak,' he whispered to her. He could hardly bear to say the words – he should have said: *This dog will not last the night.* She turned to him, pain in her eyes and tears welling. Pat returned from the kitchen.

'Sir, I think Keeper is not well. I could take him with me and look after him for the night.' Pat knew exactly what he meant.

'No.' Charlotte's voice was suddenly firm. She had stood up and was facing them both. 'No – don't you think, Papa? It's very kind, but Keeper must stay in this house in this room tonight. Emily would have wanted it.'

'Thank you, Nicholls.' Pat was struggling, but he remained calm. 'Charlotte is right, of course. My dear, you will go to bed, and I will sit here with Keeper tonight. I'm used to sleeping in chairs. The old do it more often than you can ever know.' He motioned to Nicholls to leave and kissed Charlotte to dismiss her upstairs. Then he settled in the chair, wrapped his legs around the dog's old body and embraced him till the dawn came, when Keeper sighed such a little sigh for a big dog and relaxed in death.

❧

He kept out of Charlotte's way. If they ate together it was in his study, tidying away his papers so that the sheets of *Villette* could remain untouched on the dining-room table. She wrote easily, fluently, the block of the last year forgotten, her pen gliding, tutting each time she had to pause to refill the inkwell, changing her nib the moment the slightest roughness impeded her. Pat had walked several times to Greenwood for more paper and nibs, the only service he felt he could perform for her besides his invisibility. When Nicholls called for the lonely Flossy, he found the dining-room door firmly shut and Pat shook his head at the mute enquiry. The curate sighed and made do with Flossy.

By the time Charlotte finished *Villette* she knew she was not in love with George Smith, and certainly not with James Taylor. She knew she would never be in love again. Constantin Heger had burned in her heart and mind as she wrote of Paul Emmanuel, and as she discovered her undimmed love for him she made an ambiguous end for the book. Her father's plea for a happy ending could not be granted: there would be no happy ending, neither could she endure a sad one. Lucy Snowe would endure like her creator.

'You do that so well, Nicholls, such dexterity.'

Confined by his winter bronchitis Pat lay in bed and watched his curate deal neatly with the parish papers, putting them into separate leather bags ready to be housed downstairs in the remnants of the Branwell filing system. His fine-boned, strong hands worked at the piles, tapping them into shape on the bedside table, loosening rogue sheets which became attached to others, imposing order and system. Pat sighed, stretching his own long fingers on the linen towel placed by Martha over his top sheet: she liked to change it twice a day to ensure the most pristine standards for visitors. What a help Nicholls could be to Charlotte with her mountains of pages, numbers flying out of sequence whenever a draught billowed from an opened door, or Flossy entered enthusiastically after her walk and nudged the table in her eagerness to tell Charlotte she was back. She spent hours checking the numbered sheets and often searched in vain for a page, finally rewriting it only to find it later in the discarded pile. She couldn't even tie the manuscripts up properly, her parcels having the shaggy appearance of Pat's papers. He had seen Nicholls relieve her of this task, mitring the corners, pressing the brown paper flat, tying intricate knots, sealing with the neatest splodge of wax. Nicholls smiled as he worked.

'I learned from my uncle, sir. He was the headmaster of the

Royal School in Banagher. I often worked with him in his study in Cuba House. He had a fine library and liked everything to be in perfect order, papers, books everything.'

That's a fine bit of imagination, thought Pat. *A fine library, indeed! I'm surprised he needs to try and impress me. What tosh! He must know that I know why Irishmen become Protestant clergymen.* He drifted off into a haze of memory of Thomas Tighe and the beautiful rectory at Drumballyroney.

'Do you think I would be able to help Miss Brontë with her papers?' queried Nicholls, telepathically. 'She seems overwhelmed with work at the moment, and there must be organisational things I could do for her.' His sternly handsome face had become bright, his deep voice had lifted. The love he felt for her vibrated from him. He turned to Pat for an answer. This was difficult.

Taking the mug of beef-tea left by Martha, Patrick warmed his hands around it and fixed his eyes on the church tower and carefully separated feelings from thinking. Ill again, and nearly eighty years of age, his head wanted Charlotte cared for and secure with a roof over her head; his heart wanted her to be in love with a man her intellectual equal who would excite her as he and Maria had excited each other. He knew none such existed. All the proposals she had received she had refused: like him and the rest of his children, she could only love once. Charlotte would never love a man as she had loved Constantin Heger. He had never met him, but he knew instinctively he was worthy of his daughter. Nicholls was not, intellectually or socially; that was plain. But he would love her, care for her, protect her, share with her the dearest memories of her family. He cleared his throat.

'You could try asking her,' he said. 'I have been little help to her in her present labour. Yes, you could try asking her.' He turned his head away and feigned sleep. He heard Nicholls shut the door softly and descend the stairs. A door opened and closed. Silence. Later, the front door clanged shut.

Had he spoken to her? Had she accepted his help? He turned away from the window onto his more comfortable side, where the doctor had not applied a blister. How could he make her accept a proposal from Nicholls, a contemptible curate? This could be his most important, difficult and last task.

☙

295

'What can you be thinking of!' The veins in his head stood out like whipcord. *Play the part, your last part.* He tried staggering to make his anger more convincing. Charlotte stood in front of him, her face white and body shaking.

'Papa, I have told you immediately of Mr Nicholls's proposal of marriage. There is no need to react like this. I have not accepted him, I . . .'

'You most certainly will not accept,' roared Pat. 'My distinguished daughter marry a curate! How can you even consider it – after all you have said and written about curates! You must be out of your mind even to repeat it to me!'

Charlotte trembled. She held her head high and met his enraged gaze. 'I have told you because I expected you would want me to be as I have always been to you – honest and dutiful. But apart from that I think you are very unjust to speak of Mr Nicholls in that way.' *Unjust. She cannot bear injustice.* 'He has been a great support to you personally and to this whole family. Think how he helped Branwell, and Emily.' *Yes, yes, think of that, do think of that and how comfortable it will be in the years to come to speak to him of your brother and sisters, even of your old father who appeared to lose his mind like Lear.* 'You might at least curb your snobbery and . . .'

'Snobbery!' Pat allowed his voice to rise. 'It is not snobbery to want my only remaining child to marry as she has been brought up!'

'His own relatives are well-educated and live in a good house, and he himself has been to a fine university in Ireland. Just because you went to Cambridge you need not despise . . .'

'Don't try to diminish my achievements!' shouted Pat. *Unlooked for logic here, remembering the theme of that book of hers.* 'It is ungrateful in a child for whom everything has been done to demean her elderly father in the last years of his life.' He paused. That was below the belt, given her dutiful nature. Charlotte went even whiter.

'That is not fair,' she whispered. 'I can hardly believe you are saying these things. That is really not fair. I have never thought of such a thing.' Tears welled. 'I do not wish to continue this conversation. I will refuse Mr Nicholls.'

'Of course you will, if you have the least scrap of sense left.'

'I will refuse him because I would never go against your wishes. But understand, Papa, that I am greatly disturbed by your unjust and snobbish reaction.' Still trembling, she left the room.

Pat felt a little foolish when she had gone. He had never dissembled to his children before, but the stakes this time were high: Charlotte secure with a good, dull man who could be trusted to the ends of the earth, or Charlotte alone, ageing, depressed and often ill. He had to succeed.

He had turned the house into a vortex of emotion: Charlotte's silent white-faced tension contrasted oddly with Martha's baleful looks and noisy cleaning. She couldn't bear the dissent between father and daughter and squarely blamed Nicholls rather than Pat for the miserable atmosphere of the house. John Brown declared he would like to shoot the man for the trouble he caused, while Mrs Brown feared he would die of love as he ate nothing at all. Nicholls hardly came near him; he did what he had to do in the parish, but carefully avoided Pat. This outcome Pat had foolishly overlooked: work became much harder for him, and the clear division between the two men was the talk of the village. Haworth could take sides and enjoy a fight again. He once saw Charlotte and Nicholls meeting in the lane; tracking her every movement had become necessary to know the state of the relationship, and he was pleased to see Nicholls brush away tears from his eyes. Before his curate's departure for Kirk Smeaton he scored two notable triumphs: the presentation of a fine gold watch, after the earnest enquiries of the trustees as to his reasons for going, and his last celebration of the sacrament, at which he, Charlotte and most of the women in the congregation wept openly. Despite his departure, Pat did not panic. Absence made the heart grow fonder.

⟨෴⟩

She felt his going keenly. Isolated from her friends, barely on speaking terms with Pat, Charlotte was alternately ill, depressed and unable to work – although Mrs Gaskell's visit raised her spirits temporarily. Pat, who would dearly have liked to spend time with this clever and attractive woman, limited himself to breakfast and tea; the ice between him and Charlotte did not melt. *She must think me a miserable curmudgeon as they pick me to pieces.* The two women walked the moor by day and talked late into the night, the motherly and uxorious authoress sympathising, advising and storing plot and character in her novelist's mind. Patrick began to get anxious.

He was overjoyed, therefore, when Charlotte confessed to him that she had secretly met Nicholls when he visited his friends at nearby Oxenhope and had been writing to him ever since. Her transgresson signified to him increasingly passionate feeling. She had decided, she said, that Mr Nicholls's unswerving devotion to her deserved a warmer response. She therefore was asking her father to give his permission for them to correspond further and to become better acquainted. Grudgingly he gave it, with a grand air of sacrifice and geriatric suffering. He had he played his last part, and never better.

30

The remarks concerning Mr Brontë excited in him only amusement – indeed I have not seen him laugh as much for some months as he did while I was reading the article to him. We are both well in health, but lonely and desolate . . .

The Reverend Arthur Nicholls, letter to Ellen Nussey,
11th June 1855.

They returned from their honeymoon to a house scoured, washed and polished to Martha's exacting standards; the conversion of the peat store (or pet store as Emily had called it as she shut the geese in there for the night) into Arthur's study had made a terrible mess, but she had finally achieved perfection. Pat had slept most of the time they were away in Ireland; in between services and sermons he was overcome with exhaustion, the mild stroke he had suffered as a result of his scheming rendering his body fragile and his eyes powerless. Fearfully and furtively he inspected Charlotte's tiny frame for the signs of an early pregnancy.

Frequently he fell asleep expecting to die; there was little left for him to do. Arthur managed the parish, encouraging him to preach but asking little else of him. Charlotte was the mistress, bemused at her changed station but so kind to Arthur that Patrick suspected she loved him.

'I can't decide,' she murmured one day, when she was sitting sewing with him in the afternoon, 'whether a controlling, opinionated father is better than a similar husband.' She chuckled and leant towards the light to see her work better. 'Do you know, Papa, Arthur was reading my letter to Ellen today and urging me to be discreet! Whatever fun would that be in a letter to a friend?'

'You are happy, aren't you, Char?'

'I am so very happy, Papa. I never thought I could be so happy after . . .' She paused; some things were best left unsaid. 'But my life is very full now, too full to find time to write, which is a pity, but after *Villette* I couldn't find a theme. Perhaps after this child is born I shall be full of ideas. Mrs Gaskell always was.'

His weak eyes examined her changed face. Her sisters would hardly recognise her. She glowed, and all the sad lines had dissolved. Martha came in with tea, and Arthur was behind her. He leaned over Charlotte and kissed her upturned face. *That is nice,* thought Pat, *that is very nice, such ease, such affection between them. It's really time for me to leave the stage . . .*

'Everywhere I go,' said Arthur, 'they are still taking about our tea party. It was greatly enjoyed. We'll have another for the christening!'

'You can have one for my funeral, too,' said Pat. 'I should think I deserve one for all the time I've been here.'

'Don't, Papa.' Charlotte's face clouded. 'Everything is so right, for all of us and the baby to come. I couldn't bear you to go just now.'

'Borrowed time,' replied Pat. 'Nearly eighty, still in work – it can't go on for ever. I just got you two married in time.' There was an astonished silence. 'I meant you two just got married in time,' he finished lamely.

Charlotte locked eyes with Arthur across the room. Surely, surely not?

⟋⟍

'Part of the trouble is', Pat said gently, 'that you are unused to personal grief. No amount of comforting the bereaved prepares you for your own.' He looked across at Arthur, who sat motionless in front of his food, a tiny portion provided by Martha to encourage him. He had had to leave him at Charlotte's bed, convulsed with sobs, while he went dry-eyed to his bedroom and sank to his knees. Why, he could not say. What conversation could he possibly have with God at the death of his sixth child?

'But why?' Arthur's voice was cracked and he whispered. 'Why, when we were so happy – she said we were – and all her suffering . . .?'

'Don't ask why. That will do no good at all. I stopped asking why years ago. What you do is carry on believing in Providence. Then everything that happens, bad or good, can be seen as God's will.

300

Come now, get your hat, and lean on me. I have done this seven times. I will take care of you.'

He had not been to Charlotte's wedding, asking Miss Wooler the night before if she would give her away. She was a woman of empathy and intelligence and instinctively understood that a wedding conducted over the bones of his wife and children was more than his advanced years could bear. Now he had no choice but to consign Charlotte to the remains of her sisters, brother and mother. Wrapping Arthur's arm firmly in to his own, they joined Martha in the hall and waited for Sutcliffe Sowden. To pass the time he said to Arthur, 'I'm glad your friend is able to help us out. I had such a friend – he married us, just the same, and then was always there for christenings and . . .' Fortunately Sowden arrived before he got into difficulties about funerals. Martha, her sister Eliza and her mother appeared, and with them, Nancy Garrs.

'Mrs Wainwright!' exclaimed Pat, taking both her hands. He almost wept. In her middle-aged face he could see the traces of the little girl who came to Thornton to help Maria. He kissed her hands fervently. Ellen Nussey looked away; she had not been part of this. Miss Wooler nodded kindly.

'John is waiting at the church,' sighed Mrs Brown. 'He could not believe this, so soon after Mrs Aykroyd. All our friends are going.' Martha hushed her. Pat took charge.

'Come, Sowden, let's go. There are no dogs to come with us. Since Flossy died we have been a dogless house for the first time.' *Now childless*, he thought bitterly. He squared his shoulders and kept a hold of Nicholls. It was hard, the younger man being the same height but almost twice his weight. They processed slowly to the gate in the wall to find the churchyard packed with villagers.

'This is how she was loved at home. The greater world does not yet know that Currer Bell has died.' He knew this would please Arthur, always keener on Charlotte than Currer. He kept his eyes away from the vault, holding his breath against the smell of disturbed earth, blocking out images, thoughts and feelings. He stared fixedly at the east window. Sowden touched him gently when it was all over. Keeping hold of Arthur he walked through the crowds and back to the house.

Neither of them could take the services during Holy Week, and Sowden and Grant of Oxenholme willingly helped. He sat for a week in his study; Arthur sat in the dining room. April showers pattered against the windows, fitful gleams of sun brightened the grey stone; sparse daffodils braved the graveyard. By the end of the week he had the first thought unconnected with his grief. Attired in his hat and coat, he opened the door of the dining room, where Arthur sat staring ahead.

'Come, Arthur, we're going out. We both need a dog. One can always get a new dog.' Refusing to accept Arthur's excuses, he handed him his coat and stick, and they walked to the moorland farm of Mr Summerscale. The puppy they bought had Newfoundland blood in him.

'He'll be big,' he said, observing the huge paws of the dog stretched out in front of the fire. 'He'll love going round the parish with you. I can't do names like the girls did; I'll stick to the Classics. He's Cato.'

∽

'It's so . . . *vulgar*.' Arthur shuddered as he watched Pat carefully cut Charlotte's signature from a letter. He raised his eyebrows.

'That's a bit hard, dear boy. These people admire her work and want a memento. I can't bring myself to disappoint them. Their interest is a compliment.'

'Their interest should cease with her death. She belongs to her family; our grief is private.'

'If you think that, you have greatly underestimated your wife's talent, as well as that of her sisters. There is a great interest . . .'

'I know – all these callers and letters and introductions. I hate it. We should be left alone to remember her.'

'I understand your feelings, but it sometimes soothes me to know what my children have achieved, and to talk of them to people who appreciate their genius.' Arthur looked uneasy; he was not entirely clear what genius was. 'But if the things I do distress you, then you are right to say so.'

Arthur hesitated. He had no wish to push Patrick. He wasn't even sure if the idea was good. 'Miss Nussey wrote to me about the scurrilous article in *Sharpe's London Magazine*. She feels you must be upset by it all, particularly the unjust picture given of you.'

Pat hooted with mirth. 'A man who has lost his wife and six children is not likely to be "upset" by a few scribblers who need to make a penny,' he said, wiping his eyes. 'Do you remember what

302

the mighty Wellington said? "Publish and be damned"! And what has the Brontë story got to do with me? It's Charlotte, Emily and Anne they want to hear about, not me.' He stumbled over Plato, who had soon joined Cato, to reach his spectacles. Steadying himself, he said, 'We must find a way to protect your memories.'

'Miss Nussey suggests that a biography of Charlotte, authorised by you, would stop all the speculation,' said Arthur. Uneasy as he was with Ellen, he thought she might be right on this. 'She suggests that Mrs Gaskell would be the right person to write it. An accomplished writer and one for whom Charlotte had great respect.'

Pat found himself unusually overwhelmed when Mrs Gaskell visited, suddenly unable to stop the tears he had never shed for Arthur's sake. She, embarrassed by the emotion of this venerable old man, spent little time with him and more listening with her novelist's ear to Ellen and those with a delight in gossip. Her *Life of Charlotte Brontë* was an immediate success, a sympathetic portrait of Charlotte, a damning vision of her father, and a metamorphosis of the home which they had all loved into a convincing stage set. Pat did not waver.

'The portrait of Charlotte is excellent,' he would say, twenty times a day. 'Yes, it is, Arthur, you know it is. She's going to change the bit about about me chopping up chairs for the next edition – wherever did she dig up that nurse we dismissed when Maria died? The only servant we have ever had to dismiss. But it's the writers people want to know about, the books, not their silly old father.'

∽

He was ill for nearly six months. Drifting in and out of consciousness, he sometimes mistook Martha for Charlotte, or Emily or Anne. Unable to read, he took journeys in his head through the Tighes' house, his rooms in St John's, the Bedfords' house at Lousy Thorn, the parsonage at Thornton, over and over again. When Nancy Wainwright struggled over from Bradford to see him he would check with her. 'Was there a cupboard by the fire in the parlour at Thornton, Nancy?' 'Yes, sir, Mrs Brontë used to keep your whiskey in there.' 'Oh yes, for the celebrations.' 'That's right, sir, we were always celebrating then!' 'Not much to celebrate now, Nancy.' Nancy had to agree.

Arthur read to him for hours. They went through all the girls' novels and several Scotts. Arthur was a good reader, Charlotte had said so. A deep, well-measured voice with surprising variety when required. Grant came from Oxenholme and Sowden from Kirk Smeaton, even a nervous Mrs Gaskell with her daughter as a buffer. Pat was amused by her anxiety. 'It doesn't matter,' he murmured 'It's not me they want to read about. What can it really matter what it says about me?'

One morning Greenwood the stationer, after recalling for the hundredth time how he 'always knew summat was oop' when the girls bought reams of paper from him, said to him:

'I'm going to call my little lad after you. When you're better I want you to baptise him.'

'Patrick?'

'No – Brontë; I want him called Brontë Greenwood.'

'You'd better let Mr Nicholls do it. Not much chance of me getting down there.'

But Arthur would not. It appeared to him the height of impertinence for the stationer to assume he could use the name of his wife and father-in-law.

'It's a compliment, Arthur. He was the most intelligent critic the girls had in this village. He only wants to keep the name alive.'

Arthur was adamant. Whether he felt his own failure to continue the line, whether he felt Charlotte had died because of their trying to do so – he would not. She had become Charlotte Brontë Nicholls. No one else should have that name.

Patrick felt differently. He was fond of the name. It had served him well. One morning Martha showed the Greenwoods into Pat's bedroom and filled up the bowl on his washstand. Her uncle brought the register of baptisms. Arthur was very angry when he found the entry. It was the only cross word they had had in six years.

෧෨

The two women squeezed through the crowd and took up a stand by the wall close to the north door of the church. With every shop shut in Haworth, it was not surprising that the crowd was vast, spilling onto the edges of the moor.

'I remember,' said Joan Aykroyd, 'the day he came to Haworth. I were no but a lass, but my mother had us all watching from out of our door on Kirkgate. There'd been such a fuss getting him to come that me Mam thought it might be worth watching.'

'Wor it?' murmured her companion.

'Nay. There wor just the seven carts and him at the front, dog at his heels and a bairn on his shoulders, all quiet and dignified. 'E wor a reet good-looker, lovely red hair and straight as a pole.'

'*Red* hair?'

'Aye, red like the evening sun. Reckon he's had a bit to turn it white.' She stopped, looking towards the door of the parsonage. It had just opened, and six men in clerical dress appeared, mustering to take the coffin from the undertaker and lift it onto their shoulders.

'Lovely blue eyes, too. He turned a few heads in them days. Best kind o' parson we could have had.'

'You reckon?'

'I do. Minded his own business and left folk to mind theirs, but a reet kind man. He buried four bairns for us, each as tenderly as it wor his own.'

'He should know.'

'He should that,' sighed Mrs Aykroyd. She craned her neck. 'Ee, look at how they carry that coffin – all them parsons proud to do it.' The procession entered the churchyard through the garden gate. 'He wor allus in and out of folk's houses when they were sick until he became too sick hisself. Some o' that lot' – she jerked her head in the direction of the coffin bearers, 'are too 'frit to go where there's sickness. Not Mr Brontë; he used to say he'd survived worse in Ireland.'

'Didn't your Tom's aunt work for him?'

'Aye, she did, since the childer were little bairns. Died the same year as Mrs Nicholls. She wor eighty-five, been there nigh on forty years.'

'She must 'a liked it! Did she ever say owt?'

'She said they wor like her own, and she wouldn't have nowt said agin them.'

'She should know after all that time living in t' house. You couldn't hide nowt in that sort of time.'

'You'reet. I have heard,' she lowered her voice, 'I have heard that there's a woman written a lot of nasty gossip about them, to mek a few pence. There's no end to the daftness o' folk. You'd think they'd be glad to find a good 'un and leave well alone.' She drew back against the wall as the coffin passed. The whole church-yard stood, silent, every head bowed.

'Ee look at that poor man,' whispered her companion as Nicholls paused at the door, leaning heavily on his companion. 'He can hardly bear to go in.'

'Poor soul, he looks badly. Looked after the old man six years and looks as done up as he did when his wife went.'

'He loved him, that's for sure.' She straightened her shawl. 'Coom on, that's the end of it. They don't mek 'em like him any more. Best get back.'

EPILOGUE

Arthur Bell Nicholls was refused the incumbency of Haworth, despite his sixteen years as curate. He took Cato back to Banagher in Kings County, Ireland, where he was visited frequently by Martha Brown. He gave up the church and became a farmer on his uncle's land. He married his cousin, Mary Bell Nicholls, whom Charlotte had met and liked, and died in 1906, aged eighty-eight. His wife placed his coffin beneath Richmond's portrait of Charlotte which had hung in his house ever since he had left Haworth.

ഗ൦

Patrick Bronte to Mrs Gaskell, 30th July 1855:

I do not deny that I am somewhat excentrick. Had I been among the calm, sedate, concentric men of the world, I should not have been as I now am, and I should, in all probability, never had had such children as mine have been.